A Invitation

TO JOIN THE ROYAL MINT COIN CLUB

In order to satisfy the demands of the modern collector, the Royal Mint has established its own Coin Club to provide its members with the latest information on new coins from both home and abroad. Recognised as the supreme examples of the minter's art, Royal Mint collector coins form a tangible record of our heritage.

Some of the benefits of becoming a Coin Club member are:

FREE
Coin Club Membership.
No COMMITMENT TO PURCHASE
whatsoever.
ROYAL MINT GUARANTEE
return your coins within 30 days for an immediate refund.
FREE
Quarterly Coin Club Magazine.
FREE
Postage & Packing on all purchases.
INTEREST-FREE
Payments on selected high-value products.

ROYAL MINT

ADVANCE NOTIFICATION
of rare and limited-edition issues.
OPPORTUNITY
to purchase products which are NOT offered to the general public.
SPECIAL PRE-ISSUE PRICES
(subject to status).
The **confidence** that you are dealing with one of the most prestigious and reputable numismatic organisations in the world with a history spanning over 1100 years.

A TRADITION OF EXCELLENCE

To receive your free brochure, please telephone (01443 62 34 56) or write to the address detailed below, quoting ref: CYBOO
Royal Mint Coin Club, FREEPOST, PO Box 500, Cardiff, CF1 1YY.

Regular Coin Sales

No.	Date	Features	Edge date	Obv.	Rev.	F	VF	EF
C25GM-005	1668		VICESIMO	1	1	900	1700	4500
C25GM-010	1668	elephant below head	VICESIMO	1	1	900	1700	4500
C25GM-015			VICESIMO PRIMO	1	1	950	1800	4500
C25GM-			VICESIMO PRIMO	1	1	1100	2000	5000
C25			VICESIMO SECVNDO	1	1	950	1800	4500
C2			VICESIMO TERTIO	1	1	950	1800	4500
C2			VICESIMO QVARTO	1	1	950	1800	4500
C25GM			VICESIMO QVINTO	1	1	950	1800	4500
C25GM-045			VICESIMO	1	1	950	1800	4500
C25GM-050	1675	2			1	950	1800	4500
C25GM-055	1675	ele be			1	950	1800	4500
C25GM-060	1675	e c h			1	1200	2500	7000
C25GM-065	1676	3			1	950	1800	4500
C25GM-070	1676				1	950	1800	4500
C25GM-075	1676	elephant and castle below	OCTAVO	1	1	950	1800	4500

Five Guineas — Charles II (1660 – 1685)

A 1668 "Elephant" coinage Five-Guinea piece of Charles II, from a small private collection sold at Bonhams in March, 1999 for £4,255.

The art of preparing an auction catalogue is a skill that requires more than just expertise, knowledge and integrity. At Bonhams our coin catalogues present the facts in a precise, accurate and easy to follow style. Many pieces are illustrated and standard references are given for individual coins

Our quarterly sales contain a fascinating mixture of ancient and modern coins, from Greek and Roman issues to coins of the modern world, Banknotes and Bonds, Numismatic Books, to Historical Medals and War Medals and Decorations. All our sales are on public view prior to each auction.

For a free auction valuation, or further information about buying or selling a single item or a whole collection, please call Daniel Fearon or Paul Hill of the Coin & Medal Department.

0171 393 3949
or e-mail: coins@bonhams.com

BONHAMS
AUCTIONEERS & VALUERS SINCE 1793

Montpelier Street, London SW7 1HH
Tel: 0171 393 3900 Fax: 0171 393 3905
Internet: www.bonhams.com

| Tel:
01543
473073
between
1pm and 9pm | **J. WELSH**
P.O. Box 150, Burton-on-Trent
Staffs DE13 7LB
Callers by appointment only as all coins banked | Est. 1968
Fax No.
(24 hrs)
01543
473234 |

COINS FOR SALE

UK PROOF SETS GEM UNC IN ORIG.
ROYAL MINT BOXES
1887 £5 down .... POA
1893 £5 down .... POA
1902 £5 down – Mdy 1d £1,350
1911 £5 down £2,500
1911 Sov. down £775
1927 .... £250
1937 Gold £1,350
1937 Silver (15 coins) £150
1950 .... £65
1951 .... £75
1953 .... £55

£5 + £2 PIECES
1887 £5 .... ABU £525, BU £595
1887 £2 .... ABU £250, BU £295
1937 Pe. £5 UNC £625
1937 Pr. £2 GEM UNC £320
1991 £5 BU in orig. R. Mint box £335
1993 Ditto £335
1994 Ditto £335
1995 Ditto £335
1999 Diana £5 .... £595

5 GUINEAS, 2 GUINEAS, GUINEAS, ETC
1748 5 Gns. Geo II A/UNC £3,750
1701 Wm. III Gn. UNC Extr rare £1,400
1738 2 Gns. BU Superb £1,250
1710 Gn. Anne BU Superb Extr. rare .. £1,750
1713 Gn. Anne Nice ABU. BU rare £595
1788 Gn. BU Nice £350
1793 Gn. Nice ABU £200

½ GUINEAS
1714 Anne A/UNC £595
1784 GVF £95
1801 BU £200
1804 BU £175
1806 NEF £100
1813 BU GEM Rare £250

1/3 GUINEAS
1798 NVF £50
1803 GF £45
1804 GEM BU/FDC £125
1804 GVF £58
1804 1/3 Gn. VF £48
1806 Nice BU £125
1806 VF £52
1809 BU £120
1809 ABU. BU £80
1810 BU £105

¼ GUINEAS
1718 ¼ Gn. BU Rare £175

SOVEREIGNS
George III 1761–1820
1820 A/UNC £295
1820 L EF £250

George IV 1821–1830
1822 UNC/BU £395
1826 GF £100
1827 Nice EF £250
1830 Nice BU £550

Edward VII 1902–1910
1902 MP UNC Rare £120
1906 M BU Rare £85
1906 L BU Rare £85
1907 L GVF £58
1907 L ABU/BU £68
1909 L ABU £65
1909 S ABU Scarce £68
1909 S Nice BU Rare £90

George V 1911–1936
1911 Canada UNC/BU Rare £90
1911 Canada BU GEM £125

1911 Canada BU Rare £100
1912 L ABU/BU £59
1912 S BU GEM £72
1913 L EF £56
1916 P BU GEM Rare £100
1917 L BU GEM Extr. rare £2,950
1917 S BU £85
1917 Canada BU Rare £115
1917 Canada ABU Rare £95
1917 Canada Nice BU Rare £135
1918 Canada ABU Rare £90
1918 Canada ABU/BU Rare £100
1918 Canada ABU Rare £125
1918 Canada BU GEM Rare £140
1918 India ABU/BU Rare £75
1918 India BU Rare £85
1918 Nice BU Rare £100
1918 India BU Rare £85
1920 P BU £90
1921 P ABU/BU £70
1921 P BU Rare £90
1925 P BU Extr. rare £195
1925 SA Superb BU £95
1925 L ABU £59
1928 SA BU £70
1929 P BU GEM Rare £85
1930 P BU GEM £70
1931 P BU GEM £70
1932 SA ABU Scarce £70
1932 SA BU Scarce £85
1932 SA BU GEM Scarce £95

George VI 1937–1952
1937 Pr. GEM FDC Extr. rare, mintage only 5,500 ..... £425

Elizabeth II 1953–
1957 ABU Scarce £56
1957 BU Scarce £60
1957–68 Set BU 10 coins in deluxe box
(No. 1960, 61 minted) £550
1958 BU £52
1959 BU Rare £52
1962 BU £52
1963 BU £52
1964 BU £52
1965 BU £52
1966 BU £52
1967 BU £52
1968 BU £52
1974 BU £52

CROWNS
1662 Rose below F £65
1663 Electr. copy of Simon Pet. Superb FDC
Extr. rare £450
1668 GF Rare £85
1680 4th B VF Rare £150
1691 GVF Rare £450
1718 R3. VF Extr. rare £295
1726 R&P NVF Very rare £275
1746 NEF/EF Nice £375
1818 LVIII Nice UNC £250
1821 EF A/UNC Toned £175
1821 GF £20
1821 ABU Nice £250
1822 Tert GF Scarce £18
1822 Sec GF Rare £20
1845 BU Extr. rare in this grade £750
1894 LVII Nice UNC Rare £175
1896 LX EF £48
1897 LX BU £100
1933 BU £140
1935 BU £16
1935 ABU £10
1937 ABU £12
1937 BU £18
1951 Pr. UNC £6
1953 BU £5

1960 BU £6
1960 V.I.P Proof Nice UNC Extr. rare £350
1960 Pol. Die BU £10

HALF CROWNS
1551 Edward VI VF Extr. rare £450
Charles I S.2771 MM Ton GF £50
Charles I Nice GVF £175
1673 Nice GVF Attractive, Rare £175
1677 NVF/VF £65
1683 NVF/VF Very rare £85
1686 Nice GVF+ Rare £250
1687 NVF Rare £125
1688 F Nice £60
1708 E GF £35
1720/17 F Scarce £90
1723 SSC Geo. I VF Rare £145
1735 Nice VF Rare £140
1746 Lima GF £35
1819 GEM FDC £185
1819 GF £14
1820 LH GF £13
1823 VF £30
1834 F £9
1844 Nice UNC Rare £250
1845 Nice UNC Rare £275

SHILLINGS
Charles I F £30
Edward VI GVF £195
1663 GF £50
1683 F Very rare £75
1696 NVF £28
1708 R&P NVF Very rare £55
1708 Plain UNC Nice tone £140
1709 Plain UNC Nice tone £140
1723 SSC GEM UNC £140
1723 SSC GVF £30
1729 R&P VF Extr. rare £110
1731 GVF Nice £75
1737 NVF/VF £30
1739 GVF £50
1739 NVF/VF £30
1745 Lima NVF/VF £25
1745 Roses NVF/VF £30
1758 GVF £20
1787 VF £12
1787 NEF £14
1787 EF A/UNC £20
1787 UNC £36
1787 Nice UNC £38
1816 BU GEM £45
1817 BU £38
1820 BU Rare £50
1824 BU £125
1826 Pr. Nice UNC £150
1826 NVF £8
1826 GEM UNC £75
1834 GEM UNC £110
1834 VF £12
1839 2nd B. Superb FDC lovely colour £125
1842 Nice BU £85
1844 BU £85
1853 Nice UNC £75
1853 BU GEM £95
1856 BU £75
1856 GEM UNC £85
1862 NVF/VF Rare £28
1862 EF Ext. rare £85
1865 F £4
1867 DN 6 F Scarce £10
1867 DN 22 VF/GVF £14
1868 BU £65
1871 DN9 NEF £15
1871 DN 39 NVF/VF £10
1872 DN 135 VF/GVF £12
1872 BU £60
1873 BU £45

3

4

"THE I.A.P.N. dealer, your guide to the world of numismatics"

"More than one hundred of the world's most respected coin dealers are members of the I.A.P.N. (International Association of Professional Numismatics).
I.A.P.N. members offer the collector an exceptional selection of quality material, expert cataloguing, outstanding service, and realistic pricing. The I.A.P.N. also maintain the International Bureau for the Suppression of Counterfeit Coins (I.B.S.C.C.) which, for a fee can provide expert opinions on the authenticity of coin submitted to it. A booklet listing the name, address and specialities of all I.A.P.N. members is available without charge by writing to the I.A.P.N. Secretariate". Jean-Luc van der Schueren, 14, Rue de la Bourse, B-1000, Bruxelles.
Tel: +32–2–513 3400 Fax: +32–2–512 2528 E-mail: iapnsecret@compuserve.com Web site: http://www.iapn.ch

AUSTRALIA
NOBLE NUMISMATICS Pty Ltd (Jim Noble), 169 Macquarie Street, SYDNEY NSW 2000

AUSTRIA
HERINEK, G., Josefstädterstrasse 27, A–1082 WIEN VIII
MOZELT, Erich, Vienna Marriott Hotel, Parkring 12a, A–1010 WIEN

BELGIUM
ELSEN SA, Jean, Avenue de Tervuren 65, B–1040 BRUXELLES
FRANCESCHI & Fils, B, 10, Rue Croix-de-Fer, B–1000 BRUXELLES
VAN DER SCHUEREN, Jean-Luc, 14, Rue de la Bourse, B–1000 BRUXELLES

CANADA
WEIR LTD., Randy, PO Box 64577, UNIONVILLE, Ontario, L3R 0M9

EGYPT
BAJOCCHI, Pietro 45 Abdel Khalek Sarwat Street, 11111 CAIRO

ENGLAND
BALDWIN & SONS LTD., A.H. ,11 Adelphi Terrace, LONDON WC2N 6BJ
DAVIES LTD, Paul, PO Box 17, ILKLEY, West Yorkshire LS29 8TZ
FORMAT OF BIRMINGHAM LTD 18 Bennetts Hill, BIRMINGHAM B25QJ
KNIGHTSBRIDGE COINS, 43 Duke Street. St. James's, LONDON SW1Y 6DD
LUBBOCK & SON LTD, 315 Regent Street, LONDON W1R 7YB
RUDD , Chris, PO Box 222. Aylsham, NORFOLK NR11 6TY
SPINK & SON LTD, 5/7 King Street, St. James's, LONDON SW1Y 6QS
VECCHI, Italo, 35 Dover Street, LONDON W1X 3RA

FRANCE
BOURGEY, Sabine, 7, Rue Drouot, F–75009 PARIS
BURGAN, Claude—Maison Florange, 8, Rue du 4 Septembre, F–75002, PARIS
MAISON PLATT SA, 49, Rue de Richelieu, F–75001 PARIS
NUMISMATIQUE et CHANGE DE PARIS, 3, Rue de la Bourse, F–75002 PARIS
O.G.N., 64, Rue de Richelieu, F–75002 PARIS
A POINSIGNON-NUMISMATIQUE, 4, Rue des Francs Bourgeois, F–67000 STRASBOURG
SILBERSTEIN, Claude, 39, Rue Vivienne, F–75002 PARIS
VINCHON-NUMISMATIQUE, Jean 77, Rue de Richelieu, F–75002 PARIS
WEIL, Alain, SPES NUMISMATIQUE, 54, Rue de Richelieu, F–75001 PARIS

GERMANY
DILLER, Johannes, Postfach 70 04 29, D–81304 MÜNCHEN
GARLICH, Kurt B, D–63303 DREIEICH-GOTZENHAIN
GIESSENER MÜNZHANDLUNG DIETER GORNY GmbH, Maximiliansplatz 20, D–80333 MÜNCHEN
HIRSCH, NACHF., Gerhard, Promenadeplatz 10/H, D–80333 MÜNCHEN
JACQUIER,Paul-Francis, Honsellstrasse 8, D–77694 KEHL
KAISER, Rüdiger, Münzfachgeschaft, Mittelweg 54, D–60318 FRANKFURT

KRICHELDORF Nachf., H.H. Gunterstalstrasse 16, D–79100 FREIBURG i.Br.
KÜNKER, Fritz Rudolf, Münzenhandlung, Gutenbergstrasse 23, D–49076 OSNABRUCK
KURPFALZISCHE MÜNZENHANDLUNG—KPM Augusta-Anlage 52, D–68165 MANNHEIM,
Numismatik LANZ, Luitpoldblock-Maximiliansplatz 10, D–80333 MÜNCHEN
MENZEL, Niels, Dachsteinweg 12, D–12107, BERLIN-MARIENDORF

MÜNZENETAGE-ANTIKE NUMISMATIK (Herrn Dr. M. Brandt), Marktplatz 14, D–70173 ,STUTTGART
MÜNZEN-UND MEDAILLENHANDLUG STUTTGART, Charlottenstrasse 4, D–70182 STUTTGART
NEUMANN, Ernst, Watteplatz 6, Postfach 1423, D–89312, GÜNZBÜRG
PEUS NACHF., Dr. Busso Bornweidenweg 34, D–60232 FRANKFURT/M,
Münzhandlung RITTER GmbH Postfach 24 01 26, D–40090 DÜSSELDORF
TIETJEN + CO, Spitalerstrasse 30, D–20095 HAMBURG
W E S T F A L I S C H E AUKTIONSGESELLSCHAFT oHG, Nordring 22, D–59821, ARNSBERG

ISRAEL
EIDELSTEIN, Adolfo, 61 Herzl St., HAIFA, Postal address: POB 5135, 31051 Haifa
QEDAR, Shraga, 3, Granot Street, Entrance 6, JERUSALEM. Postal address: PO Box 520, 91004 Jerusalem

ITALY
BARANOWSKY s.a.s, Via del Corso 184, I–00187, ROMA
BECKER, Roland, Parco Abate 19, I–83100, AVELLINO
BERNARDI, Giulio, Via Roma 3 & 22c, PO Box 560, I–34 121 TRIESTE
CARLO CRIPPA s.n.c., Via degli Omenoni 2 (angolo Piazza Belgioioso). I–20121 MILANO
DE FALCO, Corso Umberto 24, I–80138 NAPOLI
FALLANI, Via del Babuino 58a, I–99187 ROMA
MARCHESI GINO &Figlio (Guiseppe Marchesi), V. le Pietramellara 35, I–40121, BOLOGNA
PAOLUCCI, Raffaele, Via San Francesco 154, I–35121 PADOVA
RATTO, Mario, Via A. Manzoni 14 (Palazzo Trivulzio), I–20121 MILANO

RINALDI & Figlio, O.,Via Cappello 23 (Casa di Giulietta), I–37121 VERONA

JAPAN
DARUMA INTERNATIONAL GALLERIES, 2-16-32-301, Takanawa, Minato-ku, JP-TOKYO 108
WORLD COINS, 2 Fl. 9–6–40, Akasaka, Minato-ku, Tokyo 107.

LUXEMBOURG
LUX NUMIS, 20, rue J. P Kommes, L–6988 HOSTERT, LUXEMBOURG

MONACO
GADOURY Editions Victor, 57 rue Grimaldi, Le Panorama, MC–98000
LE LOUIS D'OR, 9, Ave. des Papalins, MC-98000 MONACO

THE NETHERLANDS
MEVIUS NUMISBOOKS Int. BV Oosteinde 97, NL 7671 VRIEZENVEEN
SCHULMAN BV, Laurens, Brinklaan 84a, NL–1404 GM BUSSUM
VAN DER DUSSEN BV, A.G., Postbus 728, NL–6211, JB, MAASTRICHT
WESTERHOF, Jille Binne, Trekpad 38–40, NL–8742 KP, Burgwerd

NORWAY
OSLO MYNTHANDEL AS, (Jan Aamlid) Postboks 355, Sentrum, N–0101, OSLO

SINGAPORE
TAISEI STAMPS & COINS (S) PTE LTD, 116 Middle Road, #09–02, ICB Enterprise House, SINGA- 188972

SPAIN
CALICO, X. & F., Plaza del Angel 2, E-08002 BARCELONA
CAYON, Juan R., JANO S.L., Alcala 35, E–28014 MADRID
VICO SA, Jesus, Jorge Juan, 83 Duplicado, E–28009 MADRID

SWEDEN
AHLSTRÖM MYNTHANDEL, AB, Norrmalstorg 1, 1, PO Box 7662, S–103 94 STOCKHOLM
NORDLINDS MYNTHANDEL AB, ULF, Karlavagen 46, PO Box 5132, S–102 43 STOCKHOLM

SWITZERLAND
HESS, Adolph A. G (H. J. Schramm) Löwenstrasse 55, CH–8001, ZURICH
HESS—DIVO AG, Löwenstrasse 55, CH–8001 ZÜRICH
LEU NUMISMATIK AG, In Gassen 20, CH-8001 ZÜRICH
MÜNZEN UND MEDAILLEN AG, Malzgasse 25, BASEL. Postal address: Postfach 3647, CH–4002 Basel

NUMISMATICA ARS CLASSICA AG, Niederdorfstrasse 43, Postfach 745, CH–8025 ZÜRICH
STERNBERG AG, Frank Schanzengasse 10 (Bhf. Stadelhofen), CH–8001 ZÜRICH

UNITED STATES OF AMERICA
BERK, LTD., Harlan J, 31 North Clark Street, CHICAGO, IL. 60602
BOWERS AND MERENA GALLERIES, INC., PO Box 1224, WOLFEBORO, NH 03894
BULLOWA, C.E. COIN HUNTER, 1616 Walnut Street, PHILADELPHIA, PA 19103
COIN AND CURRENCY INSTITUTE INC, PO Box 1057, CLIFTON, NJ 07014
COIN GALLERIES, 123 West 57 Street, NEW YORK, NY 10019
CRAIG, Freeman, PO Box 4176, SAN RAFAEL, CA 94913
DAVISSON'S LTD, COLD SPRING, MN 56320
DUNIGAN, Mike, 5332 Birchman, Fort Worth, TX 76107
FREEMAN & SEAR, PO Box 641352, LOS ANGELES, CA 90064–6352
FROSETH INC., K.M., PO Box 23116, MINNEAPOLIS, MN 55423
GILLIO Inc., Ronald J., 1103 State Street, SANTA BARBARA, CA 93101
HINDERLING, Wade, PO Box 606 MANHASSET, NY 11030
KERN, Jonathan K. Co., 441, S. Ashland Avenue, Lexington, KY 40502
KOLBE, George Frederick, PO Drawer 3100, CRESTLINE, CA 92325–3100
KOVACS, Frank L., PO Box 25300 SAN MATEO, CA 94402
KREINDLER, Herbert, 15, White Birch Drive, Dix Hills, NY11746
MALTER & CO. Inc., Joel L., 17005 Ventura Blvd., ENCINO, CA 91316
MARGOLIS, Richard, PO Box 2054, TEANECK, NJ 07666
MILCAREK, Dr. Ron, PO Box 1028, Greenfield, MA 01302
PONTERIO & ASSOCIATES, Inc 1818 Robinson Ave., SAN DIEGO, CA 92101–1683
RARE COIN COMPANY OF AMERICA, Inc, 6262 South Route 83, WILLOWBROOK, IL 60514
ROSENBLUM, William M., EVERGREEN, CO. 80437–0355
RYNEARSON, Dr Paul, PO Box 4009, MALIBU, CA 90264
SINGER, Dr Gordon Andreas, PO Box 235, GREENBELT, MD20768–0235
STACK'S, 123 West 57 Street, NEW YORK, NY 10019
STEPHENS Inc., Karl, PO Box 3038, Fallbrook, CA 92088
STREINER, Eric Inc, 119 West 57th Street, Suite 1218, NY 10019, NEW YORK
SUBAK Inc., 22 West Monroe Street, Room 1506, CHICAGO, IL 60603
TELLER NUMISMATIC ENTERPRISES 16027 Ventura Blvd., Suite 606, ENCINO, CA 91436
WADDELL, Ltd., Edward J., Suite 316, 444 N. Frederick Ave., GAITHERSBURG, MD 20877
WORLD-WIDE COINS OF CALIFORNIA, PO Box 3684, SANTA ROSA, CA 95402

VENEZUELA
NUMISMATICA GLOBUS, Apartado de Correos 50418 CARACAS 1050–A

6

THE
COIN
YEARBOOK
2000

Edited by
James Mackay, MA, DLitt
John W. Mussell
and the Editorial Team of COIN NEWS

ISBN 1 8701 92 27 3
(Hardback edition 1 8701 92 28 1)

A *Token* TITLE

Published by
TOKEN PUBLISHING LIMITED
1 Orchard House, Duchy Road, Heathpark, Honiton, EX14 1YT
Telephone: 01404 46972   Fax: 01404 44788
e-mail: info@coin-news.com. Website: http://www.coin-news.com

Printed in Great Britain by Polestar Wheatons Ltd., Exeter EX2 8RP

CONTENTS

INDEX TO ADVERTISERS

FOREWORD

WELCOME to the seventh edition of the COIN YEARBOOK. Our smaller format is now well established and our core listings now cover all the coinage of the British Isles from the earliest times right down to the present day. To encompass the entire range from Celtic staters to the Euro in a concise form is no mean feat, for it is a great problem deciding what to leave out and yet retain the essence of the subject, matched with prices that accurately reflect the current state of the market.

Moreover, in view of the fact that the momentum of British coinage is now increasing, and the issues of the offshore islands and the Republic of Ireland present a formidable volume of material in their own right, we feel justifiably proud of our achievement in presenting our price guides at just the right level for the vast majority of coin collectors.

Of course, there are much more detailed catalogues and monographs which deal with various aspects of our coinage in greater depth, but the plain fact remains that most numismatists desire a reasonably comprehensive guide that can be contained within a single volume, for ease of reference and the sheer convenience of being able to carry such a volume around with them to coin fairs and shows.

The period under review, covering the numismatic season from October 1998 to September 1999 has seen the positive momentum of the previous twelve months continuing. If growth has not been spectacular, then at least it has been steady; and that, in the long run, augurs well for the continued well-being of our hobby. We are sure that no one would wish to see a return to the roller-coaster situation of the 1970s and early 1980s.

Politically, the past year has been momentous for the dramatic constitutional changes which have resulted in the resurrection of the Scottish Parliament after almost three centuries in limbo. At the same time, the creation of a Welsh Assembly has gone a long way towards satisfying the demands of Welsh nationalism. The implementation of similar proposals affecting Northern Ireland, sadly, has not been achieved, as a result of the seeming deadlock over the decommissioning of the weapons held by the various paramilitary forces.

Apart from a pound note from the Royal Bank of Scotland celebrating the rebirth of the Scottish Parliament, these constitutional developments have not yielded anything of numismatic interest, beyond the ingenious philanumismatic cover which Royal Mail put together, using a contemporary pound coin and a set of the Scottish stamps to celebrate the ceremonial inauguration of the Edinburgh parliament by Her Majesty the Queen.

The three Scottish banks—the Bank of Scotland, the Royal Bank of Scotland and the Clydesdale Bank—will doubtless continue to issue their distinctive (and extremely attractive) notes for the foreseeable future, but there is little likelihood of a revival of Scottish coinage, as things stand at present.

The overriding political and economic development of the past year, however, was the introduction of the single European currency on January 1. During this preliminary phase commerce in the eleven countries of the European Union which have so far signed up for the Euro is being encouraged to express prices of goods and services in dual currency, in Euro as well as the indigenous francs, lire, Deutschemark or whatever. Several countries have already gone so far as to issue their stamps with values in dual currency, but at the time of going to press the definitive coinage, fully described in COIN YEARBOOK 1999, has not gone into circulation. This mammoth currency manoeuvre will swing into gear, appropriately, with the commencement of the new century, or Third Millennium.

We are sufficiently old-fashioned as to cling to the now seemingly outmoded notion that 2000 is actually the last year of the 20th century, and that the 21st century does not really get under way until January 1, 2001. But we are living in the Age of Instant Gratification and patience is not so much a virtue as a lost commodity. So Millennium fever has gripped the world and we can expect the present steady trickle of Millennium coins to swell to a positive torrent before 1999 is over with. So too, the centennial celebration of Her Majesty Queen Elizabeth the Queen Mother got under way even before she celebrated her 99th birthday; but here again we may confidently predict that by the time August 4, 2000 comes around "The Lady of the Century" will be the hottest thing in coins since the demise of Diana, Princess of Wales.

That was
THE YEAR
that was!

An at-a-glance résumé of the main events and occurrences that affected the coin hobby during the past months, as reported in COIN NEWS . . .

September 1998

On September 5 Taya Pobjoy of the Pobjoy Mint marries Robert Cunningham, a London money broker. Both bride and groom are in the business of making money, she literally and he metaphorically.

The St Albans & Hertfordshire Numismatic Society celebrates its Golden Jubilee on September 8.

Sberatel, an exhibition devoted to coins, medals, banknotes, stamps, telephone cards and fossils, is staged at the Industrial Palace, Prague, September 11–13. Highlights include the Royal Canadian Mint stand and an exhibit of coins and medals associated with Charles IV who made Prague the capital of the Holy Roman Empire.

The £5 coin celebrating the 50th birthday of the Prince of Wales goes on sale on September 28. 50p from the retail price of £9.95 on each pack is donated to the Prince's Trust.

Celebrating the St Albans & Hertfordshire NS Golden Jubilee are Secretary John Wilson (left), with guests Peter Clayton, Marion Archibald and Thomas Curtis, with Ray Wilkins (President) holding the cake.

The Royal Mint reverts to a bronze alloy for some of the 1p and 2p coins which, in 1996 and 1997, were struck in copper-plated steel. Apart from a slight difference in the colour of mint specimens, the new version does not have the magnetic property of the steel versions.

The Worldwide Bi-Metallic Collectors' Club goes live on the Internet, catering to collectors of bimetallic coins everywhere.

October 1998

On October 2 the winners of the competition jointly organised by COIN NEWS and the Royal Mint Coin Club enjoy a day trip to Llantrisant and a tour of the mint

Taya Pobjoy takes over from her father Derek as Managing Director of the Pobjoy Mint, Europe's largest private mint.

Joe Cribb on behalf of the British Museum is awarded the IAPN Book Prize, at a COINEX cocktail party held at Spink's Gallery on October 8. The award is made in respect of the two publications *Money: a History* and *The Story of Money*, and is the first time the award is made to one publisher for two books.

Over 30,000 entries are received for Centsation!, a design contest launched by the Royal Canadian Mint to obtain designs for a projected series of coins celebrating the Millennium.

November 1998

COIN NEWS celebrates its 400th issue since its inception. Originally a quarterly entitled *Coins & Medals*, it made its debut in 1964.

Marking the 80th anniversary of the Armistice that brought World War I to an end, the Victoria & Albert Museum mounts an exhibition of art medals pertaining to the war, under the title of "One by One: European Commemorative Medals of the Great War 1914–18". The exhibition, sponsored by Sotheby's, provides a rare opportunity to view the V&A Sculpture Department's incomparable collection which is normally held in store. The exhibition continues until February 11, 1999.

Krause Publications of Iola, Wisconsin, the world's largest publisher of hobby books and periodicals, launches an auction website. Collect.net plans to hold auctions live, interactive and ongoing.

The 40th anniversary of *Blue Peter*, the popular children's television show on BBC, is marked by a commemorative medal showing the programme's logo on the obverse, and the years from 1958 onwards on the reverse.

The South Wales and Monmouthshire Numismatic Society celebrates its 40th anniversary on November 10. Graham Dyer of the Royal Mint is guest of honour at the celebration.

8-year-old Andrew Hoyle, a winner of a COIN NEWS competition enjoys a numismatic day out at the British Museum and the London Coin Fair with the COIN NEWS team.

December 1998

The Royal Mint produces its first coloured coin, a $10 sterling silver coin issued by the East Caribbean Central Bank to raise funds for the Montserrat Volcano Appeal.

Andrew Hoyle, winner of the COIN NEWS competition, with his father on the steps of the British Museum.

The £5 crown commemorating the life of Diana, Princess of Wales is unveiled on January 5.

Mick Vort-Ronald, a regular contributor to COIN NEWS, receives the prestigious Tourism Award in recognition of his services and to mark the tenth anniversary of the Banking and Currency Museum which he founded at Kadina, South Australia.

The Royal Mint celebrate 30 years at Llantrisant and 21 employees who were with the Mint at the time of the move from London are invited to participate.

Mel Fisher, the chicken-farmer who became the world's most successful treasure-seeker, dies at his home in Key West, Florida on December 19. Fisher's greatest coup was the discovery of the Spanish treasure-ship *Atocha* in 1985, yielding a bonanza estimated at over $400 million.

Friary Press, printers of COIN NEWS, are chosen as Business Magazine Printer of the Year at the Printing World Awards.

January 1999

The long-awaited crown £5 coin commemorating the life of Diana, Princess of Wales, is sruck by the Royal Mint and officially unveiled on January 5. The coin carries a profile of Diana by David Cornell, FRBS.

COIN NEWS undergoes a dramatic change in appearance, adopting perfect binding instead of stapling (with an inscribed spine) and several pages of full colour. The pages themselves acquire an exciting new layout.

Celebrations marking the 400th anniversary of the birth of Oliver Cromwell commence on January 8 with an exhibition at the Museum of London entitled "Cromwell—Warts and All". Coins, patterns, essays and medals associated with the Lord Protector are prominently featured in the exhibition which runs until February 28.

An exhibition entitled "Towards a Single Currency" opens on January 16 at the National Museum of Wales in Cardiff and runs until April 6.

A display of coins from the English Civil War hoard recently discovered at Broughton Castle between Oxford and Banbury opens at the Ashmolean Museum.

Under the "Centsation!" scheme, the Royal Canadian Mint begins releasing commemorative 25 cent coins on a monthly basis, in the run-up to the Millennium. Each reverse motif pertains to a different province of Canada.

Although Britain intends remaining aloof from the Euro for the time being, an exhibition opens at the British Museum, tracing the history of previous attempts, from Roman times onwards, at monetary union, as a prelude to the introduction of the Euro in 11 countries of the European Union. The exhibition, sponsored by Visa International, analyses the successes and failures of previous monetary unions and unveils the designs of the Euro currency.

The 28th International Coin Fair takes place at Basel, January 22–24.

A retrospective exhibition of the work of the sculptor Ron Dutton opens at the Simmons Gallery in London and runs until March 26. On show are sculptures, medals and coins alongside paintings and watercolours by this versatile artist and co-founder of the British Art Medal Society. Dutton is the designer of the £2 coin commemorating the Rugby World Cup.

February 1999

John Orna-Ornstein, previously a curator of Roman coins in the British Museum's Department of Coins and Medals, is appointed as Development Curator of the Museum's new HSBC Money Gallery.

The two day coin fair organised by Whyte's and the Numismatic Society of Ireland takes place in Dublin, February 27–28.

Richard Hobbs is appointed Portable Antiques Outreach Officer by the Museums & Galleries Commission. Hobbs, based at the Department of Coins & Medals at the British Museum, liaises with the media, schools and other relevant organisations to raise public awareness of the need for the accurate and prompt recording of finds, under the terms of the new Treasure Act.

March 1999

Arnold Machin, best remembered for the coinage effigy of the Queen which was used on British and Commonwealth coins from 1964 until 1985, dies on March 9 at the age of 87. His name remains a by-word for the British definitive stamps introduced in 1967 and now holding the world record as the most prolific in terms of denominations, colours and printing processes.

Lord Lawson, former British Chancellor of the Exchequer, is the guest of honour at the Australian Gold Conference held in Perth, Western Australia, March 10–12 as part of the year-long celebrations marking the centenary of the Perth Mint.

The Duke and Duchess of Gloucester visit the Royal Mint and strike the first medal marking the 900th anniversary of the Order of St John, of which the Duke is Grand Prior.

April 1999

The Wessex Numismatic Society celebrates its 50th anniversary with a coach trip to London.

The 1999 Congress of the British Association of Numismatic Societies takes place at York, April 9–11, the host Yorkshire Numismatic Society celebrating its 90th anniversary this year.

On April 16 the British Numismatic Trade Association holds a one-day bourse at the Millennium Britannia Hotel, Grosvenor Square, London, attracting serious buyers from around the world.

The world's leading person-to-person online trading community, e-Bay, launches its UK website on April 16.

The US Mint announces its intention to re-introduce a dollar circulating coin later in the year.

John Orna-Ornstein, newly-appointed Development Curator of the HSBC Gallery at the British Museum, talks to school children on coins and currency.

Israel releases a set of medals in memory of King Hussein of Jordan who died in November 1998.

The Counterfeit Collectors Society is relaunched under the name of the Counterfeit Coin Club.

May 1999

As part of the Golden Jubilee celebrations of the Wessex Numismatic Society, a gala dinner takes place on May 6. Guest speaker is Professor Michael Metcalf who gave his very first talk, as a 16-year-old schoolboy, to the Society on May 6, 1949. On both occasions his subject was "Coins and Geography", the latter event contrasting developments over the intervening half-century.

The fifth Olympic Collectors' World Fair takes place at the Olympic Museum, Lausanne, May 21–23, catering to collectors of coins and medals, badges and insignia, stamps, cards and other mementoes associated with the modern Olympic movement.

Spink achieve a new auction record price for a single coin when they sell the Medina dinar of Al-Walid (89–96 AH) from the Turath collection for the amazing sum of £308,000 on May 25.

On May 27 Sotheby's also set a new record auction price for an Islamic coin, this time it was for a silver dirham of Jiroft which realised £99,000.

The Irish International Collectables Fair organised by Fair Aisle Promotions takes place in Dublin, May 29–30.

June 1999

COIN NEWS launches the Collector's Choice full-colour supplement, detailing a wide range of offers by mail order.

Chris Rudd, the specialist dealer in Celtic coinage, holds his first auction in London on June 4.

The Perth Mint's latest guide book celebrates its centenary.

The Perth Mint celebrates its centenary on June 20. Originally established as a branch of the Royal Mint to refine gold from the Western Australian goldfields, it produced sovereigns and half-sovereigns from 1899 till 1931 and continue to produce quality collector coins.

No fewer than 69 numismatic firms are represented at the 48th Annual Congress of the International Association of Professional Numismatists, held in Madrid—a record attendance.

The winner of the Royal Mint's competition to design a Millennium medal is named as Felicity Powell. Her design, showing a dandelion clock, is being released later in the year in nickel-brass and cupro-nickel with three optional reverse motifs.

July 1999

Her Majesty the Queen formally opens the Scottish Parliament in Edinburgh, the first since 1707. To mark the occasion, the Royal Bank releases a commemorative pound note, while Royal Mail and Royal Mint combine to produce a philanumismatic cover, encapsulating the 1999 pound coin showing the Scottish lion rampant.

The Tall Ships' Race, from St Malo to Aalborg, Denmark, takes place from July 23 to August 21, with stops at Greenock and Lerwick. To mark the event Shetland Numismatics commissions the Tower Mint to produce a set of ten Shetland kroner with a map of the route on the obverse and colour reproductions of the various ships on the reverse.

The York Coin Fair takes place at the York Racecourse Grandstand over the weekend of July 30–31, bigger and better than ever.

The dinar of Al-Walid that Spink sold for a new record price of £308,000 on May 25.

Krause Publications of Iola, Wisconsin, already the world's largest publisher of collectables handbooks and magazines, acquires Landmark Specialty Publications of Norfolk, Virginia.

August 1999

The Royal Mint reveals plans to include a minting facility in the Millennium Dome where the Millennium commemorative £5 coins will be struck.

Joe Cribb is awarded the silver medal of the Royal Numismatic Society in recognition of 30 years of distinguished service to numismatic science.

The Royal Mint's annual report for 1998–99 is published, revealing record production of 3,832 million circulating coins although there was a fall in operating profits, after an increase of £3.1 million on capital expenditure.

A new world record price is set for a coin when Bowers and Merena, USA, sell the Walter H. Childs collection in New York on August 30. The legendary 1804 Class I "Original" proof silver dollar realises $4,140,000 surpassing all expectations.

September 1999

The ninth International Coin Convention takes place at the Holiday Inn Golden Mile, Hong Kong, September 3–5, organised jointly by Taisei Gallery and China Great Wall Investments.

The Token Congress is held at the Cumbrian College of Art and Design in Carlisle, September 3–5.

Eddie and Cindy Smith inaugurate a new monthly coin show on September 5 at the Chiltern Hotel, Luton.

The Museum of London opens an exhibition on September 8 celebrating the life of King Alfred, the only English monarch to receive the title of "Great". It marks the 1100th anniversary of

Alfred's death (October 26, 899). A highlight of the show is the Alfred Jewel from the Ashmolean Museum.

Studio Coins release their 50th list. The firm was established in 1987 by Stephen Mitchell after leaving Seaby where he had been catalogue editor.

The Royal Canadian Mint releases the Millennium Gold Wafer, while the Royal Mint produces Millennium crowns in a variety of metals and finishes.

The Pobjoy Mint pioneers the Platina, a bullion coin struck in white gold.

Sheffield Coin Auctions celebrate 15 years in business.

The world record holder—the 1804 dollar which Bowers and Merena sold on August 30 for $4,140,000.

The
BEST AND
WORST
of recent coin designs

The period under review approximately covers the latter part of 1998 and the first half of 1999. It was a year in which no one theme predominated, although old faithfuls such as Sport and Royalty were still well to the fore.

Strangely enough, the forthcoming Millennium has made relatively little impact so far. To be sure, there have been further instalments of the series from San Marino and the Vatican, with strong spiritual or religious overtones. The latter in particular has concentrated on the life of Christ, and concluded its Millennium series with coins depicting the Last Supper and the Crucifixion. The Isle of Man produced a further quartet in its series of crowns charting the major landmarks of history, limitless scope for good narrative designs.

The edge of a coin as the minutes of a clock face is evident in the design for the British Millennium £5 coin, with the hands of the clock which are pointing at midnight, pivotted on the crucial meridian at Greenwich. Numismatically this is the first coin to bear three dates: 1999 and 2000 on the reverse and 2000 on the obverse. Gibraltar has also struck two Millennium £5 coins, the first showing various London landmarks with the Millennium Dome in the foreground, while the second plays on the theme of "Time is of the Essence".

Other issues are pending, and will doubtless have been launched by the time these words are in print. In particular we like the idea of the lengthy series of low-denomination circulating coins from both Canada and the United States. Rather than take a vertical approach, reaching backwards through the centuries, these relatively young countries have opted for the horizontal approach, with coins representing each state or province. From the advance publicity seen so far, we can confidently predict that both sets will be extremely popular in North America, which has, after all, the largest indigenous numismatic market.

Certain events and occasions stirred the imagination to a lesser extent. The Chinese lunar

The UK's Millennium clockface coin.

Gibraltar's theme is "Time is of the essence".

new year provoked the usual crop of coins from the Far East with variations on the rabbit theme; but the prize for the best designs in this genre must go, once again, to Western countries. Gibraltar was quick to seize the opportunity provided by the Year of the Rabbit to adapt the popular rendering of Beatrix Potter's Peter Rabbit. Canada rose to the occasion with a $5 Maple bearing a rabbit mint-mark.

Such a worthy event as the 50th anniversary of the United Nations Declaration of Human Rights

19

inspired coins from very few countries, although France and Poland brought dignity and gravitas to the occasion in their masterful motifs. As 1998 was designated by the United Nations as International Year of the Ocean it was expected that this theme would provide endless scope for coins depicting marine life; but the response from maritime countries was disappointing, to put it mildly. The Isle of Man produced four crowns and Gibraltar added eight, exploring the conflicting interests of man and nature in the seas and oceans. Why must it always be left to the smaller countries to exercise imagination and a certain flair, transforming what might otherwise be very pompous subjects into something lively and provocative?

Only one country recorded the total eclipse of the Sun which took place in certain parts of the northern hemisphere on August 11. Although such eclipses are relatively commonplace, this is the first time that we recall a coin being issued. Although the path of totality crossed southern England, France, Austria, Hungary, Romania, Turkey, Iran and India (all of which ignored the numismatic potential of the occurrence), appropriately it was left to tiny Alderney in the Channel Islands to fill the gap. Its crown-sized £2 coin shows the eclipse behind St Anne's church, while a pair of bemused gannets roost in the foreground, believing that it is night-time. It should be noted that the Royal Astronomical Society organised a trip to Alderney where the best view of the eclipse in the British Isles lived up to expectations. Alderney has cunningly catered not only to collectors of astronomical coins but also to those devoted to religion, architecture and ornithology!

The "Year of the Older Person" received symbolic treatment from Canada.

The United Nations designated 1999 as International Year of the Older Person (or the Senior Citizen, as some countries have chosen to interpret the subject). The end result was much the same: either a symbolic treatment (e.g. Canada) or a more pictorial approach (Australia). Incidentally, in addition to six coins specifically dedicated to IYOP, the latter also brought out a dollar coin as a tribute to the last of the Anzacs, the gallant veterans of the Dardanelles campaign of World War I, which ranks as one of the most poignant designs of the period under review.

After the spate of *Titanic* issues last year, interest in the ill-fated liner seems to have abated, although the Turks and Caicos Islands brought out a couple of $20 coins. The first had a reverse showing the great liner on her maiden voyage; but the second showed the submersible *Alvin* exploring the ghostly wreck on the seabed. It is no mean feat to convey the sense of mystery and tragedy in the confines of a low-relief coin, but full marks for a motif which has achieved the wellnigh impossible in both respects.

Contemporary numismatics is a subject that is largely market-led these days, which explains the popularity of serial issues. Among the top contenders, some of which have been running for several years, we may cite Portugal's Discoverers, Liberia's American Presidents, Canada's Wildlife and Gibraltar's Labours of Hercules—the last-named neatly alluding to the fact that the Rock itself forms one of the fabled Pillars of Hercules. Canada's long-running series on the history of powered flight came to an end, with the final pair of silver coins. It will be remembered that this series introduced the concept of inset portrait cartouches in another, contrasting metal, and it should be noted, in passing, that 1998–99 has been a period in which bimetallism has shown a notable increase in popularity, either as an outer ring or as a "spot" element in the field.

Arguably the longest-running serial is the Isle of Man's cat series, the latest version depicting a British Blue washing its paws. Each of these designs is a masterpiece of medallic art taken individually, but

Surprisingly Gibraltar was one of the few countries to celebrate "The Year of the Ocean"

Alderney alone marked the total eclipse of the sun with a coin which appealed to ornithologists as well as coin collectors!

the series as a whole is quite awe-inspiring. Clearly the Isle of Man feels immensely satisfied with this series, hence the special tenth anniversary coin which reproduced in miniature the motifs of the entire series!

Among the other serials which have not been under way for long one may cite the issues from Canada marking the Lunar New Year. This is billed as a five-year programme, scheduled to end in 2003. Why end it there? The Chinese lunar cycle is a 12-year one, and it makes no sense to chop it off so abruptly. It is to be hoped that as 2003 approaches better counsels will prevail and the life of this potentially exciting series is prolonged. New Zealand has begun a series devoted to its cities, showing their insignia and principal landmarks. The same theme has been adopted by Lithuania, though, we suspect, for rather different reasons. A country which has only recently regained its independence has a lot of catching up to do, and this explains the parallel series devoted to historic rulers.

The longest-running series— The Isle of Man's "Cats".

As prophesied last year, Austria's series devoted to Tragedies of the House of Habsburg has this year highlighted the worst of them all, the one which, directly or indirectly, has affected mankind ever since. We refer to the assassination of the Archduke Franz Ferdinand and his morganatic wife Countess Sophie Chotek, whose conjoined bust portraits grace the obverse of a new 100 schilling coin. The reverse shows the royal party leaving Sarajevo town hall, boarding their open tourer only minutes before the assassination. In the foreground is Count Harrach, stepping on to the running board to shield their Imperial Highnesses with his own body. Ironically, he survived the bomb outrage.

British royalty has been going through a lull lately—but only in the relative sense. Hard on the heels of last year's 50th birthday coin for the Prince of Wales has come Britain's belated contribution to Dianolatry. Usually profiles work well as coinage effigies; it is often much more effective in achieving a recognisable likeness than three-quarter or full-face portraiture. Although this genteel image contrasts with the very expressive portrait of Diana

The Archduke Ferdinand and his wife on the obverse of Austria's 100 schilling.

which appears on the cover of the coin folder, it perhaps captures the caring side of the Princess better than other similar issues.

Gibraltar has set the ball rolling in what will surely be one of the major events of 2000— Millennium and Olympic Games aside—the 100th birthday of the Queen Mother. The first four crowns in a projected series of twelve have already appeared, and the series will culminate in Her Majesty's "ton" next August, all being well. The odds are in the Queen Mum's favour; a recent report in *The Times* records that in 1998 alone Her Majesty the Queen sent out no fewer than 3,521 birthday messages to centenarians in the United Kingdom.

With Australia producing no fewer than 52 coins, in various metals, the Sydney Olympic Games are set to be the sports spectacle of 2000, numismatically at any rate, and doubtless many other countries will follow the Isle of Man (five crowns) and Gibraltar (six) in exploring every aspect of Olympic sport ad nauseam. Royal Mail is so bogged down in its Millennium stamps this year that hardly anything else gets a look-in; but the Royal Mint has fortunately avoided this with a simply splendid bi-metallic £2 coin showing a rugby ball and goalposts.

Now for a brief look at some of the other designs which, in the past twelve months, have stood out on account of their impact and high aesthetic qualities. The set of five coins, one each from the Bahamas,

Canada commenced a five-year Lunar programme with the Year of the Rabbit.

Sport—always a popular theme—well catered-for by (left) the UK £2 for the Rugby World Cup and (below) Australia's "Sydney 2000" Olympic issues.

several which fit neatly into the category of decidedly weird, but the results are thought-provoking, amusing or eye-catching. The trophy in this class must go to the coin from Slovakia to celebrate the centenary of Jan Smrek. The obverse is strange enough, in all conscience, with a rear view of a seated nude, her buttocks flopping provocatively across the bottom line (no pun intended); but the reverse has a half-length portrait of the poet smoking a cigarette (surely a first in coin design) and the smoke writhing upwards suggests the curvacious outline of a nude woman. We are not sure what the significance of this is but we can hardly wait to get hold of the collected poems of Jan Smrek to find out!

Poland issued two coins to mark the bicentenary of Adam Mickiewicz. One has a full-face portrait of the poet with hair streaming wildly, but the other has a curious treatment in which both profile and facing portraits are superimposed, creating a startling effect. When it comes to offbeat treatment of portraits, however, Switzerland takes the biscuit, with its 20 franc coin marking the centenary of the death of the poet Conrad Meyer. The obverse has a close-up of only a part of the face, mainly the bespectacled eyes and nose, and even this has his autograph signature scrawled across it.

Barbados, Belize, the Eastern Caribbean and Jamaica to mark the 50th anniversary of the University of the West Indies, is a shining example of restraint and good design, heightened by the fact that all five coins have uniform reverse showing the University's badge. The prize for the most effective use of profile portraiture must go to Israel for its 20 sheqalim coin in memory of assassinated prime minister Yitzhak Rabin. No one could claim that Rabin was the most handsome of men, but the massive, brooding profile has a majesty that many coins portraying genuine royalty sadly lack.

We hasten to add that any assessment of coin design is bound to be subjective, and this one is no exception. Personally, we are not particularly enamoured of Ian Rank-Broadley's effigy of the Queen. We do not doubt that it is a very accurate rendering of Her Majesty's profile but it seems faintly redolent of Pistrucci's handling of George III and George IV. Photographs of Queen Victoria in old age reveal heavy jowls and puffy cheeks, yet these features were tactfully toned down in the Veiled Head effigy. Perhaps Royal Mail have the right idea after all, retaining for the postage stamps the effigy of the Queen sculpted by the late lamented Arnold Machin more than 30 years ago.

There are no designs this year which one could truly castigate as poor. On the other hand there are

Both the obverse (shown here) and the reverse of Slovakia's "Nude" is certainly eye-catching.

While the Bermuda Triangles go their merry way, the latest advance in odd-shaped technology is the use of segmentation. This was first used in a (literally) joint issue from Kiribati and Western Samoa to mark the Millennium. Each country has an irregular half of the coin, the pieces fitting together along the International Dateline. This concept has been developed in a quadripartite coin, consisting of three fan-shaped outer segments as $2 coins from the Cook Islands, Fiji and Western Samoa, around a central disc which is, in fact, a silver medal celebrating the 30th anniversary of the Singapore Mint.

The same concept has been adapted by Guernsey to celebrate the Millennium. An outer ring showing hands embracing the Earth has been issued with a 1999 date, and it is intended that the central hole will be filled with a £1 gold-plated plug dated 2000. Doubtless, by the time the actual Millennium is upon us, even stranger coins will have been devised.

The most effective profile must be that of Yitzak Rabin on Israel's 20 sheqalim.

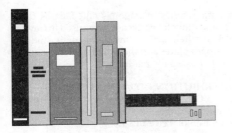

Books
of the year

Every coin collector knows that knowledge is the key to forming a good collection and each year new books or new editions of older works, as well as standard reference works, are up-dated by dedicated specialists. Here we list the most important numismatic titles that have appeared during the past year. Most have been reviewed in COIN NEWS.

AMERICA'S MONEY—AMERICA'S STORY by Richard Doty. 248 pages. Card covers. Krause Publications. Price $34.95.

This succinct account of American coins and paper money is written by the curator of numismatics at the Smithsonian Institution, Washington. It shows graphically how money has always played a major role in the development of the USA while conversely the ups and downs in American history have been faithfully reflected in the nation's currency.

ANCIENT COIN COLLECTING IV: ROMAN PROVINCIAL COINS by Wayne G. Sayles. 198 pages. Casebound. Krause Publications. Price £18.99.

Previous volumes in this series by Wayne Sayles have dealt with the coinage of the Greek world and the Roman republic, but now he turns his attention to the Roman provinces from the reign of Augustus to the end of the third century. This is a discursive overview of the primarily local coinage of client kingdoms and provinces throughout the vast, sprawling empire. There are excellent illustrations of coins, while maps of the various mint locations help to place the local coins in their imperial context. A separate section dealing with the coins of Roman Egypt has been contributed by Kerry K. Wetterstrom.

ANCIENT COIN COLLECTING V: THE ROMAION/BYZANTINE CULTURE by Wayne G. Sayles. 196 pages. Casebound. Krause Publications. Price $24.95.

Many readers may be unfamiliar with the first adjective in the sub-title, but Romaioi was a Greek word signifying the ethnic Greeks who inhabited the eastern Roman Empire. After the fall of the Empire in the west in 476, the Romaioi maintained Roman culture and traditions and later formed the bastion against incursions from barbaric tribes and the rising menace of Islam. Their civilisation lasted 1,000 years, until the collapse of the Byzantine Empire with the fall of Constantinople to the Osmanli Turks in 1453. This book is a lightning romp through this Graeco-Roman millennium, with a concise survey of its coinage, denominations, types, fabric and alloys.

The core of the book is a gallery of the emperors and empresses from Anastasius I in 491 to Constantine IX Palaeologus in 1453. No more than a page is allocated to each, but it provides a potted biography, a coin illustration and brief details of the coinage. Its saving grace is the bibliography appended to each reign. The book serves as a succinct introduction to a complex and relatively under-appreciated series.

BYZANTINE AND EARLY MEDIEVAL WESTERN EUROPEAN COINS IN THE HUNTER COIN CABINET by J. D. Bateson and I. G. Campbell. 190 pages and 29 plates. Casebound. Spink. Price £50.

Founded by Dr William Hunter, physician to George III in the 18th century, the Hunter Coin Cabinet ranks as one of the world's largest and most important coin collections. While the Greek, Roman, Anglo-Saxon and Scottish coins have been fully documented and previously published, the Byzantine and early medieval coins of Western Europe have not been the subject of a separate sylloge until now. All but 68 of the 569 Byzantine coins in the cabient were collected by Dr Hunter personally. This survey includes, for the sake of convenience, 156 Western European coins dating from the fifth to tenth centuries, notably a remarkable series of Merovingian gold which Hunter is believed to have purchased from Joseph de France during a trip to Vienna in 1782 shortly before his death. This volume fills a gap in studies of Dark Age coinage while adding useful material to our understanding of the Byzantine series.

CEYLON COINS AND CURRENCY by H. W. Codrington. 290 pages plus 7 plates. Casebound. Selous Books. Price £27.99.

A reprint of a work originally published in 1924, the book is still relevant as it follows the coinage of Ceylon since ancient times through the medieval period into the colonial history and its resultant plethora of currencies. Also covered is the fascinating series of pagodas and fanams from India and other far eastern sources used in Ceylon which so often confuse the numismatic student. The superb plates and the exhaustive index serve to further assist the reader.

CONTRIBUTIONS TO THE STUDY OF INDO-PORTUGUESE NUMISMATICS by J. Gerson da Cunha. 128 pages. Casebound. Selous Books. Price £12.95.

A reprint of a work originally published in 1880, it deals with all aspects of the coins used in Goa and other Portuguese settlements in India from 1510 onwards, with particular reference to the influence of Hindu, Moslem, Chinese and Malay cultures on them.

CONVICT LOVE TOKENS edited by Michele Field and Timothy Millet. 122 pages and 8 colour plates. Laminated card covers. Wakefield Press. Price £12.99.

The custom of converting coins into love tokens by painstakingly picking at the images and effigies by means of a pin or a sharp point is old-established, but this study looks at a particular aspect of the subject, namely those love tokens which were engraved by convicted felons, many of whom were destined for Botany Bay and other penal establishments in the Australian colonies. Not surprisingly, many of these pieces have socio-political overtones which add considerably to their interest. This fascinating subject is well illustrated with numerous monochrome photographs and line drawings as well as the colour plates of the more spectacular items.

CORPUS NUMMORUM ITALICORUM by Antonio Vessella. 80 pages and 11 plates. Card covers. Edizioni ASMV. Price 35,000 lire.

This volume dealing with the ancient coinage of Italy covers the issues made in Magna Graecia, specifically in Sannio, Frentania, Sabina and the south-eastern districts of Latium. It is a unique and innovative work, distinguished by the most meticulous research and a highly scientific approach to the subject.

LE GUIDE-ARGUS DU FRANC. 128 pages. Paperback. A special publication of La Monnaie, 12 rue Raymond-Poincare, 55800 Revigny-sur-Ornain, France. Price 39 francs.

The title is a little deceptive, for this handy paperback is in fact a price-catalogue of modern French coinage, from the end of the 19th century to the present day, arranged by denomination from the humble centime to the 100 francs, including commemorative and special issues where relevant. Appendices give details of Les Amis du Franc, an association for collectors of modern French coinage, as well as a Forum giving odd facts and feats concerning the modern coinage. Each design is copiously illustrated and described, and values are given in up to six grades of condition.

HISTORY AND COINAGE OF THE ROMAN IMPERATORS, 49-27 BC by David R. Sear. 360 pages. Casebound. Spink. Price £50.

This is the latest in a long line of authoritative texts from the able pen of David Sear whose first work, *Roman Coins and Their Values*, was published 35 years ago. This book deals with the Roman coinage in the turbulent period 49–27 BC during which Rome was transformed from a republic presided over by the Senate to a military autocracy ruled by one man, the Emperor Augustus. This was the period of the imperators, a term which originally signified a general but could more accurately be described in the context of this period as warlords, though in the end it came to be the imperial title - indeed, the word "imperial" springs from the same root. In this well-illustrated book we witness the unfolding saga of Caesar and Pompey, of Brutus and Cassius, of the triumvirs and Octavian, Caesar's great-nephew on whom the imperial mantle eventually fell.

IRISH BANKNOTES: IRISH GOVERNMENT PAPER MONEY FROM 1928 by Mártan Mac Devitt. 410 pages. Casebound. Published by the author and Whytes Auctioneers. Price £75.00.

A fully illustrated guide, complete catalogue and history of Ireland, its banks and banking history and of course its banknotes. The book is a work of

dedication by the author that updates all earlier publications on the subject from the attractive "Ploughman" notes to the present colourful issues of the current series. The author had access to the main archives of the issuing banks and is able to include much information never before made public. For the collector of the Irish series this book is an essential read.

MAGIC COINS OF JAVA, BALI AND THE MALAY PENINSULA by Joe Cribb. 208 pages and 79 plates. Casebound. British Museum. Price £75.00.

This well-illustrated volume provides the reader with a concise survey of the "magic coins" of South East Asia, the coin-shaped metal objects based on the Chinese coins that circulated in Java in the late 13th–15th centuries, which were widely used as lucky charms. They are distinguished from contemporary circulating coins by their mystic images and inscriptions which were believed to confer magical or spiritual powers on their owners. Many depict the "wayang" shadow puppets of Indonesia. The book is based on the famous Raffles collection of coin-shaped charms in the British Museum and which is compared with specimens in other famous collections.

MEDIEVAL EUROPEAN COINAGE, Volume 14, Part III: South Italy, Sicily and Sardinia. With a catalogue of the coins in the Fitzwilliam Museum, Cambridge, by Philip Grierson and Lucia Travaini. 814 pages, 63 plates, 21 tables, 7 maps and 38 diagrams. Casebound. Cambridge University Press. Price £100.00.

The first volume in this stupendous undertaking appeared in 1987 and volumes 2 to 13 are scheduled for publication some time in the next Millennium, not necessarily in numerical order, which explains why volume 14 has appeared ahead of the others. MEC 14 deals with the coinage of southern Italy and the offshore islands between the mid-10th century (where MEC 1 ended) and the reign of Ferdinand the Catholic in the 15th century. It therefore covers the pre-Norman, Norman, Hohenstauffen, Angevin and Aragonese dynasties, together with their very disparate coinages.

THE PINGO FAMILY AND MEDAL-MAKING IN 18th CENTURY BRITAIN by Christopher Eimer. 96 pages. Card covers. British Art Medal Trust. Price £19.95.

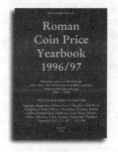

ROMAN COIN PRICE YEARBOOK edited by Morten Eske Mortensen. 525 pages. Casebound. Auction Corporation of Denmark. Price £55.00.

A concise account of one of the leading families associated with coin and medal engraving, the most notable members being Thomas and Lewis Pingo, father and son, who respectively designed many medals as well as the Spade guinea and the shillings and sixpences of 1787. The wholly original research reads like a detective story as the author explodes the myths surrounding Pingo and his origins. Far from being Italian, as all previous writers have claimed, Christopher Eimer has proved that Thomas and Lewis Pingo were English born and bred, at least four earlier generations of the family being traced in this country. Thomas Pingo Junior also deserves credit for establishing the first private mint in England, for the manufacture of medals.

PLANNING YOUR RARE COIN RETIREMENT by David L. Ganz. 227 pages. Card covers. Bonus Books, but available in UK from Gazelle (Tel: 01524 68765). Price £10.99.

The sub-title "How to select a $10,000 rare coin portfolio full of growth potential" sets the tone of this book, which is aimed at American readers and therefore, not surprisingly, selects virtually all its examples from the coins of that country. For lesser breeds beyond the pale the text is an eye-opener, for we are initiated into the arcane mysteries of Carson City silver dollars and Indian-head cents, Barber dimes and "gem proof" Eagles. At the end of the book there are eight pages devoted to foreign gold coins; by implication, therefore, there is nothing in foreign silver, let alone base metal, that is worthy of inclusion in the portfolio. The sole exception is a chapter devoted to the Cat series from the Pobjoy Mint. "There are no guarantees in life," comments the author, "but the relatively low mintages of Pobjoy Mint products, the thousand year history of the Isle of Man, and the nifty design on these coins all combine to make these a good investment for your portfolio". A true accolade, if ever there was one.

A price guide to virtually every Roman from 31 BC to AD 138 coin sold at auction throughout the world in 1995 and 1996. The references are for single coins offered as individual lots and wherever possible the item is identified by in-depth description of the piece, auction house, date of sale, lot number, standard reference number, state of preservation, estimated value and hammer price achieved. The book is part of a series also listing Scandinavian coins sold at auction during the same period.

SCOTTISH COINS: A HISTORY OF SMALL CHANGE IN SCOTLAND, by Nicholas Holmes. 112 pages. Card covers. National Museums of Scotland. Price £5.99.

This is the intriguing story of how ordinary money was used by ordinary people in Scotland. Thus it ranges from the coins of the Romans and Anglo-Saxons to the Norman and Plantagenet silver pennies which circulated widely in what is now Scotland, as evidenced by stray finds as well as hoards. There is the suggestion that even after indigenous Scottish coins were introduced, the better quality "foreign" coins were hoarded. From 1367, and certainly after 1390, the Scottish coins were progressively debased until the issue of wholly base-metal coins was officially sanctioned. The bodles, placks and bawbees of Scotland were supplemented by doits and doubles from the Low Countries. The Act of Union abolished the subsidiary coinage without putting anything in its place, and the gap had to be filled by the prolific issues of tradesmen's tokens which continued until the coinage reforms of the early 19th century.

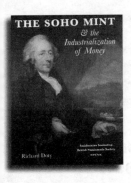

THE SOHO MINT
AND THE
INDUSTRIALIZATION
OF MONEY by
Richard Doty. 350
pages. Casebound.
Spink. Price £45.00.

This is a vivid account of Matthew Boulton and his Soho Manufactory in Birmingham in the late 18th and early 19th centuries which played such a prominent part in the mechanisation of the coin processes and produced excellent coinage not only for circulation in the British Isles but also for various overseas countries, from Australia to Chile, from India to Canada. Not content to manufacture coinage, Boulton and his partner James Watt devised state-of-the-art machinery which was exported to many of the developing nations (such as the USA) as well as supplied to long-established mints.

STANDARD
CATALOGUE OF
MALAYSIA-
SINGAPORE-BRUNEI
COINS AND PAPER
MONEY by Steven Tan.
216 pages. Card covers.
International Stamp &
Coin, Malaysia.
Price £13.00.

This is the 14th edition of a well-established catalogue, now greatly improved in illustration and layout. Mintage figures are included where known, and prices are given in up to three grades of condition.

STUDIES IN GREEK NUMISMATICS IN MEMORY OF MARTIN JESSOP PRICE, edited by R. Ashton and S. Hunter. 400 pages and 80 plates. Casebound. Spink. Price £90.00.

The sudden death of Martin Price in 1995 provoked a wish to create a suitable memorial in the form of this festschrift containing essays on various aspects of Greek coinage contributed by friends and colleagues, together with an appreciation and an introduction.

THE TREASURE ACT IN PRACTICE by Angela Sydenham. 160 pages. Spiral-bound card covers. Monitor Press. Price £65.00.

The core of this book runs to a mere 30 pages, but it is bulked out by eight appendices. Successive chapters outline the meaning of treasure and its ownership, the role of the coroner, rewards to finders, the position of finder, tenant and landowner, and the code of practice drawn up in 1997. The effect of this act on existing legislations, such as the Coroners' Act (1988) and the Merchant Shipping Act (1995) is also discussed. The sections dealing very comprehensively with metal detecting and detectorists will be particularly useful to numismatists and archaeologists.

UNITED STATES PAPER MONEY by Chester L. Krause and Robert F. Lemke. 214 pages. Casebound. Krause Publications. Price $24.95.

This is the 17th edition of the most comprehensive catalogue ever devoted exclusively to the paper currency of the United States and lists over 5,500 items, with 14,000 values and 600 monochrome illustrations. Listing, however, is confined to the period from 1812 onwards when paper money was issued by authority of the US government, and thus it excludes the colonial issues from 1690 onwards as well as the Continental 'shinplasters' of the War of Independence. Separate sections deal with military payment certificates and the issues of the Philippine Islands under American administration (1904–44).

BRITANNIA
through the ages

The figure of Britannia has been featured on milled British coins since 1672. The recent decommissioning of the Royal Yacht *Britannia* inspired RAYMOND PALERMO to outline the changes in style and presentation of Britannia that have taken place on British coinage from Roman times up to the present day. Although many proof, pattern and trial pieces have been struck for these issues, this article focuses mainly on the designs of coins bearing Britannia that were put into general circulation. Proofs and patterns are only referred to in order to preserve continuity (for example, the Edward VIII 1937 pattern penny).

Above, Hadrian's As and right, Antoninus Pius' sestertius depicting Britannia.

In ancient Rome, goddesses were used to represent the spirit of cities and regions. For example, Roma was the goddess of Rome, Africa, the goddess of what is now the northern region of Libya, and Judea, the goddess of the Holy Land. Britannia was the Roman goddess of Britain. These deities were regularly depicted on coins of the Empire for propaganda purposes.

The first image of Britannia on coins is on a Roman bronze As of Hadrian (AD 117–138), to celebrate Rome's victory over the British uprising on the Empire's northern frontier. Hadrian's Wall was built soon after this uprising between the Tyne and the Solway. Britannia is seated facing us, with one foot on a pile of stones, her left hand holding a sceptre and her right supporting her head, with a shield next to her on the right. In the exergue is the word "BRITANNIA".

The next Emperor to show Britannia on his coins was Antoninus Pius (AD 138–161). Pius extended the northern frontier of the Empire, building the Antonine Wall from the Forth to the Clyde Rivers in around AD 140. Many coins were issued over the next four years to commemorate this event, including a bronze Sesterius, showing Britannia facing left, her left arm resting on a shield, her right holding either a spear or a military standard.

In AD 155, the Brigantes, a north-eastern British tribe revolted but were quelled by the Roman forces. Once again, Britannia was depicted on the bronze Sestertius and As. Britannia is seen here in a state of melancholy, her head resting sedately on her right hand, with her shield and standard beside her. The Asses were often crudely struck, suggesting that they might have been copied and struck in Britain itself, rather than Rome.

Britannia was not seen on British coins for the next 1,500 years or so. This was because those responsible for the issue of the coinage were more concerned with using devices such as crosses, heraldry, equestrian and plain inscriptions for various protective, religious and political purposes.

In 1672, during the reign of Charles II (1660–85), the Government legislated to allow the coining of regal halfpennies and farthings in copper which began just after Christmas of that year. The obverse has the head of the King facing left while Britannia is on the reverse. She sits, facing left, holding a spray of olive leaves in her right hand and a plain spear in her left. A shield embossed with the Union Flag of England and Scotland is to the right of the field. Her figure is fully clothed although her dress is gathered coquettishly above the knee of her leg which is slightly extended. She also wears a cap. The reverse legend reads, "BRITANNIA", with the date in the exergue. John Roettier was the designer who, so it is supposed, used Frances Stewart (later

Was the King's mistress the model for Charles II's Britannia?

the Duchess of Richmond), one of the ladies at the Royal Court and the King's mistress as his model. The flans themselves were imported from Sweden because the Royal Mint was unable to produce copper blanks of a suitable quality. While clearly styled in the Baroque idiom, it is obvious that Roettier's Britannia was based on the model used on the coins of Antoninus Pius from around AD 140.

Farthings of Charles II were also minted from tin in 1684 and 1685 to help the Cornish tin industry. These pieces were similar to their copper counterparts but were somewhat thicker and contained a copper plug in the centre to make counterfeiting more difficult.

Tin halfpennies and farthings continued to be minted for most of William and Mary's reign (1689–94) using Roettier's Britannia. The electrochemical reaction between the copper plug and the tin flan caused these pieces to corrode very quickly, however, so the Government abandoned using tin to mint base coins in favour of copper in 1694. The copper halfpennies and farthings are quite common although harder to obtain in higher grades. For the copper pieces, the edge legend was omitted and the date, once again, placed in the exergue.

Britannia suffered from the shoddy minting of the copper coinage for William III's reign (1694–1702). Unsatisfactory practices such as the casting of coins and the use of cheap foreign labour led to a deterioration of the quality of these coins as a whole. The coins were weakly struck and poor Britannia even suffered the indignity of having her name spelt incorrectly. It can be argued that the decline in the standard of the copper issues was due to the Government being more concerned with ensuring that the Great Recoinage of 1696 resulted in an improved standard of gold and silver issues.

No regal copper coins were issued during the reign of Anne (1702–14) until 1714. The Master of the Mint at the time, Sir Isaac Newton, fiercely believed that the intrinsic value of the coinage should equal the face value and that the coin designs should be of a high standard. Many patterns for farthings were submitted for consideration. The potent mix of Newton's ideals and the Rococo art movement resulted in a farthing

Britannia's ankles were covered to please the prudish Queen Anne.

featuring a Britannia, designed by John Croker, struck in high relief sitting facing left, wearing an elegantly flowing robe, holding her customary sprig and spear, her Union Flag embossed shield prominently displayed, with the date in the exergue. She also appears more comfortably seated than previous Britannias. To mollify the somewhat prudish Queen, Britannia's leg was now covered to the ankle, unlike many of the previous models, which often left a leg bare from the knee down. Because of the high quality of these coins and the occurrence of the Queen's death in the same year as issue, the Anne farthing is commonly found in high states of preservation and is keenly sought by collectors.

The same Britannia punch was used for the copper coins of George I (1714–27), with the minting of both halfpennies and farthings being recommended in 1717.

The 1717 and 1718 halfpenny, and 1717 farthings are known as "dump" issues because they were struck on thick and compact flans. Subsequent issues were struck on normal flans.

Croker's Britannia was used for all of George II's (1727–60) farthings but two reverses were used for the halfpenny. The earlier reverse (1729–39), in the finest Rococo style, was probably designed by the ageing Croker, while the later version (1740–54) was possibly designed by either John Tanner or John Ochs, Junior, although it has been suggested that Croker was responsible, due to its high artistic quality.

Many counterfeit copper coins were in circulation in the 18th century, especially during the reigns of George II and George III. These pieces varied enormously in quality from virtual copies of Croker's Britannia to extremely poor imitations. The general population's attitude did not help matters for it regarded the copper coinage as having little importance compared to the gold and silver issues.

George III's (1760–1820) first issues of copper halfpennies were dated 1770 to 1775 and farthings, 1771, 1773 to 1775. The reverses had a new Britannia, engraved by Richard Yeo whose Britannia was similar in quality and style to Tanner's (or Och's) model.

Britannia was completely redesigned for the

William III's Britannia, although sometimes badly struck, showed a shapely leg.

famous "cartwheel coinage" of 1797, so-called because of the extreme thickness of their flans and raised rims. The one penny and two penny pieces, comprising one and two ounces of pure copper respectively, were struck at Matthew Boulton's Soho Mint in Birmingham, using James Watt's steam technology. This change in general style and weight was implemented to make counterfeiting more difficult and to comply with Boulton's philosophy (echoing Newton) that a coin's intrinsic value should equal its face value.

The German artist, Conrad Kuchler engraved Britannia for the 1797 issue. Britannia is seated on a rock, facing left. For the first time, she is seen amidst the sea. For the first time also, she holds a trident (as opposed to a spear previously), and olive spray. Her shield, proudly displaying the Union Flag, is beside her to the right. On the rock, just below the shield is the world "SOHO" in small script. In the left background is a man-o-war bravely sailing the high seas. Britannia is dressed in a flowing gown that clings to her body. The legend, "BRITANNIA 1797", is engraved in incuse on a raised rim. The obverse, also by Kuchler, carries an equally magnificent portrait of the King. These coins must have provided much inspiration to the British sailors as they prepared for battle against Napoleon's equally patriotic forces.

Halfpennies and farthings were issued from the Soho mint in 1799, with a similar Britannia, complete with warship, again by Kuchler. These pieces were lighter than the "cartwheels" but still closely matched intrinsic and face values. Unlike the previous issue, the rim was not significantly raised and the edge was grained diagonally. The legends were engraved in relief. On the farthing, as well as the word, "BRITANNIA" and the date, is the inscription, "1 FARTHING", the first time that the name of a denomination appears on any English coin. It was also the first time that the date appears on the obverse of an English coin.

In 1806 and 1807, the Soho Mint produced another issue of copper coins, namely the penny, halfpenny and farthing, featuring Kuchler's Britannia of similar style to the 1799 issue. The obverse shows the ageing King, facing right, with the date below.

Between 1797 and 1808, numerous patterns of the minor denominations were struck at the Soho Mint. While some were genuine trial pieces, many, including mules, were minted privately by Boulton. This situation did not improve when the Soho Mint closed down in 1848 and much of the machinery, including some dies, were sold to the Clerkenwell die sinker, W. J. Taylor, who experimented with the striking of unauthorised patterns as well.

To alleviate the problem of a silver coin shortage in circulation in the early years of the 19th century, the Bank of England overstruck Spanish-American eight reales pieces, which it had in surplus. These were Bank of England dollars and were current for

Kuchler's design for the famous "Cartwheel" coinage placed Britannia firmly on the sea.

five shillings. The obverse has a laureate bust of the King, while the reverse has Britannia, by Kuchler, seated facing left, amidst the sea, with a battleship in the background, within an oval garter inscribed, "FIVE SHILLINGS DOLLAR". Outside the garter is the legend, "BANK OF ENGLAND" and the date, 1804, below. Some examples show traces of the original coin's design. Although all of these coins carry the same date, they were actually struck until 1811.

The Royal Mint moved to Tower Hill in 1816, followed by the Great Recoinage. It was, however, in 1821, during the reign of George IV (1820–30), that Britannia made her next appearance. This was on the farthing (1821–22), the only base metal denomination minted for the first issue of this reign. She was, once again, completely redesigned. The artist this time was the famous Italian, Benedetto Pistrucci. Against tradition, his Britannia sits facing to the right, holding her trident in her left hand and resting her right hand on a rather oval shield, which partly obscures a spray of leaves. As well as her robes, Britannia now wears a crested helmet in the ancient Roman style. The legend reads, "BRITANNIAR REX FID DEF" and the date occupies the exergue. The sea and ship have been omitted. Pistrucci's Britannia looks rather stiff and is less endearing than Kuchler's efforts but his model nonetheless serves as a fine example of neoclassical coin design.

The Bank of England chose Britannia to overstrike Spanish-American silver.

William Wyon took over most of the coin designing duties following the removal of Pistrucci, precipitated by the latter refusing to copy Sir Francis Chantrey's bust of the King for the second coinage. Wyon's Britannia, on the penny (1825–27), halfpenny (1825–27), farthing (1826–30), half farthing (1828–30, for use in Ceylon) and third farthing (1827 only, for use in Malta) is extremely elegant. She sits, facing right, with her left hand curled around her trident. Her shield is more rounded than Pistrucci's and the exergue contains a lovely arrangement of an English rose, a Scottish thistle and an Irish shamrock. The legend is the same as that of Pistrucci's model. The field is devoid of sea, ships or sprays, resulting in an altogether clear and perfectly balanced design.

Two interesting varieties of the pennies of George IV are a slightly thicker or thinner line representing St Andrew's saltire on Britannia's shield.

William Wyon's Britannia for George IV's copper issues was extremely elegant although devoid of any background.

William Wyon's Britannia continued to be used for the copper denominations of William IV (1830–37), which were the same as his brother, George IV.

The silver groat was reintroduced in 1836–37, with Wyon's Britannia and the legend, "FOUR PENCE" on the reverse. Whilst being quite small, at only 16mm in diameter, Wyon's talent for design can still be appreciated.

The base metal coinage of Victoria (1837–1901) can be divided into three distinct periods: the Young Head (copper, 1836–1860), Bronze Young (Bun) Head (bronze, 1860–1895) and Old Head (bronze, 1895–1901), reflecting the portrait style.

The reverse designs of the first young head coinage were similar in style to the copper issues of Victoria's uncles, George IV and William IV. The obverse carries a charming effigy of the Queen, by William Wyon. The penny, halfpenny, farthing and third farthing (the latter for use in Malta) are of interest to us because they each have Wyon's Britannia on the reverse. Unlike the previous two reigns, however, many varieties occur on Victoria's copper issues. Some of the most interesting examples are the style of the trident's head (either plain or ornamental) on some pennies, the presence of two prongs on the trident instead of three on the 1839 farthing, and the presence of incuse dots on and above Britannia's shield on some halfpennies of 1851, 1852 and 1857, as well as all halfpennies dated 1853 to 1855. Overdates on the obverse, and variations in the spelling and punctuation of the reverse legend are also frequently encountered with these issues,

although the denomination most commonly seen with these variations is the penny.

From 1860, the base metal coinage was minted from bronze, due to the rising price of copper and to overcome the inconvenience of the larger and heavier (though artistically beautiful) copper pieces.

The bronze young head, or "bun" issue featuring Britannia comprises the penny (1860–94), the halfpenny and the farthing (1860–95). Both the obverse, showing the Queen with her hair tied in a bun (hence the nickname of this issue) and the reverse were designed by William Wyon's eldest son, Leonard Charles Wyon. Britannia has been, once again, redesigned. She sits, looking a little more relaxed than on the copper issue, facing right. She holds her trident in her left hand while resting her right hand on her shield. In the left field, on the sea, we see a lighthouse and in the right field is a three masted ship. Britannia is now smaller in size to accommodate the reduced flan size and the date is in the exergue. The legend has also been changed. The Royal titles are now on the obverse while the value of the coin is on the reverse. The whole design is enclosed within a beaded border.

The obverse of Victoria's "Old Head" coinage (1893–1901) was designed and engraved by Thomas Brock. Of interest to us, Britannia was on the reverse of the penny, halfpenny and farthing, depicted using another design. Brock designed the new Britannia while the very talented George William de Saulles was responsible for the engraving. Brock's Britannia is larger than L. C. Wyon's, the crest of her helmet shorter and her shield larger and more oval in shape. Her trident is also more plain than before and the date is, once more, in the exergue. The lighthouse and ship are omitted.

The silver groat, with Victoria's young head on the obverse and William Wyon's Britannia on the reverse was struck between 1838 and 1855. It was issued again, in 1888 only, for use in British Guyana, this time with Boehm's Jubilee Head on the obverse.

The reign of Edward VII (1901–10) saw pennies and halfpennies being struck in 1902 using Brock's and the de Saulles' Britannia with both "high" and "low" tide varieties. From 1903 onwards, only the former was used. The farthing was minted using "low tide" dies in 1903, otherwise "high tide" dies were employed.

Edward VII's reign is especially important as far as a study of Britannia on the coinage is concerned because, for the first time on British coins, a standing Britannia design was used. De Saulles designed this device for the silver florin. Britannia is proudly standing on the prow of a ship, holding her trident and shield. Her helmeted head is turned slightly to the right, her cloak blowing behind her to the left. This denomination proved very popular with the public and has remained so with collectors today.

The model for de Saulles' standing Britannia was the 24 year old Miss Susan Hicks-Beach (later Lady Susan Hicks-Beach), daughter of the Chancellor of the Exchequer (and therefore Master of the Mint), Sir Michael Hicks-Beach.

A similar standing Britannia was used on the

obverse of the silver British Trade Dollar, between 1895 and 1935, again engraved by de Saulles and possibly with Miss Hicks-Beach as the model. These pieces were minted mainly at Bombay and Calcutta for use in promoting trade with Great Britain in the Far East. The reverse, incidentally, is inscribed with the value written in Malay script and Chinese characters.

The penny, halfpenny and farthing issues of George V (1910–36) carried the (seated) Britannia of the previous reign but the standing Britannia on the florin was dropped in favour of a cruciform shield design.

The pattern penny for Edward VIII (1936), dated 1937, has a Britannia designed by Thomas Humphrey Paget that is similar to the Brock/de Saulles' model. The new Britannia sits facing right, holding her trident a little more erect in her left hand. Her left arm is more bent than before. There is more sea visible to the left of Britannia, where we also find, once again, a lighthouse.

The halfpenny and farthing no longer depicted Britannia because it was felt that, while the reducing machine faithfully reproduced Britannia on these smaller pieces, her aesthetic qualities could not be fully appreciated. The halfpenny now depicted Drake's ship, the Golden Hind, while the farthing had a wren on the reverse.

Paget's Britannia was used on George VI's (1936–52) pennies. Between 1944 and 1946, pennies were made from a bronze alloy containing a higher proportion of copper than normal, thus making the coins tarnish rather unattractively. To counter this problem, the pennies were artificially blackened prior to release by the Mint.

A slightly modified Britannia was used on the predecimal pennies of Elizabeth II. One difference was that the toothed border used on the penny of the previous reign now became a beaded border.

Throughout the 20th century, slight changes were made from time to time on the detail of the Britannia design. *The Bronze Coinage of Great Britain* by Michael Freeman (1985), published by Barrie and Jenkins, London, is an excellent reference for those interested in pursuing this topic.

In 1969, the decimal 50 new pence in cupro-nickel was released to circulate on parity with the ten shilling note. The new coin was seven sided and measured 30mm across. The obverse bust was designed by Arnold Machin, while Christopher Ironside was responsible for Britannia on the reverse. Britannia is seated to the right, holding a spray of olive branches in her left hand and gently resting her right hand on her trident, which also leans on her shield. A lion proudly sits next to Britannia, and looks in the same direction as his mistress. The legend reads, "FIFTY NEW PENCE" with the value in the exergue. The graceful pose of Britannia and the perfect balance of the design makes this the finest example of a seated Britannia since William Wyon's superb model which graced the copper coinage of George IV, William IV and Victoria. Apart from various commemorative issues, this has remained the basic design for the 50 pence piece.

The daughter of the Chancellor of the Exchequer was the artist's model for Britannia on Edward VII's florin.

In 1985, for the first time since the reign of Edward VII, Britannia was depicted in a standing position on British coinage. This was the new design for the gold bullion issue £100, £50, £25 and £10 pieces. Designed by Philip Nathan, the new standing Britannia, whilst strongly reminiscent of de Saulles' version, is nevertheless an outstanding example of later 20th century design and a worthy Coin of the Year winner in 1987. Britannia stands, with her body turned towards us. Her long, flowing garments and hair dramatically windswept to the left, in which direction her head is turned. Her helmet has a prominent, pointed visor and is adorned by a long, yet graceful crest. She stands on a rock, with a wavy sealine on a low horizon to each side. She holds her trident, almost vertically, in her right hand and grasps her oval shield, together with an olive spray in her left. The legend is within a ringed border and reads (for the £100 piece) "ONE OUNCE FINE GOLD BRITANNIA" along with the date.

To celebrate the 10th anniversary of the gold Britannia issue and the tercentenary of the Britannia silver hallmarking standard, the Royal Mint released a special edition set of bullion coins in 0.958 silver with the face values of £2, £1, 50 pence and 20 pence. Philip Nathan was commissioned to design a special standing Britannia for this commemorative issue and his efforts, once again, do not disappoint. Britannia is attired in the battle dress of a Roman soldier, complete with breastplate, holding her trident and being drawn in a chariot by two very spirited horses. The legend, enclosed by an inner ring is partly obscured by Britannia and reads (for the £2 piece), "ONE OUNCE FINE SILVER 1997 BRITANNIA".

Britannia has been depicted on British coinage continuously for over three centuries. May this, the most important of British icons, continue to fascinate with her graceful presence for many years to come.

On this design, originally issued in 1997 to celebrate the 10th anniversary of the British "Britannia" bullion coins, she was given a chariot.

36

Talking TOKENS

Strictly speaking, a token is any piece of money whose intrinsic value is less than its face value. In that sense, therefore, all modern coins are mere tokens, because their metallic worth is invariably less than their nominal, legal tender value. Until the 19th century, however, most countries issued coins which contained metal up to the value at which they circulated. This applied mainly to gold and silver coins, but it should be noted that Britain's first copper penny and twopence (1797) were so cumbersome because they contained one and two ounces of metal respectively, copper being then valued at a penny an ounce.

The desire for parity between intrinsic and nominal value led to copper coins containing a small plug of silver to bring them up to their full value. The UK abandoned full value in 1816; as a result of the recoinage of that year the gold sovereign became the absolute standard and all silver and copper coins became mere tokens. The difference between real and nominal value widened in subsequent years with the debasement of silver coins and finally the replacement of silver altogether by cupro-nickel and other base alloys. Oddly enough, there have been many instances of small copper or bronze coins in recent years which had a greater intrinsic value than their face value and actually cost twice as much to produce as they were worth in circulation.

A token is an outward sign or pledge, something given or shown as a guarantee of authority or good faith. The word comes from German zeichen and Old English tacen, meaning a sign or mark. From this developed the notion of a promise, symbol or keepsake. In the numismatic sense, however, the term is restricted to any coinlike object, either issued by a body other than a government, or something which is used in place of money and can be exchanged for specified goods and services. Broadly speaking, tokens include any unofficial coins supplied by local bodies or occasionally even private individuals and tolerated in general circulation at times of shortage of government issues of small change.

Tokens go back a surprisingly long way. The earliest issues in base metal with limited local validity were produced by Sicily in the middle of the fifth century BC, the bronze litra being easier to handle than its tiny silver counterpart. Himera was one of the first towns to issue such tokens, but by the end of the century many Sicilian towns had adopted small bronze pieces as token currency, the intrinsic value of which was considerably below the circulating value placed on them by the issuing authorities.

This concept gradually spread to all other parts of the Greek world. Under the Roman Empire, base-metal tokens were issued from the time of Augustus to the late third century AD. Sometimes referred to as quasi-autonomous coinage, these pieces were struck mostly in bronze with the nominal value of drachmae or sestertii, and have portraits of local deities instead of the Roman emperor and members of his family. These tokens were struck by every town and city and their range and variety is enormous.

This concept survived the fall of the Roman Empire and many towns in medieval Europe continued to strike small base-metal pieces for use as local currency. They were usually accorded a measure of legality because they were authorised by the royal or imperial government, even if their actual design and metal content were decided by the municipal authorities. In addition to the tokens which served as small change there are other categories of coinlike material which deserve comment.

Jetons (from French jeter, to throw) originated in medieval France as counters used on the chequerboard by merchants and bankers as well as royal treasurers to do their monetary calculations. These pieces spread rapidly all over Europe, but found their greatest expression at Nuremberg where, in the hands of Hans Krauwinckel (flourished 1580–1620), they attained the status of an art form and were often produced in thematic sets.

While many jetons were struck in gold or silver and were eventually used (especially in France) as a form of New Year bonus to servants, the vast majority of them were struck in debased silver alloys (billon) or in copper, bronze, brass or pewter. Base-metal Nuremberg jetons, in fact, often circulated as small change in countries where there was a shortage of total lack of government issues of small change. This situation arose in England early in the 14th century, Nuremberg jetons circulating freely until 1335 when they were banned by statute.

English tokens

The first indigenous tokens in England were cast or struck in lead and have been recorded as circulating in 1404. For many years these local farthings and half-farthings were tolerated but had no official sanction. They were certainly well-established in Tudor times and it was not until 1598 that any attempt was made to regulate them. Queen

The prolific issues of 18th century tokens were banned on the introduction of the "Cartwheel" coinage in 1797.

Elizabeth then licensed Bristol to issue lead tokens, to be valid within a ten-mile radius of the city. At the same time, private tokens were expressly forbidden, so that the municipal tokens were given a monopoly. By the end of the Civil War (1649) there was an acute shortage of small change, and illicit tokens, mainly in lead and including pewter, brass, copper or even leather pieces, were revived in England and Wales.

Almost 4,000 types of token were issued in London alone, by tradesmen and shopkeepers of all kinds, and often circulating no farther than the end of the street. As the vast majority were produced before the Great Fire of 1666 they form an invaluable record of London streets and their occupants from this period. Following the introduction of regal copper farthings and halfpence in 1672 these tradesmen's tokens were banned, but they continued in some parts of England until 1674, and survived in Ireland until 1679. By contrast there was virtually no need for tokens in 17th century Scotland because of an abundant supply of copper coinage, and only two Scottish tokens (c. 1668) have so far been recorded.

In many ways tokens benefited the poor, who were no longer compelled to purchase more than they actually required because the smallest coin available was a penny. Tokens were also used as alms, as people would gladly give a farthing but would think twice about giving a halfpenny or penny. For this reason many tokens of the 17th century were inscribed "Remember the Poore",

17th century tokens come in a variety of shapes and sizes.

"For the Poore's Advantage" or "For Change & Charitie" or some other pious slogan.

There were even tokens inscribed in verse: "To supply the poore's need is charitie indeed". Other poetic inscriptions include "When you please, I'll change thee", "Although but brass, yet let me pass", "Welcome you be to trade with me" or "Take these that will, I'll change them still".

Eighteenth century tokens

Tokens were revived in the British Isles in 1787 to fill a gap in the regal coinage. Silver pennies for general circulation were only sporadically produced in the reign of George III and none at all was minted after 1786. The dearth of copper halfpence and farthings was even greater as none was minted after 1775. On this occasion the way was led by the Angelsey Copper Mining Company which began striking pennies with the effigy of a Druid on the obverse. This triggered off an immense deluge of token pennies, halfpennies and farthings. The range was not as great as it had been in the 17th century as fewer individual shopkeepers now issued them.

There was a greater concentration of tokens issued by municipal authorities and the more important merchant companies. On the other hand, the quality of design and execution improved beyond all recognition and latterly they were aimed at the contemporary collector market, with emphasis on heraldry, landmarks, scenery, historic events and portraits of local and national celebrities. These tokens enjoyed a decade of use before they were banned following the introduction of the "Cartwheel" coinage in 1797.

Nineteenth century tokens

Silver tokens were issued between 1804 and 1816 as a result of a continuing shortage of silver coins. At first countermarked Spanish dollars and half-dollars were issued but in 1811–12 the Bank of England released silver pieces inscribed BANK TOKEN on the reverse, with the value and date below. The obverse portrayed George III and had his name and titles round the circumference like the proper silver coins. Denominations of 1s6d and 3s were issued; though 9d pieces exist they were only patterns. The Bank of Ireland had silver tokens in the same period, but denominated in a decimal system of 5, 10 and 30 pence, as well as 6 shillings. Many private silver tokens were issued in 1811–12 in denominations from 3d to 5s, mainly by private banks, local authorities and large companies.

Copper or bronze tokens were again issued in the British Isles from 1811 to the 1830s. As no copper subsidiary coins were issued between 1807

and 1821 (no halfpence or pennies until 1825–26) the range of tokens in this period was far greater than ever. Significantly a high proportion of these tokens were now issued by banks rather than by private individuals.

Other types of tokens

Tokens have been produced in most countries at some time or another. Very extensive series, for example, were produced in Canada and Australia before these countries introduced subsidiary coinage. They were also produced on a number of occasions in the USA, from the revolutionary period onwards, and notably during the Hard Times (1834–44) during a shortage of copper cents and half-cents. There was a further spate of local tokens during the Civil War (1861–65), often with patriotic motifs and having a propaganda purpose as well as filling the gap in the coinage. Many countries issued tokens during and after the First World War, every type of material from pasteboard and wood to leather and even rubber being pressed into service. A special category consists of trade dollars issued all over Canada. These are often commemorative or intended as tourist mementoes, but they have a nominal value, redeemable for cash within a certain area and over a fixed period, usually twelve months. They are immensely

Banks and local authorities produced hundreds of different tokens in the early 19th century.

Hop tokens, although simple and sometimes crudely made, can make an interesting collection.

popular and now have a wide following in North America.

In Britain from the 18th century onwards tokens were often issued by textile mills, collieries, iron foundries and other industrial undertakings in exchange for a day's work. These tokens could only be used to obtain goods from the company stores, and were eventually outlawed by the Truck Act in 1844. Nevertheless they survived in various parts of Britain, often in specific forms of labour. A very prolific series, for example, consists of hop-pickers' tokens, associated mainly with the hopfields of Kent and Sussex. In Scotland, however, fruit-pickers' tokens were also issued by many of the farms in the Clyde Valley and the fruit-growing areas of Perthshire and Angus.

Another vast area consists of the checks and tokens issued by co-operative societies, often in proportion to the money spent by the member in the societies' stores, as a form of dividend. When a certain quantity of checks had been accumulated they could be exchanged for goods or services. The same concept underlay the discount schemes, premium giveaways and trading stamps of more recent items.

Tokens of metal, pasteboard or even plastic have been used as a method of controlling the use of public transport by employees of companies, the Post Office or local authorities, being given out whenever it was necessary for an employee to travel on official business. Such tokens were produced by local authorities or the private companies operating buses, ferries, trams and other services. At the other end of the spectrum are the tokens and passes, often in silver or even gold, or ivory, which were issued to directors of the railway companies to enable them to travel free of charge. Tokens in the same materials, and for the same purpose, were produced for the use of the directors and shareholders of theatres and other places of entertainment, and were often highly ornate in design.

Gaming tokens

This is another vast field, ranging from the brass halfpenny and penny tokens issued by many pubs and taverns in the 19th century for use in games of chance, to the modern tokens, often in cupro-nickel, bronze or aluminium-bronze, used in one-armed bandits and fruit machines. These tokens range from the fairly utilitarian designs showing perhaps a company name and a unit of value only, to the very elaborate tokens used by casinos and gaming clubs, often with special security features built into their design and composition. Many of the gaming tokens of more recent years have a quasi-commemorative or publicity character.

A new world record price for a British token was set at Noble Numismatic's sale on July 7/8, 1998, when Richard Orchard's Sawbridgeworth token realised £24,400.

Squashed
PENNIES

Paranumismatica is a term used to encompass anything vaguely numismatic or coin-like. Tokens are the prime candidates for this all-embracing heading but some items are less obvious—elongates definitely fall in the category but until recent years have been the prerogative of the US collecting scene. However, their popularity is spreading rapidly (the internet is helping!) and each year more and more become available to the collector looking for something different—and affordable as PAUL BAKER explains . . .

Elongates are unusual in that they are made by further processing a standard coin—they are produced when a coin is rolled through a press which brings about that distinctive ovoid shape.

So why turn a coin into something else? Producing a coin, especially in small numbers, is expensive so why not save some of this expense by cutting out the blank production process and use a circulated coin instead? British elongates are all made from one penny coins. Elongates are one of the few examples of one coin or coin-like object being effectively turned into another—a practice that, perhaps surprisingly, is not illegal in Great Britain.

To produce an elongate a small coin is forced through two rollers and as the coin passes through the rollers the image from a die on one of the rollers is pressed on to the coin. Such a pressure is applied that the original design of the coin almost disappears. The compression of the coin through the dies also causes the newly-produced elongate to be ovoid and on a somewhat curved planchet which is initially quite hot. In fact this pressure is believed to be in the region of 2,500 pounds per square inch. Designs always seem to include a feature called the start-bar. This is a lip at the end of the piece that passes through the dies first. The start-bar's purpose is to aid the rolling process by giving the dies something to grip on.

The commercial purpose of the elongate is to be an inexpensive, novel, advertising souvenir. This is found to be of great use to tourist attractions. Thousands of designs from zoos, theme parks, museums and the like in the USA

A number of museum's issue elongates including this one from the Royal Museum of Scotland, Edinburgh.

Deep Sea World, Inverkeithing, and Highland Mystery World, Glencoe, are two other Scottish tourist attractions where elongates can be purchased.

The Verdant Works at the Dundee Heritage Trust is a keen supporter of elongates.

Chocoholics are also well catered for!

are known. Often, but not always, the host coin is the lowest denomination, hence the most common host in the US is the cent (the cent coin is often referred to a "penny"). There is obviously a lot of material available to the collector of US elongates and dies for new designs are continually coming into use over there. Here in Britain we have relatively few designs, perhaps less than 100, so there is a greater challenge in getting hold of these. The most obvious way to obtain an elongate is to

visit a tourist attraction either knowing or hoping that they have a machine for making elongates. These are basically just another variety of vending machine though perhaps a little larger than usual. Often it is possible to view the route of the coin as it is being procesed which makes it more interesting. The cost of having a one penny coin elongated varies around 40 or 50 pence, although sourcing a machine in Britain could itself involve a lot of travelling, which of course is another expense. Your second option for acquiring elongates is to keep looking in coin shops and on dealers lists. Pieces usually cost around a pound—when you can find them. At the moment it seems that very few, if any, dealers know of the relative abundance of the different designs and so prices seem to be the same irrespective of design.

Many elongates exhibit a further feature of great relevance, this being the maker's mark—a lower case "e" in place of one of the beads in the border near to the start-bar. The "e" is the trademark for Eurolink whose British base, EurolinkGB, is in Linlithgow, Scotland. This company's location accounts for there being so many British elongates with designs related to Scottish tourist attractions. Eurolink also has a base in California, USA, run by its sister company, Eurolink Design Corporation.

The best advice for collecting British elongates would be to collect one of each and every type you can find. There is perhaps only one way that the series could be broken down at all and that would be to either collect Scottish pieces or those from anywhere else in Britain. Collecting just those depicting say animals, would probably narrow one's scope down too much. Of course a few animal elongates would certainly make an interesting addition to a general collection of animals in numismatics. In contrast a collector in

The famous Sea Life Centre on Weymouth's golden mile is an attraction visited by thousands of holidaymakers every season—and most of them take an elongate home with them

the USA could go for themes in US elongates of just animals, zoos, people or even Disney characters, etc, and still have plenty to look for.

Those most similar to the elongates of Great Britain are those from the Republic of Ireland. A number are known and these could easily be mistaken for British pieces since the one penny coins there are of identical specification to the British ones. So of course Irish elongates can be made from British one penny coins and vice-versa. At least one Irish piece (Blarney Castle) is on a British penny and it has the "e" trademark for EurolinkGB, so perhaps a collection of elongates of Great Britain could easily turn into one of the British Isles.

A little more challenging than this would be a collection of one elongate from each country for which pieces exist. Apart from the USA, Great Britain and Ireland, this could also include countries such as France, Germany, Sweden and even New Zealand. In many countries legislation still forbids doing such defacement of current coins—in Japan elongates have been made using specially-made blanks, in Australia obsolete pre-decimal coins are known to have been used for this purpose and the machines in Canada swap the tourist's Canadian one cent for a US one cent and it is onto this that the new design goes.

It was only through the relaxation of similar legislation in Britain in the early 1980s that the use of the elongate as a commercial item ever came about. Prior to the relaxation of our laws no one would have dared to sell such machines for the defacement of coins, for fear of the severe penalties.

Before elongates, another way of making an advertising piece from a small coin was the framing or encasing of a coin. A relatively small number of types of British encased farthings are known (perhaps less than 20) and all of these are apparently over 30 years old, although in the USA there is a different story. Hundreds of encased coin designs exist and new ones continue to be produced. Going back even further into the history of British paranumismatica we have, from late Victorian times, coins stamped with words such as "PEARS' SOAP" as a means of advertising. Legal action was avoided by the choice of host coins—foreign coins such as the bronze French 10 centimes were used, and of course the British government wasn't going to worry about the defacement of foreign coins. Coins which were similar in size to the British pennies current at the time were intentionally chosen as they often circulated as pennies and hence carried around their advertisement.

The minute "e" (seen at the top of the elongate) is Eurolink's own "mintmark"

For further information an organisation based in the US called "The Elongated Collectors" (TEC) exists as a world-wide organisation for those with a particular interest in elongates. TEC meets annually and produces a regular newsletter. For details write to The Elongated Collectors (TEC), Adele Vogel, TEC Secretary, PO Box 352, Butler, WI 53007-0352, USA.

One website to note is Bert Creighton's "Smashed Coin Locator" which can be found at http://www.smashedcoin.com. This site includes a list of all countries world-wide which are known to have elongates. Another useful website, is to be found at http://www.pennypage.com, this has plenty of information with images accompanying a listing of US elongates.

DATES
on coins

The vast majority of modern coins bear the date prominently on one side. In most cases dates are expressed in modified Arabic numerals according to the Christian calendar and present no problem in identification. There have been a few notable exceptions to this general rule, however. Morocco, for example, has used European numerals to express dates according to the Moslem calendar, so that a coin dated 1321 actually signifies 1903. Dates are almost invariably written from left to right—even in Arabic script which writes words from right to left. An exception, however, occurred in the Philippines quarto of 1822 where the date appeared as 2281, and the "2s" back to front for good measure.

	ARABIC-TURKISH	CHINESE, JAPANESE KOREAN, ANNAMESE (ORDINARY)	CHINESE, JAPANESE KOREAN, ANNAMESE (OFFICIAL)	INDIAN	SIAMESE	BURMESE
1	١	一	壹	٩	໑	၁
2	٢	二	貳	২	๒	၂
3	٣	三	叁	३	๓	၃
4	٤	四	肆	४	๔	၄
5	٥	五	伍	५	๕	၅
6	٦	六	陸	६	๖	၆
7	٧	七	柒	७	๗	၇
8	٨	八	捌	८	๘	၈
9	٩	九	玖	९	๙	၉
0	٠			٥	๐	၀
10	١٠	十	拾		๑๐	
100	١٠٠	百			๑๐๐	
1000	١٠٠٠	千				

Dates in Roman numerals have been used since 1234 when this practice was adopted by the Danish town of Roskilde. Such Roman numerals were used sporadically throughout the Middle Ages and survive fitfully to this day. This was the system used in England for the first dated coins, the gold half-sovereigns of Edward VI struck at Durham House in 1548 (MDXLVIII). This continued till 1550 (MDL) but thereafter Arabic numerals were used, beginning with the half-crown of 1551. Notable exceptions of more recent times include the Gothic coinage of Queen Victoria (1847–87).

The first coin with the date in European numerals was a plappart of St Gallen, Switzerland dated 1424, but this was an isolated case. In 1477 Maria of Burgundy issued a guldiner which bore a date on the reverse, in the form of two pairs of digits flanking the crown at the top. The numerals in this instance were true Gothic, an interesting transition between true Arabic numerals and the modified Arabic figures now used in Europe. The Tyrolese guldengroschen of 1484–6 were the first coins to be regularly dated in European numerals and thereafter this custom spread rapidly.

For the numismatist, the problem arises when coins bear a date in the numerals of a different alphabet or computed according to a different era. Opposite is a table showing the basic numerals used in different scripts. The various eras which may be found in coin dates are as listed and explained overleaf.

Hijra

The era used on Moslem coins dates from the flight of Mohammed from Mecca to Medina on July 15, 622 and is often expressed as digits followed by AH (*Anno Hegirae*). Moslems employ a lunar calendar of twelve months comprising 354 11/30 days. Tipu Sultan of Mysore in 1201 AH (the fifth year of his reign)introduced a new era dating from the birth of Mohammed in AD 570 and using a luni-solar system. Tipu also adopted the Hindu cycle of sixty years (the Tamil Brihaspate Cycle), but changed this two or three years later, from Hijra to Muludi.

Afghan coins used the lunar calendar until 1920 and during 1929–31, but at other times have used the solar calendar. Thus the Democratic Republic began issuing its coins in SH 1358 (1979).

To convert an AH date to the Christian calendar you must translate the Arabic into European numerals. Taking an Arabic coin dated 1320, for example, first deduct 3% (to convert from the Moslem lunar year to our solar year). This gives 39.6 which, rounded up to the nearest whole number, is 40. Deduct 40 from 1320 (1280), then add 622. The answer is 1902.

There have been a few notable exceptions. Thus the Khanian era of Ilkhan Ghazan Mahmud began on 1st Rajab 701 AH (1301). This era used a solar calendar, but was shortlived, being confined to coins of Mahmud and his nephew Abu Said down to year 34 (1333).

The era of Tarikh Ilahi was adopted by the Mughal emperor Akbar in the thirteenth year of his reign (922 AH). This era dated from his accession on 5th Rabi al-Sani 963 AH (February 19, 1556). The calendar had solar months and days but no weeks, so each day of the month had a different name. This system was used by Akbar, Jahangir and Shah Jahan, often with a Hijra date as well.

Saphar

The era of the Caesars began on January 1, 38 BC and dated from the conquest of Spain by Augustus. Its use on coinage, however, seems to have been confined to the marabotins of Alfonso VIII of Castile and was expressed in both Latin and Arabic.

Samvat

The era of Vikramaditya began in 57 BC and was a luni-solar system used in some Indian states. Coins may be found with both Samvat and Hijra dates. Conversion to the Christian date is simple; merely subtract 57 from the Samvat to arrive at the AD date.

Saka

This originated in the southwestern district of Northern India and began in AD 78. As it used the luni-solar system it converts easily by adding 78 to the Saka date.

Nepal

Nepalese coins have used four different date systems. All coins of the Malla kings were dated in Nepal Samvat (NS) era, year 1 beginning in 881. This system was also used briefly by the state of Cooch Behar. Until 1888 all coins of the Gurkha dynasty were dated in the Saka era (SE) which began in AD 78. After 1888 most copper coins were dated in the Vikram Samvat (VS) era from 57 BC. With the exception of some gold coins struck in 1890 and 1892, silver and gold coins only changed to the VS era in 1911, but now this system is used for all coins struck in Nepal. Finally, dates in the Christian era have appeared on some commemorative coins of recent years.

Ethiopian

This era dates from August AD 7, so that EE 1885 is AD 1892. Ethiopian dates are expressed in five digits using Amharic numerals. The first two are the digits of the centuries, the third is the character for 100, while the fourth and fifth are the digits representing the decade and year. On modern coins dates are rendered in Amharic numerals using the Christian era.

Thailand

Thai coins mainly use the Buddhist era (BE) which dates from 543 BC, but some coins have used dates from the Chula-Sakarat calendar (CS) which began in AD 638, while others use a Ratanakosind Sok (RS) date from the foundation of the Chakri dynasty in AD 1781.

Hebrew

The coins of Israel use the Jewish calendar dating from the beginning of the world (Adam and Eve in the Garden of Eden) in 3760 BC. Thus the year 1993 is rendered as 5753. The five millennia are assumed in dates, so that only the last three digits are expressed. 735 therefore equates with AD 1975. Dates are written in Hebrew letters, reading from right to left. The first two characters signify 400 and 300 respectively, totalling 700. The third letter denotes the decades (*lamedh* = 30) and the fourth letter, following the separation mark (") represents the final digit (*heh* = 5). The Jewish year runs from September or October in the Christian calendar.

Dates from the creation of the world

This system was also used in Russia under Ivan IV. The dating system *Anno Mundi* (AM) was established by the Council of Constantinople in AD 680 which determined that the birth of Christ had occurred in 5508 AM. Ivan's coins expressed the date as 7055 (1447).

Dynastic dates

The system of dating coinage according to regnal years is a feature of Chinese and Japanese coins. Chinese coins normally have an inscription stating that they are coins of such and such a reign period (not the emperor's name), and during the Southern Sung dynasty this was joined by the numeral of the year of the reign. This system was continued under the republic and survives in Taiwan to this day, although the coins of the Chinese Peoples Republic are dated in western numerals using the Christian calendar.

Early Japanese coins bore a reference to the era (the title assumed by each emperor on his accession) but, like Chinese coins, could not be dated accurately. From the beginning of the Meiji era (1867), however, coins have included a regnal number. The Showa era, beginning in 1926 with the accession of Hirohito, eventually ran to sixty-three (expressed in western numerals on some denominations, in Japanese ideograms on others) to denote 1988, although the rest of the inscription was in Japanese characters.

Dynastic dates were used on Korean milled coins introduced in 1888. These bore two characters at the top *Kae Kuk* (founding of the dynasty) followed by quantitative numerals. The system dated from the founding of the Yi dynasty in 1392. Curiously enough, some Korean banknotes have borne dates from the foundation of the first dynasty in 2333 BC.

Iran adopted a similar system in 1975, celebrating the 15th anniversary of the Pahlavi regime by harking back to the glories of Darius. The new calendar dated from the foundation of the Persian Empire 2535 years earlier, but was abolished only three years later when the Shah was overthrown.

Political eras

France adopted a republican calendar in 1793 when the monarchy was abolished. Coins were then inscribed L'AN (the year) followed by Roman numerals, but later Arabic numerals were substituted. This continued to the year 14 (1806) but in that year the Emperor Napoleon restored the Christian calendar.

The French system was emulated by Haiti whose coins dated from the revolution of 1803. The date appeared as AN followed by a number until AN 31 (1834) on some coins; others had both the evolutionary year and the Christian date from 1828 until 1850 (AN 47). Coins with a date in the Christian calendar appeared only in 1807–9 and then from 1850 onwards.

Mussolini introduced the Fascist calendar to Italy, dating from the seizure of power in October 1922. This system was widely employed on documents and memorials, but was first used on silver 20 lire coins of 1927 and then only in addition to the Christian date and appearing discreetly as Roman numerals. Subsequently it was extended to gold 50 lire and 100 lire coins in 1931 and the subsidiary coinage in 1936, being last used in the year XXI (1943).

Around the WORLD

Listed here are the names of all the coins of the world, many of which have been around for hundreds of years, others are no longer in use. Some of the denominations have been introduced only recently, whilst others are familiar household words. A number of the names are shared by different countries and a few have even been used by different civilisations.

Abazi Caucusus
Abbasi, Abbassi Afghanistan, Georgia, Persia
Ackey Gold Coast
Adli Altin Ottoman Empire
Afghani Afghanistan
Agnel France
Agora (ot) Israel
Ahmadi Mysore, Yemen
Akce Turkey
Akcheh Turkestan
Albertusdaler Denmark
Albus German States, Swiss Cantons
Altin, Altun Egypt, Turkey
Altinlik Turkey
Altyn, Altynnik Russia
Amani Afghanistan
Amman Cash Mewar Udaipur, Pudukota, India
Angel England, Scotland, Isle of Man
Angelet France
Angelot France
Angster Lucerne
Anna Burma, India, Pakistan, Kenya, Muscat & Oman
Antoninianus Rome
Ardite Navarre
Argentino Argentina
Ariary Malagasy Republic
As Rome
Asarfi Nepal
Ashrafi Afghanistan, Awadh, Bahawalpur, Egypt, Hyderabad
Asper Algeria, Egypt, Libya, Trebizond, Tunisia, Turkey
Asses Luxembourg
At Laos
Atia Portuguese India
Atribuo Frankfurt
Att Cambodia, Laos, Siam (Thailand)
August d'Or Saxony

Augustale Sicily
Aurar (plural **Eyrir**) Iceland
Austral Argentina
Avo Macau, Timor
Bagarone Bologna
Bagattino Venice
Baggliangster Lucerne
Baht Thailand
Baiocco (plural **Baiocchi**) Papal States
Baisa Oman
Baiza Kuwait
Baizah Muscat & Oman
Balboa Panama
Ban (plural **Bani** or **Banu**) Roumania
Banica Croatia
Barbarina Mantua
Barbonaccio Lucca
Barbone Lucca
Barbuda Portugal
Barilla Philippines
Batzen German States, Swiss Cantons
Bawbee Scotland
Bazaruco Portuguese India
Bazaruk Dutch Settlements in India
Belga Belgium
Benduqi Morocco
Besa (plural **Bese**) Ethiopia, Somalia
Beshlik Soviet Central Asia
Bezant Byzantine Empire, Cyprus, Jerusalem
Bezzo Italian States
Bianco (plural **Bianchi**) Bologna, Papal States
Biche French Indian Settlements
Binio Roman Empire
Bipkwele Equatorial Guinea
Bir (r) Ethiopia
Bisti Caucasia
Bit Guyana, West Indies
Bitt Danish Virgin Islands
Black Dog Nevis
Blaffert Switzerland

Blanc France
Blodsklipping Sweden
Bluzger Swiss Cantons
Bodle Scotland
Bogach Yemen
Bolivar Venezuela
Boliviano Bolivia
Bolognino Papal States
Bonk Ceylon, Dutch East Indies
Bonnet Scotland
Boo Japan
Braspenning Flanders
Broad England
Bu Japan
Budju Algeria
Buqsha Yemen Arab Republic
Burbe(ns) Tunisia
Butut Gambia
Cache French Indian Settlements
Cagliareso Italian States
Calderilla Spain
Candareen China
Carbovanetz Ukraine
Carlin Sicily
Carlino Papal States
Carolin Austria,German States, Sweden
Cash China, Hong Kong, India, Mysore,
Travancore, Turkestan, Vietnam
Cassathaler German States
Cauri Guinea
Ceitil Portugal
Cent Australia, Bahamas, Barbados, Belize,
Bermuda, Botswana, British East Caribbean
Territories, British Honduras, British North
Borneo, British Virgin Islands, Brunei,
Canada, Cayman Island, Ceylon, China,
Cochin China, Cocos (Keeling) Islands, Cook
Islands, Curacao, Cyprus, Danish West Indies,
East Africa, Ethiopia, Fiji, French Indochina,
Gilbert and Ellice Islands, Guyana, Hawaii,
Hong Kong, Indonesia, Jamaica, Kenya, Kiao
Chau (Kiatschau), Kiribati, Laos, Liberia,
Malaya, Malaysia, Malta, Mauritius,
Netherlands, Netherlands Antilles,
Netherlands Indies, New Zealand, Nova
Scotia, Panama, Prince Edward Island,
Sarawak, Seychelles, Sierra Leone, Singapore,
Solomon Islands, South Africa, Sri Lanka,
Straits Settlements, Suriname, Swaziland,
Tanzania, Trinidad and Tobago, Tuvalu,
Uganda, United States of America, Virgin
Islands, Zanzibar, Zimbabwe
Centas (plural **Centa, Centu**) Lithuania
Centavo Angola, Argentina, Bolivia, Brazil,
Cape Verde Islands, Chile, Colombia, Costa
Rica, Cuba, Dominican Republic, Ecuador, El
Salvador, Guatemala, Guinea-Bissau,

Honduras, Mexico, Mozambique, Nicaragua,
Paraguay, Peru, Philippines, Portugal,
Portuguese Guinea, Portuguese India, Puerto
Rico, St Thomas and Prince Islands, Timor,
Venezuela
Centecimo Bolivia
Cententionalis Roman Empire
Centesimo Bolivia, Chile, Dominican Republic,
Ethiopia, Italian East Africa, Italy, Panama,
Paraguay, San Marino, Somalia, Uruguay,
Vatican
Centime Algeria, Antwerp, Belgian Congo,
Belgium, Cambodia, Cameroon, Cochin
China, Comoro Islands, Djibouti, France,
French Equatorial Africa, French Guiana,
French Indochina, French Oceania, French
Polynesia, French Somali Coast, French West
Africa, Guadeloupe, Guinea, Haiti, Laos,
Monaco, Morocco, New Caledonia, Reunion,
Senegal, Switzerland, Togo, Tunisia, Vietnam,
Westphalia, Yugoslavia, Zaire
Centimo Costa Rica, Mozambique, Paraguay,
Peru, Philippines, Puerto Rico, St Thomas and
Prince Islands, Spain, Venezuela
Centu Lithuania
Chaise Antwerp, Bavaria, France
Chervonetz (plural **Chervontzy**) Russia
Chetrum Bhutan
Cheun South Korea
Chiao China, Formosa, Manchukuo
Chi'en China
Chio China
Cho-gin Japan
Chomseh Yemen
Chon Korea
Christian d'Or Denmark
Chuckram Travancore
Colon Costa Rica, El Salvador
Condor Chile, Colombia, Ecuador
Cordoba Nicaragua
Cornado Spain
Cornuto Savoy
Coroa de Prata Portugal
Coroin Eire
Corona Austrian provinces of Italy, Naples
Coronato Castile, Naples
Couronne d'Or France
Crocione Italian States
Crossazzo Genoa
Crown Ascension, Australia, Bermuda,
England, Ghana, Gibraltar, Ireland, Isle of
Man, Jamaica, Jersey, Malawi, New Zealand,
Nigeria, Rhodesia, Rhodesia and Nyasaland,
St Helena, Scotland, Southern Rhodesia,
Tristan da Cunha, Turks and Caicos Islands
Cruzadinho Brazil, Portugal
Cruzado Brazil, Portugal

Cruzeiro Brazil
Cuartillo, Cuartino Mexico
Cuarto Bolivia, Spain
Daalder Netherlands
DakBler Danish West Indies, Denmark, Sweden
Dam Afghanistan, India, Nepal
Daric Persia
Dauphin France
Decime France
Decimo Argentina, Chile, Colombia, Ecuador, Galapagos
Decussis Roman Republic
Dekadrachm Syracuse, Hellenistic kingdoms
Dekanummion Byzantine Empire
Dekobolon Greece
Demareteion Syracuse
Demer France
Demy Scotland
Denar Hungary
Denarius Rome
Denaro Italian States
Denga Russia
Dengi Roumania
Denier France and colonies, Haiti, Swiss Cantons
Denning Denmark
Deut Rhineland, Westphalia
Deutschemark Germany
Dhofari Riyal Yemen
Diamante Ferrara
Diamantino Ferrara
Dicken Swiss Cantons
Didrachm Greece
Dime Canada, Hawaii, USA
Dinar Afghanistan, Algeria, Bahrain, Hejaz, Iraq, Kuwait, Morocco, Persia, Saudi Arabia, Serbia, Tunisia, Turkey, Yugoslavia
Diner Andorra
Dinero Peru, Spain
Diobol Greece
Dirham Jordan, Libya, Morocco, United Arab Emirates
Dirhem Dubai, Iraq, Morocco, Qatar
Dio, Diu Portuguese India
Disme USA
Dobla Genoa, Naples and Sicily
Doblado Spanish colonies
Doblenca, Doblenga Aragon, Barcelona
Dobler Mallorca
Doblon Chile, Spain, Urugay
Dobra St Thomas and Prince
Dodekadrachm Carthage
Doit Netherlands, Netherlands Indies, Indonesia
Dokdo Junagadh, Kutch, Nawanagar (Indian States)

Dollar Anguilla, Antigua and Barbuda, Australia, Bahamas, Belize, Bermuda, Canada, Cayman Islands, China, Cocos (Keeling) Islands, Cook Islands, East Caribbean Territories, Fiji, Great Britain, Grenada, Guyana, Hawaii, Hong Kong, Indonesia, Jamaica, Japan, Kiribati, Liberia, Malaysia, Mauritius, Montserrat, Newfoundland, New Zealand, Panama, St Kitts-Nevis, St Lucia, St Vincent, Scotland, Sierra Leone, Singapore, Solomin Islands, Straits Settlements, Trinidad and Tobago, Tuvalu, USA, Virgin Islands, Western Samoa, Zimbabwe
Dolya Russia
Dong Annam, Vietnam
Doppia Italian States
Doppietta Sardinia
Double Guernsey
Dou Dou French Indochina
Douzain France
Drachma Crete, Greece
Dram Armenia
Dreibatzner Austria, German States
Dreigroscher Lithuania, Prussia
Dreiling German States
Dub Hyderabad, India
Dubbeltje Holland
Ducat Austria, Austrian States, Courland, Czechoslovakia, Denmark, German States, Hungary, Italian States, Liechtenstein, Liege, Netherlands,Poland, Roumania, Sweden, Swiss Cantons, Russia, Yugoslavia
Ducaton Belgium, Netherlands
Ducatone Italian States
Dudu India
Duetto Italian States
Duit Ceylon, German States, Netherlands, Netherlands Indies
Dukat Czechoslovakia, German States, Hungary, Poland, Sweden, Yugoslavia
Duplone Swiss Cantons
Duro Spain
Dyak Nepal
Ecu Belgium, Bosnia, France, Gibraltar
Ekuele Equatorial Guinea
Elisabeth d'Or Russia
Emalangeni Swaziland
Escalin Belgium, Guadeloupe, Haiti, Liege, Martinique
Escudillo Spain
Escudo Angola, Argentina, Azores, Bolivia, Cape Verde Islands, Central American Republic, Chile, Colombia, Costa Rica, Ecuador, Guadeloupe, Guatemala, Guinea-Bissau, Madeira, Mexico, Mozambique, Peru, Portugal, Portuguese Guinea/India, St Thomas and Prince Islands, Spain, Timor

Espadin   Portugal
Esphera   Goa
Excelente   Spain
Eyrir (singular Aurar) Iceland
Fals   Iraq
Faluce   Ceylon
Falus   Afghanistan, China, India, Iran, Morocco,
   Turkestan
Fanam   Ceylon, Dutch East Indies, Travancore
Fano   Tranquebar (Danish Indian Settlements)
Fanon   French Indian Settlements
Farthing   Antigua, Ceylon, Great Britain, Isle of
   Man, Jamaica, Malta, Scotland, South Africa
Fels   Algeria
Fen   People's Republic of China, Manchukuo
Fenig (ow)   Poland
Feoirling   Eire
Ferding   Courland, Livonia
Filiberto   Savoy
Filippo   Italian States
Filler   Hungary
Fils   Bahrain, Iraq, Jordan, Kuwait, South
   Arabia, United Arab Emirates, Yemen
Fiorino   Italian States
Flitter   South German States
Floirin   Eire
Florin   Australia, Austria, East Africa, Fiji,
   Great Britain, Hungary, Ireland, Malawi, New
   Zealand, Rhodesia and Nyasaland, South
   Africa, Swiss Cantons
Follis   Rome, Byzantine Empire
Forint   Hungary
Franc   Algeria, Belgian Congo, Belgium,
   Burundi, Cambodia, Cameroon, Central
   African Republic, Chad, Comoro Islands,
   Congo, Danish West Indies, Djibouti,
   Dominican Republic, Ecuador,
   France, French colonies, Gabon, Guadeloupe,
   Guinea, Ivory Coast, Katanga, Luxembourg,
   Madagascar, Malagasy Republic, Mali,
   Martinique, Mauretania, Monaco, Morocco,
   New Caledonia, New Hebrides, Reunion,
   Ruanda-Urundi, Rwanda, St Pierre and
   Miquelon, Senegal, Switzerland, Togo,
   Tunisia, West African States
Francescone   Italian States
Franchi   Switzerland
Franco   Dominican Republic, Ecuador, Italian
   States, Swiss Cantons
Frang   Luxembourg
Frank(en)   Belgium, Liechtenstein, Saar,
   Switzerland, Westphalia
Franka Ara   Albania
Frederik d'Or   Denmark
Friedrich d'Or   German States
Fyrk   Sweden
Gabellone   Papal States

Gayah   Sumatra
Gazetta   Venice
Genovino   Genoa, Florence, Venice
Genevoise   Geneva
George Noble   England
Georgstaler   German States
Gersh   Ethiopia
Gigliato   Hungary, Naples, Rhodes
Gigot   Brabant, Flanders
Gin   Japan
Giorgino   Ferrara, Modena
Giovannino   Genoa
Girsh   Hejaz, Nejd, Saudi Arabia, Sudan
Giulio   Italian States
Golde   Sierra Leone
Goldgulden   German States, Swiss Cantons
Goldpfennig   German States
Goryoban   Japan
Gourde   Haiti
Gourmier   Morocco
Gram   Afghanistan
Gramme   Burma
Gramo   Bolivia, Tierra del Fuego
Grana   Italian States
Grano   Italian States, Mexico,
   Sovereign Order of Malta
Grenadino   Colombia, New Granada
Greschl   Roumania, Transylvania
Grivenka   Russia
Grivennik   Russia
Grivna (plural Grivny)   Ukraine
Groat   Great Britain
Groeschl   Bohemia
Groot   Netherlands
Gros   France
Groschel   German States
Groschen   Austria, German States, Poland,
   Swiss Cantons
Groshen   Austria, German States
Grossetto   Dalmatia, Illyria, Venice
Grosso   Italian States
Grossone   Italian States
Grosspfennig   Pomerania, Rhineland
Grossus   Courland, Poland
Grosz (plural Grosze or Groszy)   Poland
Grote   German States
Grush   Albania
Guarani   Paraguay
Guerche   Egypt, Saudi Arabia
Guinea   Great Britain, Saudi Arabia
Gulden   Austria, Curacao, German States,
   Netherlands, Netherlands Indies, Swiss
   Cantons
Guldiner   Austria, South German States, Swiss
   Cantons
Gutegroschen   North and Central German
   States

Guterpfennig   German States
Habibi   Afghanistan
Halala   Saudi Arabia, Yemen
Halbag   Frankfurt
Haler (plural **Halere, Haleru**)   Czechoslovakia, Czech Republic
Halierov   Slovakia
Haller   Swiss Cantons
Hao   China, Vietnam
Hapalua   Hawaii
Hardhead   Scotland
Hardi   France, Turin
Hau   Tonga
Hayrir Altin   Iraq, Turkey
Hekte   Lesbos, Mytilene
Heller   Austria, German States, German East Africa
Helm   England
Henri d'Or   France
Hryvnia   Ukraine
Hsien   China
Hvid   Denmark
Hwan   Korea
Hyperpyron   Byzantine Empire
Ichibu-gin   Japan
Ikilik   Russia
Imadi   Yemen
Imami   Mysore
Imperial   Russia
Isabella   Spain
Ischal   Russia
Ishu Gin   Japan
Jacondale   France
Jawa   Nepal
Jeon   Korea
Jerome d'Or   Westphalia
Jiao   People's Republic of China
Jedid   Egypt
Jefimok (plural **Jefimki**)   Russia
Joachimico   Italy
Joachimik   Poland
Joachimstaler   Bohemia
Joao   Portugal
Johanna   Portugal
Johannes   Portugal
Jokoh   Kelantan, Malaysia
Judenpfennig   Frankfurt
Justo   Portugal
Kapang   Sarawak
Kapeikas   Latvia, Belarus
Karolin   German States
Kas   Danish Indian Settlements
Kasu   Mysore
Kazbeg   Caucasia, Safavid Persia
Khayriya   Egypt
Khoum   Mauretania
Kin   Japan

Kina   Papua New Guinea
Kip   Laos
Koban   Japan
Kobo   Nigeria
Kopec   Poland
Kopejek   Outer Mongolia (Tannu Tuva)
Kopek   Russia
Kori   Kutch
Korona   Bohemia and Moravia, Hungary, Slovakia
Kortling   German States
Korun(a) (plural **Koruny** or **Koruncic**)   Czechoslo-vakia
Koula   Tonga
Krajczar   Hungary
Kran   Iran, Persia
Kreu(t)zer   Austria, Austrian States, Czechoslovakia, German States, Hungary, Liechtenstein, Poland, Roumania, Swiss Cantons
Krona (plural **Kronor** or **Kronur**)   Iceland, Sweden
Krona (plural **Kroner** or **Kronen**)   Austria, Denmark, German States, Greenland, Liechtenstein, Norway
Kroon(i)   Estonia
Krugerrand   South Africa
Kuna (plural **Kune**)   Croatia
Kupang   Malaysia, Thailand
Kurus   Turkey
Kuta   Congo-Kinshasa, Zaire
Kwacha   Malawi, Zambia
Kwanza   Angola
Kwartnik   Poland
Kyat   Burma, Myanmar
Kyrmis   Russia
Lang   Annam
Laree, Lari, Lariat or Larin   Maldive Islands
Lati, Lats   Latvia
Laurel   England
Lei   Roumania
Lek (plural **Leke** or **Leku**)   Albania
Lempira   Honduras
Leone   Sierra Leone
Leopard   England
Lepton (plural **Lepta**)   Crete, Greece, Ionian Islands
Leu (plural **Lei**)   Roumania
Lev(a)   Bulgaria
Li   Manchukuo
Liang   China, Laos
Liard   Belgium, France, Luxembourg
Libra   Peru
Licente   Lesotho
Likuta   Zaire
Lilangeni   Swaziland
Lion   Scotland

Lion d'Or   Austrian Netherlands
Lira (plural Lire)   Eritrea, Italian East Africa,
   Italy, San Marino, Syria, Turkey, Vatican
Lira (plural Lirot)   Israel
Lisente   Lesotho
Litas (plural Litai or Litu)   Lithuania
Litra   Sicily, Syracuse
Livre   France, Guadeloupe, Lebanon,
   Martinique, Mauritius, Reunion
Louis d'Argent   France
Louis d'Or   France
Luhlanga   Swaziland
Lumma   Armenia
Lweis   Angola
Mace   China
Macuta   Angola
Magdalon d'Or   Aix-en-Provence, Tarascon
Mahalek   Ethiopia
Mahallak   Harar
Mahbub   Egypt, Ottoman Empire
Mahmudi   Saudi Arabia
Makuta   Zaire
Maloti   Lesotho
Manat   Azerbaijan
Manghir   Crimea
Marabotin   Moorish kingdoms, Southern Spain
Maravedi   Spain
Marchetto   Italian States
Marck   German States
Marengo   France
Mariengroschen   German States
Mark   Germany, German States, German New
   Guinea, Norway, Poland, Sweden
Marka   Estonia
Markka(a)   Finland
Mas   Malaysia
Masriya   Egypt
Masson   Lorraine and Bar
Mat   Burma
Matapan   Venice
Mathbu   Morocco
Maticaes   Mozambique
Matona   Ethiopia
Mattier   German States
Maximilian d'Or   German States
Mazuna   Morocco
Medin   Egypt
Mehmudiye Altin   Ottoman Empire
Meinhard   Austria, German States
Melgarejo   Bosnia
Merk   Scotland
Metica   Mozambique
Meung   Japan
Mil   Cyprus, Hong Kong, Israel, Malta,
   Palestine
Milan d'Or   Serbia
Miliarense   Byzantine Empire

Milesima   Spain
Millieme   Egypt, Libya
Millime   Tunisia
Milreis   Brazil
Miscals   China
Mohar   Nepal
Mohur   Afghanistan, Bikanir, Cooch Behar,
   Gwalior, Hyderabad, India (Mughal Empire),
   Maldive Islands, Netherlands Indies, Rajkot
Moidore (Moeda de ouro)   Portugal
Momme   Japan
Mon   Japan, Ryukyu Islands
Mongo   Mongolia
Mouton d'Or   France
Mu   Burma
Mun   Korea
Mung   Mongolia
Munzgulden   Swiss Cantons
Muzuna   Algeria
Naira   Nigeria
Nami-sen   Japan
Napoleon   France
Naya Paisa   Bhutan, India
Negotiepenning   Netherlands
Neugroschen   German States
New Pence   Gibraltar, Great Britain, Guernsey,
   Isle of Man, Jersey
Ngultrum   Bhutan
Ngwee   Zambia
Nisar   Afghanistan, India
Nisfiya   Egypt
Noble   Austria,England, Scotland, Isle of Man
Nomisma   Byzantine Empire
Nonsunt   Scotland
Nummion (plural Nummia)   Byzantine Empire
Oban   Japan
Obol   Greece, Ionian Islands
Ochavo   Spain
Octavo   Mexico, Philippines
Omani   Oman
Onca   Mozambique
Oncia   Italian States
Onlik   Crimea
Onluk   Turkey
Onza   Bolivia, Chile, Costa Rica, Mexico
Or   Sweden
Ore   Denmark, Faroe Islands, Greenland,
   Norway, Sweden
Ort(e)   Poland, Prussia
Ortug (plural Ortugar)   Sweden
Ouguiya   Mauretania
Pa'anga   Tonga
Pagoda   India (Madras)
Pahlavi   Iran
Pai   India, Siam (Thailand)
Paisa   Afghanistan, Bhutan, India, Nepal,
   Pakistan

Panchia   India
Pano   Portuguese Africa
Paoli   Italian States
Papetto   Papal States
Para (plural **Paras** or **Parades**)   Crimea, Egypt,
   Greece, Iraq, Libya, Nejd, Roumania, Saudi
   Arabia, Serbia, Sudan, Syria, Turkey,
   Walachia, Yugoslavia
Pardao   Portuguese India
Parisis d'Or   France
Pataca   Macau
Pataco   Portugal
Patagon   Belgium
Patrick   Ireland
Pavillon d'Or   France
Pe   Burma, Cambodia
Peca   Portugal
Pengo   Hungary
Penni(a)   Finland
Penning(ar)   Denmark, Sweden
Penny (plural **Pence**)   Australia, Bahamas,
   Barbados, Bermuda, Biafra, British Guiana,
   British East Africa British West Africa,
   Canada, Ceylon, Falkland Islands, Fiji,
   Gambia, Ghana, Gibraltar, Gold Coast, Great
   Britain, Guernsey, Ireland, Isle of Man,
   Jamaica, Jersey, Malawi, Montserrat, New
   Guinea, New Zealad, Nigeria, Rhodesia and
   Nyasaland, St Helena, St Kitts-Nevis, South
   Africa, Southern Rhodesia, Trinidad &
   Tobago, Tristan da Cunha, Zambia
Pentekontalitron   Sicily
Pentekontedrachm   Hellenistic kingdoms
Pentenummion   Byzantine Empire
Perper(a)   Montenegro
Pesa   German East Africa
Peseta   Andorra, Equatorial Guinea, Peru, Spain
Pesewa   Ghana
Peso   Argentina, Bolivia, Cambodia, Chile,
   Colombia, Costa Rica, Cuba, Dominican
   Republic, El Salvador, Guatemala, Guinea-
   Bissau, Honduras, Mexico, Netherlands
   Antilles, Nicaragua, Paraguay, Peru,
   Philippines, Puerto Rico, Uruguay, Venezuela
Pessa   Yemen (Lahej), Zanzibar
Petermannchen   Trier
Pfennig(e)   Austria, Bohemia, Germany,
   German States, Poland, Swiss Cantons
Pfenning   Austrian States, German States
Philippeioi   Macedon
Phoenix   Greece
Piastra   Italian States
Piastre   Annam, Cambodia, Cochin China,
   Cyprus, Denmark, Egypt, French Indochina,
   Hejaz, Iraq, Khmer, Lebanon, Libya, Nejd,
   Saudi Arabia, Syria, Sudan, Tonkin, Tunisia,
   Turkey, Vietnam, Yemen

Piataltynny   Russia
Picciolo   Sovereign Order of Malta
Piccolo   Italian States
Pice   Bhutan, Ceylon, East Africa, India, Kenya,
   Malaysia
Pinto   Portugal
Piso   Philippines
Pistole   France, German States, Ireland,
   Scotland, Swiss Cantons
Pitis   Brunei, Java, Sumatra, Siam
Plack   Scotland
Plappart   Switzerland
Poisha   Bangladesh
Poltina   Russia
Poltura   Hungary, Roumania
Poludenga   Russia
Polupoltinnik   Russia
Polushka   Russia
Pond   Transvaal
Pound   Ascension, Australia, Biafra, Cyprus,
   Egypt, Falkland Islands, Ghana, Gibraltar,
   Great Britain, Guernsey, Iran, Isle of Man,
   Israel, Jersey, Malta, Nigeria, Rhodesia, St
   Helena, South Arabia, South Africa, Sudan,
   Syria
Protea   South Africa
Pruta(ot)   Israel
Puffin   Lundy
Pul   Afghanistan, China, Turkestan
Pula   Botswana
Puli   Caucasia
Pultorak   Poland
Pya(t)   Burma
Pysa   Zanzibar
Qindar(ka)   Albania
Qiran   Afghanistan
Qirsh   Egypt
Quadrans   Roman Republic
Quan   Annam
Quart   Gibraltar, Swiss Cantons
Quart d'Ecu   France
Quartenses   Silesia
Quartillo   Spain
Quartinho   Portugal
Quarto   Ecuador, Mexico, Philippines, Spain
Quartuncia   Rome
Quaternio   Rome
Quattrino   Italian States
Qepiq   Azerbaijan
Quetzal   Guatemala
Quinarius   Rome
Quint   USA
Quinto di Scudo   Papal States
Rand   South Africa
Rappen   Switzerland
Rasi   Netherlands Indies
Reaal   Curacao

Real(es) Argentina, Bolivia, Central American Republic, Chile, Colombia, Costa Rica, Dominican Republic, Ecuador, El Salvador, Venezuela
Real Batu Indonesia
Reichsmark Germany
Reichspfennig Germany
Reichsthaler Germany
Reis Angola, Azores, Brazil, Madeira, Mozambique, Portugal, Portuguese India
Reisedaler Denmark
Rentenmark Germany
Rentenpfennig Germany
Reul Eire
Rial Iran, Morocco, Muscat and Oman, Oman, Persia, Yemen Arab Republic
Rider Scotland
Riel Kampuchea
Rigsbankdaler Denmark
Rigsbankskilling Denmark
Rigsdaler, Denmark, Norway
Rigsmontskilling Denmark
Rijder Friesland, Guelderland, United Provinces
Rijksdaalder Netherlands
Riksdaler Sweden
Riksdaler Riksmynt Sweden
Riksdaler Specie Sweden
Rin Japan
Ringgit Malaysia
Rio Japan
Rixdollar Ceylon
Riyal Iran, Iraq, Saudi Arabia, United Arab Emirates, Yemen Arab Republic
Rose Noble England
Rouble Russia, USSR
Royal d'Or France
Royalin(er) Tranquebar, Danish Indian Settlements
Rub Ethiopia
Rubel German occupation of Russia
Rubiya Egypt
Ruble Poland, Transnistria
Rublis Latvia
Rufiyaa Maldive Islands
Rumi Altin Ottoman Empire
Rupee Afghanistan, Andaman Islands, Bhutan, Burma, China, Cocos Keeling Islands, India, Iran, Kenya, Mauritius, Nepal, Pakistan, Saudi Arabia, Seychelles, Sri Lanka, Tanzania, Tibet, United Arab Emirates, Yemen
Rupia Portuguese India, Somalia
Rupiah Indonesia
Rupie German East Africa
Ruspone Italian States
Ryal England, Hejaz, Iran, Muscat and Oman, Nejd, Oman, Persia, Quaiti State, Saudi Arabia, Yemen, Zanzibar

Ryo Japan
Rytterpenning Denmark, Hanseatic League
Saidi Oman
Saiga Merovingian Empire
Salung Siam (Thailand)
Salut d'Or France
Sampietrino Papal States
Sanar Afghanistan
Sanese Siena
Santa Croce Italian States
Santim(at) Morocco
Santims (plural **Santimi** or **Santimu**) Latvia
Sapeque Annam, Cochin China, French Indochina
Sar Sinkiang
Sarrazzino Crusader kingdoms
Satang Siam (Thailand)
Sceat Anglo-Saxon England
Scellino Somalia
Schilling Austria, German States, Poland, Swiss Cantons
Schoter Breslau, Silesia
Schwaren German States
Scilling Eire
Scudo Bolivia, Italian States, Mexico, Malta, Papal States, Peru, San Marino
Sechsling German States
Semis Rome
Semuncia Rome
Sen Brunei, Cambodia, Indonesia, Irian Barat, Japan, Kampuchea, Malaysia, Riau Lingga, West New Guinea
Sene Samoa
Sengi Zaire
Seniti Tonga
Sent Estonia
Sente Lesotho
Senti Estonia, Somalia, Tanzania
Sentimo Philippines
Serebrnik Bulgaria
Sertum Bhutan
Sesena Spain
Sesino Italian States
Sestertius Rome
Sestino Italian States
Shahi Afghanistan, Iran, Turkestan
Sheqal(im) Israel
Shilingi Tanzania
Shilling Australia, Biafra, British West Africa, Canada, Cyprus, East Africa, Fiji, Gambia, Ghana, Great Britain, Grenada, Guernsey, Ireland, Isle of Man, Jamaica, Jersey, Kenya, Malawi, Malta, New Guinea, New Zealand, Nigeria, Scotland, Somalia, South Africa, Trinidad and Tobago, Uganda, Zambia
Sho Nepal, Tibet
Shokang Tibet
Shu Japan

Siglos Achaemenid Empire
Sik Siam (Thailand)
Silbergroschen German States,Luxembourg
Silbergulden South Germany
Sizain France
Skar Tibet
Skilling Danish West Indies, Denmark,
  Norway, Sweden
Skillingrigsmont Denmark
Skot Prussia, Silesia
Sol(es) Argentina, Belgium, Bolivia, France,
  Haiti, Luxembourg, Mauritius, Peru, Reunion,
  Switzerland, Windward Islands
Soldo (plural **Soldi**) Italian States, Swiss
  Cantons, Papal States, Yugoslavia
Solidus Argentina, Bolivia, Peru, Rome
Solot Siam
Som Kyrgyzstan
Somalo Somalia
Sosling Denmark
Sou Canada, French colonies, Guadeloupe,
  Mauritius, Reunion, Spain
Souverain d'Or Austrian Netherlands
Sovereign Australia, Canada, England,
  Falkland Islands, India, Isle of Man, Saudi
  Arabia, South Africa, United Kingdom
Sovrano Italian States
Speciedaler Denmark, Norway
Species Ducat Denmark
Srang Tibet
Stater Greece
Stella USA
Stiver British Guiana, Ceylon, Demerara and
  Essequibo, Dutch East Indies, Netherlands
Stotinka Bulgaria
Stuber German States
Stuiver Curacao, Dutch East Indies,
  Netherlands, Netherlands Antilles
Styca Northumbria
Styver Sweden
Su South Vietnam
Sucre Ecuador, Galapagos
Sueldo Bolivia, Spain
Sukus Indonesia
Sultani Algeria, Libya, Tunisia
Surre Altin Ottoman Empire
Syli Guinea
Tackoe Gold Coast
Tael China, Laos
Taka Bangladesh
Tala Samoa, Tokelau
Talar(a) Poland
Talaro Ethiopia
Taler German States, Poland, Swiss Cantons
Talirion Greece
Tallero Ethiopia, Italian States, Ragusa
Tambac-tron Annam

Tambala Malawi
Tamlung Siam
Tanga Portuguese India
Tangka Tibet
Tanka Nepal
Tankah Burma
Tarin Naples, Sicily
Taro (plural **Tari**) Italian States, Malta
Tek Altin Ottoman Empire
Tenga China, Bokhara, Turkestan
Ternar Poland
Tester England
Testern British East Indies
Testone Italian States
Testoon England
Tetartemorion Greece
Tetarteron Byzantine Empire
Tetradrachm Greece
Tetrobol Greece
Thaler Austria, Austrian States, Courland,
  Czechoslovakia, German States, Hungary,
  Liechtenstein, Poland, Roumania, Switzerland
Thebe Botswana
Theler Frankfurt
Thistle Crown England
Thistle Merk Scotland
Thistle Noble Scotland
Thrymsa Anglo-Saxon England
Tical Cambodia, Thailand
Tien Annam, Vietnam
Tilla Afghanistan, Sinkiang, Turkestan
Timasha Afghanistan
Tostao Portugal
Toea Papua New Guinea
Tola India, Nepal
Tolar Slovenia
Toman Iran, Persia, Azerbaijan
Tornese Italian States
Tournois France
Trade Dollar Great Britain, Japan, USA
Trah Malaysia
Tremissis Rome, Byzantine Empire, Franks,
  Lombards, Visigoths
Tressis Rome
Triens Rome
Trihemiobol Greece
Triobol Greece
Tritartemorion Greece
Tughrik Mongolia
Turner Scotland
Tympf Poland
Tyyn Kyrgyzstan
Unghero Italian States
Unicorn Scotland
Unit Scotland, French West Africa
Unite England
Van Vietnam

Vatu   Vanuatu
Veld Pond   South African Republic
Venezolano   Venezuela
Vereinstaler   Austria-Hungary, German States
Victoriate   Rome
Vierer   Swiss Cantons
Vintem   Portugal
Wan   Korea
Wark   Ethiopia
Warn   Korean
Wen   China
Whan   Korea
Won   South Korea
Xerafim   Portuguese India
Xu   Vietnam
Yang   Korea

Yarim   Turkey
Yen   Japan
Yirmilik   Ottoman Empire
Yuan   China
Yuzluk   Ottoman Empire
Zaire   Zaire
Zalat   Yemen Arab Republic
Zecchino   Italian States, Malta
Zelagh   Morocco
Zeri Mahbub   Egypt, Libya, Turkey
Zloty (plural **Zlote** or **Zlotych**)   Poland
Zolota   Turkey
Zolotnik   Russia
Zolotoj   Russia
Zweidritteltaler   German States
Zyfert   East Friesland

Glossary of
COIN
TERMS

In this section we list all the terms commonly encountered in numismatics or in the production of coins.

Abbey Coins Medieval coins struck in the abbeys, convents and other great religious houses which were granted coinage rights. These coins were often used also by pilgrims journeying from one monastery to another.

Abschlag (German for "discount") A *restrike* from an original die.

Accolated Synonym for *conjoined* or *jugate* and signifying two or more profiles overlapping.

Acmonital Acronym from *Aciaio Monetario Italiano*, a stainless steel alloy used for Italian coins since 1939.

Adjustment Reduction of metal in a *flan* or *blank* to the specified weight prior to striking, accomplished by filing down the face. Such file marks often survived the coining process and are occasionally met with in coins, especially of the 18th century.

Ae Abbreviation for the Latin *Aes* (bronze), used for coins made of brass, bronze or other copper alloys.

Aes Grave (Latin for heavy bronze) Heavy circular coins first minted at Rome in 269 BC.

Aes Rude (Latin for rough bronze) Irregular lumps of bronze which gradually developed into ingots of uniform shape and were the precursors of coins in Rome.

Aes Signatum (Latin for signed bronze) Bronze ingots of regular size and weight, bearing marks of authority to guarantee their weight (289–269 BC).

Agonistic (Greek) Term for coins issued to commemorate, or pertaining to, sporting events.

Alliance Coinage struck by two or more states acting together and having common features of design or inscription.

Alloy Coinage metal composed of two or more metallic elements.

Altered Deliberately changed, usually unofficially, with the aim of increasing the numismatic value of a coin, medal or note. This applies particularly to dates, where a common date may be altered to a rare date by filing or re-engraving one of the digits.

Aluminium (American *Aluminum*) Silvery lightweight metal, developed commercially in the late 19th century for commemorative medals, but used for tokens and emergency money during the First World War and since 1940 widely used in subsidiary coinage.

Aluminium-bronze Alloy of aluminium and copper. Hard-wearing and gold-coloured, it is now widely used in tokens and subsidiary coinage.

Amulet Coin or medal believed to have talismanic qualities, such as warding off disease and bad luck. Many Chinese and Korean pieces come into this category. See also *Touchpiece*.

Androcephalous Heraldic term for creatures with a human head.

Anepigraphic Coins or medals without a legend.

Annealing Process of heating and cooling applied to metal to relieve stresses and prepare it for striking into coins.

Annulet Small circle often used as an ornament or spacing device in coin inscriptions.

Antimony Brittle white metal, chemical symbol *Sb*, virtually impractical as a coinage metal but used for the Chinese 10 cents of Kweichow, 1931. Alloyed with tin, copper or lead, it produces the white metal popular as a medallic medium.

Antoniniani Silver coins minted in Imperial Rome. The name derives from the Emperor Caracalla (Marcus Aurelius Antoninus) in whose reign they were first struck. The silver content was progressively reduced and by the time of the last issue (AD 295) they were reduced to *billon*.

Ar Abbreviation for Latin *Argentum* (silver), used for coins struck in this metal.

Assay Mark Mark applied to a medal struck in

precious metal by an assayer or assay office as a guarantee of the fineness of the metal.

Assignat Type of paper money used in France 1789–96, representing the land assigned to the holders.

Attribution Identification of a coin by characteristics such as issuing authority, date or reign, mint, denomination, metal, and by a standard reference.

Au Abbreviation for *aurum* (Latin for gold), denoting coins of this metal.

AU Abbreviation for "About Uncirculated", often found in catalogues and dealers' lists to describe the condition of a numismatic piece.

Autodollar Name given to the silver yuan issued by Kweichow, 1928, and having a contemporary motor car as the obverse motif.

Auxiliary Payment Certificate Form of paper money intended for use by American military personnel stationed in overseas countries. See also *Baf* and *Scrip*.

Babel Note Nickname given to the paper money of the Russian Socialist Federated Soviet Republic (1919) because it bore the slogan "workers of the world unite" in seven languages, a reference to the biblical tower of Babel.

Baf Acronym from British Armed Forces, the popular name for the vouchers which could only be exchanged for goods in service canteens from 1945 onwards.

Bag Mark Minor scratch or abrasion on an otherwise uncirculated coin, caused by coins in mint bags knocking together.

Banknote Form of paper money issued by banks and usually promising to pay the bearer on demand in coin of the realm.

Barbarous Imitation of Greek or Roman coins by the Celtic and Germanic tribes who lived beyond the frontiers of the civilised world.

Base Non-precious metals or alloys.

Bath Metal Inferior bronze alloy, named after the English city where it was used for casting cannon. Used by William Wood of Bristol for Irish and American tokens and by Amos Topping for Manx coins of 1733/4.

Beading Ornamental border found on the raised rim of a coin.

Behalfszahlungsmittel German term for auxiliary payment certificates used in occupied Europe from 1939 to 1945.

Bell Metal Alloy of copper and tin normally used for casting bells, but employed for the subsidiary coinage of the French Revolutionary period.

Billon Silver alloy containing less than 50 per cent fine silver, usually mixed with copper. In Spain this alloy was known as *vellon*.

Bi-metallic Coins struck in two separate metals or alloys. Patterns for such coins exist from the 19th century but actual coins with a centre of one metal surrounded by a ring of another did not appear till 1982 (Italy, San Marino and Vatican). Canada introduced coins with a tiny plaque inset in a second metal (1990). See also *Clad*, *Plugged* and *Sandwich*.

Bi-metallism Monetary system in which two metals are in simultaneous use and equally available as legal tender, implying a definite ratio between the two. A double standard of gold and silver, with a ratio of 16:1, existed till the mid-19th century.

Bingle American term for a trade token, more specifically the US government issue of tokens for the Matacuska, Alaska colonization project, 1935.

Birthday Coins Coins celebrating the birthday of a ruler originated in Roman Imperial times, notably the reigns of Maximianus (286–305) and Constantinus I (307–37). Birthday talers were issued by many German states, and among recent examples may be cited coins marking the 70th, 80th and 90th birthdays of Gustaf Adolf VI of Sweden, 80th and 90th birthday coins from the British Commonwealth for the Queen Mother, and coins honouring Queen Elizabeth, the Duke of Edinburgh and the Prince of Wales.

Bit Term denoting fragments of large silver coins, cut up and circulating as fractional values. Spanish dollars were frequently broken up for circulation in the American colonies and the West indies. Long bits and short bits circulated at 15 and 10 cents respectively, but the term came to be equated with the Spanish real or eighth of a peso, hence the American colloquialism "two-bit" signifying a quarter dollar.

Black Money English term for the debased silver deniers minted in France which circulated freely in England until they were banned by government decree in 1351.

Blank Piece of metal, cut or punched out of a roller bar or strip, and prepared for striking to produce coins. Alternate terms are *flan* and *planchet*.

Blundered Inscription Legend in which the lettering is jumbled or meaningless, indicating the illiteracy of the tribes who copied Greek and Roman coins.

Bonnet Piece Scottish gold coin, minted in 1539–40. The name is derived from the obverse portraying King James V in a large, flat bonnet.

Bon Pour French for "good for", inscribed on Chamber of Commerce brass tokens issued in 1920–7 during a shortage of legal tender coinage.

Bouquet Sou Canadian copper token halfpenny

of 1837 deriving its name from the nosegay of heraldic flowers on the obverse.

Box Coin Small container formed by *obverse* and *reverse* of two coins, hollowed out and screwed together.

Bracteate (Latin *bractea*, a thin piece of metal). Coins struck on blanks so thin that the image applied to one side appears in reverse on the other. First minted in Erfurt and Thuringia in the 12th century, and later produced elsewhere in Germany, Switzerland and Poland till the 14th century.

Brass Alloy of copper and zinc, widely used for subsidiary coinage. The term was also formerly used for bronze Roman coins, known numismatically as first, second or third brass.

Breeches Money Derisive term given by the Royalists to the coinage of the Commonwealth, 1651, the conjoined elongated oval shields on the reverse resembling a pair of breeches.

Brockage Mis-struck coin with only one design, normal on one side and *incuse* on the other. This occurs when a coin previously struck adheres to the die and strikes the next blank to pass through the press.

Broken Bank-note Note issued by a bank which has failed, but often applied more generally to banknotes which have been demonetised.

Bronze Alloy of copper and tin, first used as a coinage metal by the Chinese c. 1000 BC. Often used synonymously with copper, though it should be noted that bronze only superseded copper as the constituent of the base metal British coins in 1860.

Bull Neck Popular term for the coins of King George III, 1816–17.

Bullet Money Pieces of silver, *globular* in shape, bearing various *countermarks* and used as coins in Siam (Thailand) in the 18th and 19th centuries.

Bullion Precious metal in bars, ingots, strip or scrap (i.e. broken jewellery mounts, watch-cases and plate), its weight reckoned solely by weight and fineness, before being converted into coin.

Bullion Coin A coin struck in platinum, gold or silver, whose value is determined solely by the prevailing market price for the metal as a commodity. Such coins do not generally have a nominal face value, but include in their inscriptions their weight and fineness. Good examples of recent times include the Krugerrand (South Africa), the Britannia (UK), the Maple Leaf (Canada), Libertad (Mexico), the Nugget (Australia) and the Eagle (USA).

Bun Coinage British coins of 1860–94 showing Queen Victoria with her hair in a bun.

Bungtown Coppers Derisive term (from Anglo-American slang *bung*, to swindle or bribe) for halfpence of English or Irish origin, often counterfeit, which circulated in North America towards the end of the colonial period.

Carat (American *Karat*) Originally a unit of weight for precious stones, based on carob seeds (ceratia), it also denotes the fineness or purity of gold, being 1/24th part of the whole. Thus 9 carat gold is .375 fine and 22 carat, the English sovereign standard, is .916 fine. Abbreviated as ct or kt.

Cartwheel Popular term for the large and cumbersome penny and twopenny pieces of 1797 weighing one and two ounces, struck by Matthew Boulton at the Soho Mint, Birmingham.

Cased Set Set of coins in mint condition, housed in the official case issued by the mint. Formerly leather cases with blue plush or velvet lining were used, but nowadays many sets are encapsulated in plastic to facilitate handling.

Cash (from Portuguese *caixa*, Hindi *kasu*). Round piece of bronze or brass with a square hole in the centre, used as subsidiary coinage in China for almost 2000 years, till the early 12th century. In Chinese these pieces were known as *Ch'ien* or *Li* and strung together in groups of 1000 were equivalent to a silver tael.

Cast Coins Coins cast from molten metals in moulds. This technique, widespread in the case of early commemorative medals, has been used infrequently in coins, the vast majority of which are struck from *dies*. Examples of cast coins include the Chinese cash and the Manx coins of 1709.

Check A form of *token* given as a means of identification, or issued for small amounts of money or for services of a specific nature.

Cheque (American *Check*) A written order directing a bank to pay money.

Chop (Hindi, to seal). Countermark, usually consisting of a single character, applied by Chinese merchants to precious metal coins and ingots as a guarantee of their weight and fineness. Coins may be found with a wide variety of chop marks and the presence of several different marks on the same coin considerably enhances its interest and value. See also *Shroff mark*.

Christmas Coins issued as Christmas gifts date from the Middle Ages when the Venetian Doges struck *Osselle* as presents for their courtiers. In modern times, however, the custom has developed only since the late 1970s, several countries having issued attractive coins at Christmas since then.

Cistophori (Greek for chest bearing), a generic term for the coins of Pergamum with an obverse motif of a chest showing a serpent crawling out of the half-opened lid. Cistophori became very popular all over Asia Minor in the 3rd and 2nd centuries BC and were struck also at mints in Ionia, Phrygia, Lydia and Mysia.

Clad Coins Coins with a core of one alloy, covered with a layer or coating of another. US half dollars from 1965 to 1970, for example, had a core of 21 per cent silver and 79 per cent copper, bonded to outer layers of 80 per cent silver and 20 per cent copper. More recently, however, coins usually have a body in a cheap alloy, with only a thin cladding of a more expensive material, such as the British 1p and 2p coins of stainless steel with a copper cladding, introduced late in 1992.

Clash Marks Mirror image traces found on a coin which has been struck from a pair of dies, themselves damaged by having been struck together without a blank between.

Clipped Coins Precious metal coins from which small amounts have been removed by clipping the edges. It was to prevent this that *graining* and *edge inscriptions* were adopted.

Cob Crude, irregularly shaped silver piece, often with little more than a vestige of die impressions, produced in the Spanish American mints in the 16th–18th centuries.

Coin Piece of metal, marked with a device, issued by government authority and intended for use as money.

Collar Retaining ring within which the *dies* for the *obverse* and *reverse* operate. When the *blank* is struck under high pressure between the dies the metal flows sideways and is formed by the collar, taking up the impression of *reeding* or *edge inscription* from it.

Commemorative Coin, medal, token or paper note issued to celebrate a current event or the anniversary of a historic event or personality.

Communion Token Token, cast in lead, but later struck in pewter, brass, bronze or white metal, issued to members of a congregation to permit them to partake of the annual communion service in the Calvinist and Presbyterian churches. John Calvin himself is said to have invented the communion token in 1561 but they were actually referred to in the minutes of the Scottish General Assembly in 1560. Later they were adopted by the Reformed churches in many parts of Europe. They survived in Scotland till the early years of this century. Each parish had its own tokens, often bearing the names or initials of individual ministers, with dates, symbols and biblical texts.

Conjoined Term denoting overlapped profiles of two or more rulers (e.g. William and Mary).

Contorniate (from Italian *contorno*, edge). Late 4th and 5th century Roman bronze piece whose name alludes to the characteristic grooving on the edges.

Contribution Coins Coins struck by Bamberg, Eichstatt, Fulda and other German cities in the 1790s during the First Coalition War against the French Republic. The name alludes to the fact that the bullion used to produce the coins necessary to pay troops was raised by contribution from the Church and the civilian population.

Convention Money Any system of coinage agreed by neighbouring countries for mutual acceptance and interchange. Examples include the Amphictyonic coins of ancient Greece, and the Austrian and Bavarian talers and gulden of 1753–1857 which were copied by other south German states and paved the way for the German Monetary union.

Copper Metallic element, chemical symbol *Cu*, widely used as a coinage medium for 2,500 years. Pure or almost pure copper was used for subsidiary coinage in many countries till the mid-19th century, but has since been superseded by copper alloys which are cheaper and more durable: *bronze* (copper and tin), *brass* (copper and zinc), *Bath metal* or *bell metal* (low-grade copper and tin), *aluminium-bronze* (copper and aluminium), *potin* (copper, tin, lead and silver) or *cupro-nickel* (copper and nickel). Copper is also alloyed with gold to give it its reddish hue, and is normally alloyed with silver in coinage metals. When the copper exceeds the silver content the alloy is known as *billon*.

Copperhead Popular term for a copper *token* about the size and weight of an American cent which circulated in the USA during the Civil War (1861–65) during a shortage of subsidiary coinage. Many different types were produced, often of a political or patriotic nature.

Coppernose Popular name for the debased silver shillings of Henry VIII. Many of them were struck in copper with little more than a silver wash which tended to wear off at the highest point of the obverse, the nose on the full-face portrait of the king.

Counter A piece resembling a coin but intended for use on a medieval accountancy board or in gambling. See also *jeton*.

Counterfeit Imitation of a coin, token or banknote intended for circulation to deceive the public and defraud the state.

Countermark Punch mark applied to a coin some time after its original issue, either to alter its nominal value, or to authorise its circulation in some other country.

Cowrie Small shell (*Cypraea moneta*) circulating as a form of primitive currency from 1000 BC (China) to the present century (East and West

Africa) and also used in the islands of the Indian and Pacific Oceans.

Crockard Debased silver imitation of English pennies produced in the Netherlands and imported into England in the late 13th century. Edward I tried to prevent their import then, in 1299, allowed them to pass current as halfpennies. As they contained more than a halfpennyworth of silver this encouraged their trading in to be melted down and they disappeared from circulation within a year. Sometimes known as *pollards*. See also *lushbourne*.

Crown Gold Gold of 22 carat (.916) fineness, so called on account of its adoption in 1526 for the English gold crown. It has remained the British standard gold fineness ever since.

Cumberland Jack Popular name for a counter or medalet of sovereign size, struck unofficially in 1837 in brass. The figure of St George was replaced by the Duke of Cumberland on horseback with the inscription "To Hanover" a reference to the unpopular Duke of Cumberland, uncle of Queen Victoria, who succeeded to the Hanoverian throne since Victoria, as a female, was debarred by Salic law from inheritance.

Cupellation (Latin *cupella*, a little cup). Process by which gold and silver were separated from lead and other impurities in their ores. A cupel is a shallow cup of bone-ash or other absorbent material which, when hot, absorbs any molten material that wets its surface. Lead melts and oxidises with impurities into the cupel, whereas gold and silver remain on the cupel. Cupellation is also used in assaying the fineness of these precious metals.

Cupro-nickel Coinage alloy of 75 per cent copper and 25 per cent nickel, now widely used as a base metal substitute for silver. A small amount of zinc is added to the alloy in modern Russian coins.

Currency Coins, tokens, paper notes and other articles intended to pass current in general circulation as money.

Current Coins and paper money still in circulation.

Cut Money Coins cut into smaller pieces to provide correspondingly smaller denominations. The cross on many medieval coins assisted the division of silver pennies into halfpence and farthings. Spanish dollars were frequently divided into *bits* which themselves became units of currency in America and the West Indies.

Darlehnskassen (German for "state loan notes"). Paper money issued during the First World War in an abortive bid to fill the shortage of coinage in circulation. These low-denomination notes failed to meet demand and were superseded by local issues of small *Notgeld* in 1916.

Debasement The reduction in the precious metal content of the coinage, widely practised since time immemorial by governments for economic reasons. British coins, for example, were debased from sterling (.925 fine) silver to .500 in 1920 and then from silver to cupro-nickel in 1947.

Decimalisation A currency system in which the principal unit is subdivided into ten, a hundred, or a thousand fractions. Russia was the first country to decimalise, in 1534 when the rouble of 100 kopeks was introduced, but it was not till 1792 that France adopted the franc of 100 centimes and 1793 when the USA introduced the dollar of 100 cents. Most European countries decimalised their currency in the 19th century. Britain toyed with the idea, introducing the florin or tenth of a pound in 1849 as the first step, but did not complete the process till 1971. The last countries to decimalise were Malta and Nigeria, in 1972 and 1973 respectively.

Demidiated Heraldic term to describe the junction of two armorial devices, in which only half of each is shown.

Demonetisation The withdrawal of coins or paper money from circulation and declaring them to be worthless.

Device Heraldic term for the pattern or emblem on coins or paper notes.

Die Hardened piece of metal bearing a mirror image of the device to be struck on one side of a coin or medal.

Die Proof An impression, usually pulled on soft carton or India paper, of an *intaglio* engraving of a banknote, usually taken during the progress of the engraving to check the detail. Banknote proofs of this nature usually consist of the portrait or some detail of the design, such as the border, rather than the complete motif.

Dodecagonal Twelve-sided, a term applied to the nickel-brass threepence of Great Britain, 1937–67.

Dump Any primitive coin struck on a very thick *flan*, but more specifically applied to the circular pieces cut from the centre of Spanish dollars, countermarked with the name of the colony, a crown and the value, and circulated in New South Wales at 15 pence in 1813. See *Holey Dollar*.

Duodecimal Currency system based on units of twelve, i.e. medieval money of account (12 denarii = 1 soldo) which survived in Britain as 12 pence to the shilling as late as 1971.

Ecclesiastical Coins Coins struck by a religious authority, such as an archbishop, bishop, abbot,

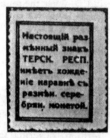

Examples of Emergency Money: Top left, Civil War Pontefract shilling; left, Russian stamp money and above, a Mafeking siege note.

prior or the canons of a religious order. Such coins were common in medieval times but survived as late as the early 19th century, the bishops of Breslau (1817) and Gurk (1823) being the last prelates to exercise coinage rights. Coins were struck by authority of the Pope at Rome till 1870 but since 1929 coinage has been struck at the Italian state mint on behalf of the Vatican City State.

Edge Inscription Lettering on the edge of a coin or medal to prevent clipping. Alluding to this, the Latin motto *Decus et Tutamen* (an ornament and a safeguard) was applied to the edge of English milled coins in the reign of Charles II.

Edge Ornament An elaboration of the *graining* found on many milled coins to prevent clipping, taking the form of tiny leaves, florets, interlocking rings, pellets and zigzag patterns. In some cases the ornament appears between layers of more conventional reeding.

EF Abbreviation for Extremely Fine.

Effigy An image or representation of a person, normally the head of state, a historical personage, or an allegorical figure, usually on the *obverse* or "heads" side of a coin or medal.

Electrotype A reproduction of a coin or medal made by an electrolytic process.

Electrum Alloy of gold and silver, sometimes called white gold, used for minting the staters of

Lydia, 7th century BC, and other early European coins.

Elongated Coin An oval *medalet* created by passing a coin, such as an American cent, between rollers under pressure with the effect of squeezing it out and impressing on it a souvenir or commemorative motif.

Emergency Money Any form of money used in times of economic and political upheaval, when traditional kinds of currency are not available. Examples include the comparatively crude silver coins issued by the Royalists during the *Civil War* (1642–49), *obsidional* money, issued in time of siege, from Tyre (1122) to Mafeking (1900), the *Notgeld* issued by many German towns (1916–23), *encased money, fractional currency, guerrilla notes, invasion, liberation* and *occupation money* from the two World Wars and minor campaigns. Among the more recent examples may be cited the use of sweets and cheques in Italy (1976–77) and the issue of coupons and vouchers in many of the countries of the former Soviet Union pending the introduction of their own distinctive coins and notes.

Enamelled Coins Coins decorated by enamelling the obverse and reverse motifs in contrasting colours was an art practised by many jewellers in Birmingham and Paris in the 19th century, and revived in Europe and America in the 1970s.

Encased Money Postage and revenue stamps enclosed in small metal and mica-faced discs, circulated as small change in times of emergency. The practice was invented by John Gault, a Boston sewing-machine salesman, during the American Civil War (1862). The face of the stamp was visible through the transparent window, while the back of the disc was embossed with firms' advertisements. This practice was revived during and after the First World War when there was again a shortage of small coins. Encased stamps have also been recorded from France, Austria, Norway, Germany and Monaco. See also *Stamp Money*.

Engrailing Technical term for the close serrations or vertical bars round the edge of a coin, applied as a security device.

Engraving The art of cutting lines or grooves in plates, blocks or dies. Numismatically this takes the form of engraving images into the face of the dies used in striking coins, a process which has now been almost completely superseded by *hubbing* and the use of *reducing machinery*. In the production of paper money, *intaglio* engraving is still commonly practised. In this process the engraver cuts the design into a steel die and the printing ink lies in the grooves. The paper is forced under great pressure into the grooves and picks up the ink, and this gives banknotes their characteristic ridged feeling to the touch. Nowadays many banknotes combine traditional intaglio engraving with multicolour lithography or photogravure to defeat the would-be counterfeiter.

Epigraphy The study of inscriptions, involving the classification and interpretation of coin legends, an invaluable adjunct to the study of a coin series, particularly the classical and medieval coins which, in the absence of dates and mintmarks, would otherwise be difficult to arrange in chronological sequence.

Erasion The removal of the title or effigy of a ruler from the coinage issued after his or her death. This process was practised in imperial Rome, and applied to the coins of Caligula, Nero and Geta, as part of the more general practice of *damnatio memoriae* (damnation of the memory) ordered by the Senate.

Error Mistakes on coins and paper money may be either caused at the design or engraving stage, or as a result of a fault in the production processes. In the first category come misspellings in legends causing, in extreme cases, *blundered inscriptions*, or anachronisms or inaccuracies in details of the design. In the second, the most glaring error is the mule caused by marrying the wrong dies. Faulty alignment of dies can cause obverse and reverse to be out of true. Although many coins are issued with obverse and reverse upside down in relation to each other, this can also occur as an error in coins where both sides should normally be facing the same way up. Other errors caused at the production stage include striking coins in the wrong metal or with the wrong *collar* thus creating a different edge from the normal (e.g. British 10p with scalloped Hong Kong edge).

Essay (From the French *essai*, a trial piece). The term is applied to any piece struck for the purposes of examination, by parliamentary or financial bodies, prior to the authorisation of an issue of coins or paper money. The official nature of these items distinguishes them from *patterns*, which denote trial pieces often produced by mints or even private individuals bidding for coinage contracts.

Evasion Close copy or imitation of a coin, with sufficient deliberate differences in the design or inscription to avoid infringing counterfeit legislation. A good example is the imitation of Sumatran coins by European merchants, inscribed SULTANA instead of SUMATRA.

Exergue Lower segment of a coin or medal, usually divided from the rest of the *field* by a horizontal line, and often containing the date, value, ornament or identification symbols.

Exonumia Generic term for numismatic items not authorised by a government, e.g. *patterns, tokens, medalets* or *model coins*.

Face The surface of a coin, medal or token, referred to as the *obverse* or the *reverse*. The corresponding faces of a paper note are more correctly termed *verso* and *recto*, but the coin terms are often used instead.

Facing Term for the portrait, usually on the obverse, which faces to the front instead of to the side (profile).

Fantasy Piece of metal purporting to be the coinage of a country which does not exist. Recent examples include the money of Atlantis and the Hutt River Province which declared its independence of Western Australia.

FDC Abbreviation for *Fleur de Coin*, a term denoting the finest possible condition of a coin.

Fiat Money Paper notes issued by a government but not redeemable in coin or bullion.

Field Flat part of the surface of a coin or medal, between the *legend*, the *effigy* and other raised parts of the design.

Fillet Heraldic term for the ribbon or headband on the effigy of a ruler or allegorical figure.

Find Term applied to an archaeological discovery of one or more coins. A large quantity of such material is described as a *hoard*.

Flan Alternative name for *blank* or *planchet*, the piece of metal struck between dies to produce a coin or medal.

Forgery An unauthorised copy or imitation, made with the intention of deceiving collectors. Forgeries intended to pass current for real coins or notes are more properly called *counterfeits*.

Fractional Currency Emergency issue of small-denomonation notes by the USA in 1863–5, following a shortage of coins caused by the Civil War. This issue superseded the *Postage Currency* notes, but bore the inscription "Receivable for all US stamps", alluding to the most popular medium of small change at that time. Denominations ranged from 3c to 50c.

Franklinium Cupro-nickel alloy developed by the Franklin Mint of Philadelphia and used for coins, medals and gaming tokens since 1967.

Freak An *error* or *variety* of a non-recurring type, usually caused accidentally during production.

Frosting Matt surface used for the high relief areas of many proof coins and medals, to give greater contrast with the mirrored surface of the field.

Funeral Money Imitations of banknotes, used in China and Latin America in funeral ceremonies.

Geat (Git) Channel through which moten metal is ducted to the mould. Cast coins and medals often show tiny protrusions known as geat marks.

Ghost Faint image of the design on one side of a coin visible on the other. Good examples were the British penny and halfpenny of George V, 1911–27, the ghosting being eliminated by the introduction of a smaller effigy in 1928.

Globular Coins struck on very thick *dumps* with convex faces. The term is applied to some Byzantine coins, and also the *bullet money* of Siam (Thailand).

Godless (or *Graceless*) Epithet applied to any coin which omits the traditional reference to the deity, e.g. the British florin of 1849 which omitted D.G. (*Dei Gratia*, "by the Grace of God").

Gold Precious metal, atomic symbol and numismatic abbreviation *Au*, from the *Latin Aurum*, used as a coinage medium from the 7th century BC till the present day. The purity of gold is reckoned in *carats* or a decimal system. Thus British gold sovereigns are 22 carat or .916 fine. Medieval coins were 23.5 carat or .995 fine, and some modern bullion coins are virtually pure gold, denoted by the inscription .999. Canadian maple leaves are now struck in "four nines" gold and bear the inscription .9999.

Goodfor Popular name for token coins and *emergency money* made of paper or card, from the inscription "Good for" or its equivalent in other languages (e.g. French *Bon pour* or Dutch *Goed voor*) followed by a monetary value. They have been recorded from Europe, Africa and America during times of economic crises or shortage of more traditional coinage.

Gothic Crown Popular name for the silver crown issued by the United Kingdom (1847–53), so-called on account of its script (more properly Old English, rather than Gothic).

Grain The weight of a single grain of wheat was taken as the smallest unit of weight in England. The troy grain was 1/5760 of a pound, while the avoirdupois grain was 1/7000 pound, the former being used in the weighing of precious metals and thus employed by numismatists in weighing coins. A grain is 1/480 troy ounce or 0.066 gram in the metric system.

Graining Term sometimes used as a synonym for the *reeding* on the edge of milled coins.

Gripped Edge Pattern of indentations found on the majority of American cents of 1797, caused by the milling process. Coins of the same date with a plain edge are rather scarcer.

Guerrilla Money Money issued in areas under the control of guerrillas and partisans during wartime range from the *veld ponds* of the Boers (1900–2) to the notes issued by the Garibaldi Brigade in Italy and the anti-fascist notes of Tito's forces in Yugoslavia. The most prolific issues were those produced in Luzon, Mindanao and Negros Occidental by the Filipino resistance during the Japanese occupation (1942–5).

Guilloche French term signifying the intricate pattern of curved lines produced by the rose engine and used as a security feature in the production of banknote, cheques, stocks and share certificates.

Gun Money Emergency coinage of Ireland (1689–91) minted from gunmetal, a type of bronze used in the casting of cannon. All denominations of James II, from the sixpence to the crown, normally struck in silver, were produced in this base metal.

Gutschein German word for voucher or coupon, denoting the paper money used aboard ships of the Imperial Navy during the First World War. The last issue was made at Scapa Flow, 1918–19, during the internment of the High Seas Fleet.

Hammered Term denoting coins produce by the traditional method of striking a *flan* laid on an anvil with a hammer. A characteristic of hammered coins is their uneven shape which tended to encourage *clipping*. This abuse was gradually eliminated by the introduction of the screw press in the 15th century and the mechanisation of coining processes in the course of the 16th and 17th centuries.

Hard Times Token Copper piece the size of the

large cent, issued in the USA, 1834–44, during a shortage of coins caused by the collapse of the Bank of the United States, the panic of 1837 and the economic crisis of 1839, the landmarks in the period known as the Hard Times. Banks suspended *specie* payments and the shortage of coinage was filled by tradesmen's tokens. Many of these were more in the nature of satirical *medalets* than circulating pieces.

Hat Piece Alternative name for the *bonnet piece* of James VI of Scotland, 1591.

Hell Notes Imitation paper money used in Chinese funeral ceremonies and buried with the dead to pay for services in the next world.

Hoard Accumulation of coins concealed in times of economic or political upheaval and discovered, often centuries later. Under English common law, such hoards are subject to th law of *treasure trove* if they contain precious metal.

Hog Money Popular name for the early coinage of Bermuda, issued about 1616. The coins were minted in brass with a silver wash and circulated at various values from twopence to a shilling. They derived their name from the hog depicted on the obverse, an allusion to the pigs introduced to the island in 1515 by Juan Bermudez.

Holed Term denoting two different categories: (a) coins which have been pierced for suspension as a form of jewellery or talisman, and (b) coins which have a hole as part of their design. In the latter category come the Chinese *cash* with a square hole, and numerous issues of the 19th and 20th centuries from many countries, with the object of reducing weight and metal without sacrificing overall diameter.

Holey Dollar Spanish silver peso of 8 reales with the centre removed. The resultant ring was counter-marked "New South Wales" and dated 1813, with "Five Shillings" on the reverse, and placed into circulation during a shortage of British coin. The centre, known as a *dump*, was circulated at 15 pence.

Hub Heavy circular piece of steel on which the *die* for a coin or medal is engraved. The process of cutting the die and transferring the master die, by means of intermediary *punches*, to the die from which the coins will be struck, is known as hubbing. Soft steel is used in the preliminary process, and after the design has been transferred, the hub is hardened by chemical action.

Hybrid Alternative name for a *mule*.

Imitation Money Also known as play money or toy money, it consists of coins and notes produced for games of chance (like Monopoly), children's toy shops and post offices, as tourist souvenirs, or for political satire (e.g. the shrinking

pound or dollar). See also *funeral money*, *hell notes*, *model coins* and *skit notes*.

Imprint Inscription on a paper note giving the name of the printer.

Incuse Impression which cuts into the surface of a coin or medal, as opposed to the more usual raised relief. Many of the earliest coins, especially those with a device on one side only, bear an incuse impression often in a geometric pattern. An incuse impression appears on one side of the coins, reflecting the image on the other side. Few modern coins have had an incuse design, notable examples being the American half and quarter eagle gold coins of 1908–29 designed by Bela Pratt. Incuse inscriptions on a raised rim, however, are more common, and include the British *Cartwheel* coins of 1797 and the 20p coins since 1982.

Inflation Money Coins produced as a result of inflation date back to Roman times when bronze minimi, little bigger than a pinhead, circulated as denari. Nearer the present day inflation has had devastating effects on the coinge and banknotes of Germany (1921–3), Austria (1923), Poland (1923), Hungary (1945–6), Greece (1946) and many Latin American countries since the 1980s. Hungary holds the record for the highest value of any note ever issued—one thousand million adopengos, equivalent to 20,000,000,000,000,000,000,000,000 pengos.

Ingot Piece of precious metal, usually cast in a mould, and stamped with the weight and fineness. though mainly used as a convenient method of storing bullion, ingots have been used as currency in many countries, notably Russia and Japan.

Intaglio Form of *engraving* in which lines are cut into a steel die for the recess-printing of banknotes.

Intrinsic The net metallic value of a coin, as distinguished from the nominal or face value.

Iron Metal, chemical symbol Fe (from Latin *Ferrum*), used as a primitive form of currency from classical times onwards. Iron spits (obeliskoi) preceded the obol as the lowest unit of Greek coinage, a handful of six spits being worth a drachma (from *drassomai*, "I grasp"). Cast iron coins were issued in China as a substitute for copper *cash*. Many of the emergency token issues of Germany during the First World War were struck in iron. Iron coins were issued by Bulgaria in 1943. See also *Steel*.

Ithyphallic (Greek for "erect penis"). Term descriptive of coins of classical Greece showing a satyr.

Janiform Double profiles back to back, after the Roman god Janus.

Jeton (From French *jeter*, to throw). Alternative term for *counter*, and used originally on the chequerboard employed by medieval accountants. Nuremberg was the most important centre for the production of medieval jetons, often issued in lengthy portrait series. In modern parlance the term is often synonymous with *token*, though more specifically confined to pieces used in vending equipment, parking meters, laundromats, telephones and urban transport systems in many European countries. Apart from security, removing the temptation of vandals to break into the receptacles, the main advantage of such pieces is that they can be retariffed as charges increase, without any alteration in their design or composition, a method that is far cheaper than altering costly equipment to take larger coins.

Jugate (From Latin *jugum*, a yoke). Alternative to *accolated* or *conjoined* to denote overlapping profiles of rulers.

Key Date Term describing the rarest in a long-running series of coins with the dates changed at annual intervals.

Kipperzeit German term meaning the time of clipped money, denoting the period during and after the Thirty Years War (1618–48) in which debased and clipped money was in circulation.

Klippe Rectangular or square pieces of metal bearing the impression of a coin. Coins of this type were first struck in Sweden in the 16th century and were subsequently produced in many of the German states. The idea has been revived in recent years as a medium for striking commemorative pieces.

Knife Money Cast bronze pieces, with an elongated blade and a ring at one end to facilitate stringing together in bunches, were used as currency in China from the 9th century BC until the 19th century.

Kreditivsedlar (Swedish for "credit notes"). The name given to the first issue of paper money made in the western world. Paper money of this type was the idea of Johan Palmstruch at Riga in 1652, but nine years elapsed before it was implemented by the Stockholm Bank. The notes were redeemable in copper *platmynt*.

Laureate Heraldic term for a laurel wreath, often framing a state emblem or shown, in the Roman fashion, as a crown on the ruler's forehead.

Leather Money Pieces of leather embossed with an official device have been used as money on several occasions, during the sieges of Faenza and Leiden and in the Isle of Man in the 15th and 16th centuries. Several towns in Austria and Germany produced leather tokens during and after the First World War.

Legal Tender Coins or paper money which are declared by law to be current money and which tradesmen and shopkeers are obliged to accept in payment for goods or services. (See *Money and the Law*).

Legend The inscription on a coin or medal.

Liberation Money Paper money prepared for use in parts of Europe and Asia, formerly under Axis occupation. Liberation notes were used in France, Belgium and the Netherlands in 1944–5, while various Japanese and Chinese notes were overprinted for use in Hong Kong when it was liberated in 1945. Indian notes overprinted for use in Burma were issued in 1945–6 when that country was freed from Japanese occupation.

Ligature (From Latin *ligatus*, bound together). Term denoting the linking of two letters in a *legend*, e.g. Æ and Œ.

Long Cross Coinage Type of coinage introduced by King Henry III in 1247, deriving its name from the reverse which bore a cross whose arms extended right to the edge to help safeguard the coins against *clipping*. This remained the style of the silver penny, its fractions and multiples, till the reign of Henry VII, and vestiges of the long cross theme can be seen in the silver coins throughout the remaining years of the Tudor period.

Love Token A coin which has been altered by smoothing one or both surfaces and engraving initials, dates, scenes, symbols of affection and messages thereon.

Lushbourne English word for base pennies of inferior silver, said to have emanated from Luxembourg, from which the name derived. These coins were first minted under John the Blind who adopted the curious spelling of his name EIWANES in the hope that illiterate English merchants might confuse it with EDWARDVS and thus be accepted as coin issued in the name of Edward III. Lushbournes were also minted by Robert of Bethune, William I of Namur and the bishops of Toul during the mid-14th century.

Lustre The sheen or bloom on the surface of an uncirculated coin resulting from the centrifugal flow of metal caused by striking.

Magnimat Trade name used by VDM (*Verein Deutscher Metallwerke*) for a high-security alloy containing copper, nickel and magnetised steel. First used for the 5 deutschemark coin of 1975, it has since been adopted for other high-value coins in Germany and other countries.

Manilla Copper, bronze or brass rings, sometimes shaped like horseshoes and sometimes open, with flattened terminals, used as currency in West Africa until recent years.

Matrix Secondary die for a coin or medal, produced from the master die by means of an intermediate punch. In this way dies can be duplicated from the original cut on the reducing machine.

Matt or Matte Finely granulated surface or overall satin finish to proof coins, a style which was briefly fashionable at the turn of the century. The Edward VII proof set of 1902 is a notable example. In more recent years many issues of the Franklin Mint have been issued in this finish.

Maundy Money Set of small silver coins, in denominations of 1, 2, 3 and 4 pence, distributed by the reigning British monarch to the poor and needy on Maundy Thursday. The custom dates back to the Middle Ages, but in its present form, of distributing pence to as many men and women as the years in the monarch's age, it dates from 1666. At first ordinary silver pennies and multiples were used but after they went out of everyday use distinctive silver coins were produced specifically for the purpose from the reign of George II (1727–60) onwards. For centuries the ceremony took place in Westminster Abbey but since 1955 other venues have been used in alternate years.

Medal (French *medaille*, Italian *medaglia*, from Latin *metallum*). A piece of metal bearing devices and legends commemorating an event or person, or given as an award. Military medals date from the 16th and 17th centuries, but were not generally awarded to all ranks till the 19th century. Commemorative medals can trace their origin back to Roman times, but in their present form they date from the Italian Renaissance when there was a fashion for large-diameter cast portrait medals.

Medalet A small medal, generally 25mm or less in diameter.

Medallion Synonym for medal, but usually confined to those with a diameter of 50mm or more.

Milling Process denoting the mechanical production of coins, as opposed to the handmade technique implied in *hammering*. It alludes to the use of watermills to drive the machinery of the screw presses and blank rollers developed in the 16th century. As the even thickness and diameter of milled coins permitted a security edge, the term milling is popularly, though erroneously, used as a synonym for *graining* or *reeding*.

Mint The place in which coins and medals are produced. Mint condition is a term sometimes used to denote pieces in an uncirculated state.

Mint Set A set of coins or medals in the package or case issued by the mint. See also *year set*.

Mintmark A device appearing on a coin to denote the place of minting. Athenian coins of classical times have been recorded with up to 40 different marks, denoting individual workshops. In the 4th century AD the Romans adopted this system to identify coins struck in provincial mints. This system was widely used in the Middle Ages and survives in France and Germany to this day. Initials and symbols are also used to identify mints, especially where the production of a coin is shared between several different mints. From 1351 onwards symbols were adopted in England to denote periods between trials of the *Pyx*, and thus assist the proper chronological sequence of coins, in an era prior to the adoption of dating. These mintmarks continued into the 17th century, but gradually died out as the use of dates became more widespread. See also *countermark* and *privy mark*.

Mionnet Scale Scale of nineteen diameters covering all sizes of coins belonging to the classical period, devised by the French numismatist, Theodore-Edme Mionnet (1770–1842) during the compilation of his fifteen-volume catalogue of the numismatic collection in the Bibliotheque Nationale in Paris.

Mirror Finish The highly polished surface of proof coins.

Misstrike A coin or medal on which the impression has been struck off-centre.

Model Coin Tiny pieces of metal, either reproducing the designs of existing coins (used as play money by children) or, more specifically, denoting patterns produced by Joseph Moore and Hyam Hyams in their attempts to promote an improved subsidiary coinage in 19th century Britain. These small coins were struck in bronze with a brass or silver centre and were designed to reduce the size of the existing cumbersome range of pence, halfpence and farthings.

Modified Effigy Any coin in which the profile on the obverse has been subtly altered. Examples include minor changes in the Victorian Young Head and Old Head effigies and the George V profile by Sir Bertram Mackennal.

Money Order Certificate for a specified amount of money, which may be transmitted by post and encashed at a money order office or post office. This system was pioneered by Britain and the United States in the early 19th century and is now virtually worldwide. The term is now confined to certificates above a certain value, the terms *postal order* and *postal note* being used for similar certificates covering small amounts.

Mule Coin whose obverse is not matched with its official or regular reverse. Mules include the erroneous combination of dies from different reigns, but in recent years such hybrids have arisen in mints where coins for several countries are struck. Examples include the Coronation Anniversary crowns combining Ascension and Isle of Man dies and the 2 cent coins with Bahamas and New Zealand dies. *Restrikes* of rare American coins have been detected in which the dated die has been paired with the wrong reverse die, e.g. the 1860 restrike of the rare 1804 large cent.

Mute An *anepigraphic* coin, identifiable only by the devices struck on it.

Nail Mark Small indentation on ancient coins. The earliest coins of Asia Minor developed from the electrum *dumps* which merchants marked with a broken nail as their personal guarantee of value, the ancient counterpart of the *chop* marks used in China and Japan.

NCLT Coins Abbreviation for "Non Circulating Legal Tender", a term devised by modern coin catalogues to denote coins which, though declared *legal tender*, are not intended for general circulation on account of their precious metal content or superior finish.

Nicked Coin Coin bearing a tiny cut or nick in its edge. Silver coins were tested by this method, especially in the reign of Henry I (1100–35) when so many base silver pennies were in circulation. Eventually people refused to accept these nicked coins a problem which was only overcome when the state decreed that all coins should have a nick in them.

Nickel Metallic element, chemical symbol *Ni*, a hard white metal relatively resistant to tarnish, and extensively used as a cheap substitute for silver. It was first used for the American 5 cent coin in 1866, hence its popular name which has stuck ever since, although nowadays the higher denominations are minted in an alloy of copper and nickel. Although best known as a silver substitute, nickel was widely used in Jamaica (1869–1969) for halfpence and pennies and in British West Africa for the tiny 1/10th pennies (1908–57). Pure nickel is used for French francs and German marks, but usually it is alloyed with copper or zinc to produce *cupro-nickel* or nickel brass.

Notaphily Hybrid word from Latin *nota* (note) and Greek philos (love), coined about 1970 to denote the branch of numismatics devoted to the study of paper money.

Notgeld German word meaning emergency money, applied to the *tokens*, in metals, wood, leather and even ceramic materials, issued during the First World War when coinage disappeared from circulation. These tokens were soon superseded by low-denomination paper money issued by shops and businessmen in denominations from 10 to 50 pfennige and known as *kleine Notgeld* (small emergency money). These notes were prohibited in September 1922 but by that time some 50,000 varieties are thought to have been issued. Inflation raced out of control and the government permitted a second issue of local notes, known as *large Notgeld*, as the denominations were in thousands, and latterly millions, of marks. Some 3,600 types appeared in 1922 and over 60,000 in 1923 alone. These quaint and colourful mementoes of the German hyperinflation ceased to circulate in 1924 when the currency was reformed.

Numismatics The study of coins, medals and other related fields, a term derived from the Latin *numisma* and Greek *nomisma* (money).

Obsidional Currency (From Latin *obsidium*, a siege). Term for *emergency money* produced by the defenders of besieged towns and cities. These usually took the form of pieces of silver plate, commandeered for the purpose, crudely marked with an official device and the value. Instances of such siege coinage have been recorded from the 12th to the 19th centuries. Paper money was issued in Venice during the Austrian siege of 1848, and by Mafeking in 1900 during the Boer War.

Obverse The "heads" side of a coin or medal, generally bearing the effigy of the head of state or an allegorical figure (e.g. Liberty—Argentina, USA; Helvetia or William Tell—Switzerland; or La Semeuse—France).

Off Metal Term denoting a piece struck in a metal other than the officially authorisied or issued alloy. This originally applied to *patterns* which were often struck in lead or copper instead of gold and silver as trial pieces or to test the dies; but in recent years it has applied to collectors' versions, e.g. proofs in platinum, gold or silver of coins normally issued in bronze or cupro-nickel.

Overdate One or more digits in a date altered by superimposing another figure. Alterations of this kind, by means of small hand punches, were made to dated dies so that they could be used in years other than that of the original manufacture. Coins with overdates invariably show traces of the original digit.

Overstrike Coin, token or medal produced by using a previously struck pieces as a flan. The Bank of England dollar of 1804 was overstruck on Spanish pieces of eight, and examples showing traces of the original coins are worth a good premium.

Paduan Name given to imitations of medals and bogus coins produced in Italy in the 16th century, and deriving from the city of Padua where forgeries of bronze sculpture were produced for the antique market.

Patina Oxidation forming on the surface of metallic objects. So far as coins and medals are concerned, this applies mainly to silver, brass, bronze and copper pieces which may acquire oxidation from the atmosphere, or spectacular patination from salts in the ground in which they have been buried. In extreme forms patina leads to verdigris and other forms of rust which corrode the surface, but in uncirculated coins it may be little more than a mellowing of the original *lustre*. Coins preserved in blue velvet presentation cases often acquire a subtle toning from the dyes in the material.

Pattern Piece resembling a coin or medal, prepared by the mint to the specifications or on the authorisation of the coin-issuing authority, but also applied to pieces produced by mints when tendering for coinage or medal contracts. Patterns may differ from the final coins as issued in the type of alloy used (*off metal*) but more often they differ in details of the design.

Pellet Raised circular ornament used as a spacing device between words and abbreviations in the *legend* of coins and medals. Groups of pellets were also used as ornaments in the angles of the cross on the reverse of English silver pennies.

Piece de Plaisir (French for "fancy piece"). Term given to coins struck in a superior precious metal, or to a superior finish, or on a much thicker flan than usual. See *off metal*, *piedfort* and *proof*.

Piedfort (Piefort) Piece struck with coinage dies on a *flan* of much more than normal thickness. This practice originated in France in the late 16th century and continues to the present day. In recent years it has been adopted by mints in Britain and other countries as a medium for collectors' pieces.

Pile Lower die incorporating the obverse motif, used in striking coins and medals. See also *trussel*.

Planchet French term used as an alternative for *blank* or *flan*.

Plaque or **Plaquette** Terms sometimes used for medals struck on a square or rectangular flan.

Plaster Cast taken from the original model for a coin or medal sculpted by an artist, and used in modern reducing machines in the manufacture of the master *die*.

Plated Coins Coins stuck in base metal but given a wash of silver or some other precious metal. This expedient was adopted in inflationary times, from the Roman republic (91 BC) till the Tudor period. American cents of 1943 were struck in steel with a zinc coating, and in more recent years *clad* coins have produced similar results.

Platinum The noblest of all precious metals, platinum has a higher specific gravity than gold and a harder, brighter surface than silver. Until an industrial application was discovered in the mid-19th century, it was regarded as of little value, and was popular with counterfeiters as a cheap substitute for gold in their forgeries which, with a light gold wash, could be passed off as genuine. It was first used for circulating coins in Russia (the chief source of the metal since 1819) and 3, 6 and 12 rouble coins were mined at various times between 1828 and 1845. In recent years platinum has been a popular metal for limited-edition proof coins.

Platmynt (Swedish for "plate money"). Large copper plates bearing royal cyphers and values from half to ten dalers produced in Sweden between 1643 and 1768. They represented laudable attempts by a country rich in copper to produce a coinage in terms of its silver value, but the net result was far too cumbersome to be practical. The weight of the daler plate, for example, ranged from 766 grams to 1.1kg, and special carts had to be devised to transport them!

Plugged Coins Coins struck predominantly in one metal, but containing a small plug of another. This curious practice may be found in the farthings of Charles II (1684–85) and the halfpence or farthings of James II (1685–87), which were struck in tin, with a copper plug, to defeat forgers.

Pollard Alternative name for *crockard*.

Porcelain Money Tokens made of porcelain circulated in Thailand from the late 18th century till 1868. The Meissen pottery struck tokens in 1920–22 as a form of small *Notgeld*, using reddish-brown Bottger stoneware and white *bisque* porcelain. These ceramic tokens circulated in various towns of Saxony.

Postage Currency Small paper notes in denominations of 5, 10, 25 and 50 cents, issued by the US federal government in 1862–63, were thus inscribed and had reproductions of postage stamps engraved on them — five 5c stamps on the 25c and five 10c stamps on the 50c notes. The earliest issue even had perforations in the manner of stamps, but this unnecessary device was soon done away with. See also *stamp money*.

Postal Notes or Orders Low-value notes intended for transmission by post and encashable at post offices. Introduced by Britain in 1883, they were an extension of the earlier *money order* system, and are now issued by virtually every country.

Potin (French for pewter). Alloy of copper, tin, lead and silver used as a coinage metal by the Celtic tribes of eastern Gaul at the beginning of the Christian era.

Privy Mark Secret mark incorporated in the design of a coin or medal to identify the minter, or even the particular die used. The term is also used more loosely to denote any small symbol or initials appearing on a coin other than a *mint mark*, and is sometimes applied to the symbols associated with the trial of the *Pyx* found on English coins.

Prize Coins Coins of large size and value struck primarily as prizes in sporting contests. this principle dates from the late 5th century BC when Syracuse minted decadrachms as prizes in the Demareteian Games. The most notable example in modern times is the lengthy series of talers and five-franc coins issued by the Swiss cantons since 1842 as prizes in the annual shooting festivals, the last of which honoured the Lucerne contest of 1939.

Profile A side view of the human face, widely used as a coinage effigy.

Proof Originally a trial strike testing the *dies*, but now denoting a special collectors' version struck with dies that have been specially polished on *flans* with a mirror finish. Presses operating at a very slow speed, or multi-striking processes, are also used.

Propaganda Notes Paper money containing a political slogan or a didactic element. During the Second World War forgeries of German and Japanese notes were produced by the Allies and additionally inscribed or overprinted with slogans such as "Co-Prosperity Sphere—What is it worth?" (a reference to the Japanese occupied areas of Southeast Asia). Forged dollars with anti-American propaganda were airdropped over Sicily by the Germans in 1943 and counterfeit pounds with Arabic propaganda over Egypt in 1942–43. Various anti-communist organi-sations liberated propaganda forgeries of paper money by balloon over Eastern Europe during the Cold War period.

Provenance Mark Form of *privy mark* denoting the source of the metal used in coins. Examples include the plumes or roses on English coins denoting silver from Welsh or West of England mines, and the elephant or elephant and castle on gold coins denoting bullion imported by the African Company. Coins inscribed VIGO (1702–03) or LIMA (1745–46) denote bullion seized from the Spaniards by Anglo-Dutch privateers and Admiral Anson respectively. Other provenance marks on English coins include the letters EIC and SSC, denoting bullion imported by the East India Company or the South Sea Company.

Pseudo Coins Derisory term coined in recent years to signify pieces of precious metal, often struck in *proof* versions only, aimed at the international investment market. Many of these pieces, though bearing a nominal face value, are not *legal tender* in the countries purporting to issue them and in many cases they go straight from the overseas mint where they are produced to coin dealers in America and western Europe, without ever appearing in the so-called country of origin. See also *NCLT coins*.

Punch or Puncheon Intermediate *die* whereby working dies can be duplicated from the master die, prior to the striking of coins and medals.

Pyx Box in which a specimen from every 15 pounds troy weight of gold and every 60 pounds of silver minted in England is kept for annual trial by weight and assay. Many of the *mintmarks* on English coins of the 14th–17th centuries were in use from one trial to the next and still exist today and can therefore be used to date them.

Reducing Machinery Equipment designed on the pantographic principle for transferring the image from a *plaster* to a *hub* and reducing it to the size of the actual coin or medal. The image is transferred by means of a stylus operating rather like a gramophone needle, but working from the centre to the outer edge.

Reeding Security edging on coins, consisting of close vertical ridges. As a rule, this appears all round the edge but some coins, e.g. New Zealand's 50c (1967) and the Isle of Man's £1 (1978) have segments of reeding alternating with a plain edge, to help blind and partially sighted persons to identify these coins.

Re-issue A coin or note issued again after an extended lapse of time.

Relief Raised parts of the *obverse* and *reverse* of coins and medals, the opposite of *incuse*.

Remainder A note from a bank or issuing authority which has never been circulated, due to inflation, political changes or bank failure. Such notes, some-times in partial or unfinished state (e.g. missing serial numbers or signatures), are generally unloaded on to the numismatic market at a nominal sum and provide a good source of inexpensive material for the beginner.

Restrike Coin, medal or token produced from *dies* subsequent to the original use. Usually restrikes are made long after the original and can often be identified by marks caused by damage, pitting or corrosion of the dies after they were taken out of service.

Retrograde Term describing inscriptions running from right to left, or with the letters in a mirror image, thought to arise from unskilled die-cutters failing to realise that inscriptions have to be engraved in negative form to achieve a positive impression. Retrograde inscriptions are common on ancient Greek coins, but also found on Roman and Byzantine coins.

Reverse The side of a coin or medal regarded as of lesser importance; in colloquial parlance, the "tails" side.

Saltire Heraldic term for a cross in the shape of an X.

Sandwich Coin *blank* consisting of thin outer layers in one alloy bonded to a core in another. See *clad coins*.

Sceat (Anglo-Saxon for "treasure", or German *Schatz*). Money of account in Kent early in the 7th century as the twelfth part of a shilling or Merovingian gold tremissis. As a silver coin, it dates from about AD 680–700 and weighed about 20 grains, putting it on par with the Merovingian denier or penny. Sceats spread to other parts of England in the 8th century but tended to decline in weight and value, but from about 760 it was gradually superseded by the silver penny minted under Offa and his successors.

Scissel The clippings of metal left after a *blank* has been cut. Occasionally one of these clippings accidentally adheres to the blank during the striking process, producing characteristic crescent-shaped flaws on the finished coin.

Scrip Paper money of restricted validity or circulation, e.g. *Bafs* and other military scrip used in canteens and post exchanges.

Scyphate (Greek *scypha*, a skiff or small boat). Byzantine coin with a concave *flan*.

Sede Vacante (Latin for "Vacant See"). Coins struck at *ecclesiastical mints* between the death of a prelate and the election of his successor are often thus inscribed. This practice originated at Rome in the 13th century and spread to every part of Europe.

Seignorage or Seigneurage Royalty or percentage paid by persons bringing *bullion* to a mint for conversion into coin, but nowadays synonymous with the royalty paid by mints in respect of the precious metal versions of coins sold direct to collectors. It arises from the medieval right of the king to a small portion of the proceeds of a mint, and amounted to a tax on moneying. It has also been applied to the money accruing to the state when the coinage is re-issued in an alloy of lesser fineness, as, for example, the debased sovereigns of Henry VIII in 20 instead of 23 carat gold, the king's treasury collecting the difference.

Series Term applied to sets of medals of a thematic character, which first became fashionable in the early 18th century. Jean Dassier pioneered the medallic series in the 1720s with his set of 72 medals portraying the rulers of France till Louis XV. The idea was developed by J. Kirk, Sir Edward Thomason, J. Mudie and A. J. Stothard in Britain, and by Moritz Fuerst and Amedee Durand in Europe. The fashion died out in the 19th century, but has been revived in America and Europe since 1964.

Serrated Having a notched or toothed edge, rather like a cogwheel. Coins of this type, struck in *electrum*, are known from Carthage in the 2nd century BC, and some silver denarii of Rome in the 2nd century AD also come into this category.

Sexagesimal System Monetary system in which the principal unit is divided into 60 parts. The oldest system in the Western world was based on the gold talent of 60 minae and the mina of 60 shekels. In medieval Europe 60 groschen were worth a fine mark; in England from 1551, the silver coinage was based on the crown of 60 pence, and in the south German states till 1873 the gulden was worth 60 kreuzers.

Shin Plasters Derisory term originally applied to the Continental currency notes issued during the American War of Independence, the fractional currency of the Civil War period and also the low-denomination notes of Canada between 1870 and 1935, but often applied indiscriminately to any other low-denomination, small-format notes.

Short Cross Coinage Term for the silver coinage introduced by Henry II in 1180 and minted till 1247 when it was replaced by the *Long Cross* type. The termination of the arms of the cross on the reverse well within the circumference encouraged the dishonest practice of *clipping*.

Shroff Mark A *countermark* applied by Indian bankers or merchants to attest the full weight and purity of coins. See also *chop*.

Siege Money See *Obsidional Currency*

Silver Precious metal, chemical symbol *Ag*, numismatic abbreviation *Ar*, from Latin *Argentum*, used as a coinage metal from the 6th century BC to the present day. **Sterling silver** denotes an alloy of .925 fine silver with .075 copper. Fine silver alloys used over the past 2,500 years have ranged from .880 to .960 fine, but base silver has also been all too common. British coins from 1920 to 1946 were struck in .500 fine silver, while alloys of lesser fineness are known as *billon* or *vellon*. Silver alloyed with gold produces *electrum*, used for the earliest coinage of the western world, the staters of Lydia in the 7th century BC. Since 1970 silver as a medium for circulating coinage has virtually disappeared, yet the volume of silver coins for sale to collectors has risen considerably in recent years.

Skit Note Piece of paper masquerading as a bankntoe. It differs from a *counterfeit* in that its design parodies that of a genuine note, often for political, satirical or advertising reasons. Others were produced as April Fools' Day jokes or a form of Valentine (e.g. the Bank of Lovers). In recent years they have been produced as advertising gimmicks, or as coupons permitting a discount off the list price of goods.

Slug Popular name for the $50 gold pieces produced by private mints in California in the mid-19th century. The term is also applied nowadays to *tokens* intended for use in gaming machines.

Spade Guinea Name given to the guineas of George III issued between 1787 and 1799 because the shield on the reverse design resembled the shape of a spade. In Victorian times the spade guinea was extensively copied in brass for gaming counters.

Spade Money Cast bronze pieces resembling miniature spades and other agricultural implements, used as money and derived from the actual implements which had previously been used in barter. Often referred to as *Pu* or *Boo* money.

Specie Financial term denoting money in the form of precious metals (silver and gold), usually struck as coin, as opposed to money in the form of paper notes and bills of exchange. It occurs in the name of some European coins (e.g. *speciedaler*, *speciestaler* and *speciesducat*) to denote the use of fine silver or gold.

Specimen Generally used to denote a single piece, but more specifically applying to a coin in a special finish, less than *proof* in quality but superior to the general circulating version. It also denotes paper notes intended for circulation between banks or for press publicity and distinguished from the generally issued version by zero serial numbers, punch holes or a security endorsement.

Spintriae Metal tokens produced in Roman imperial times, with erotic motifs, thought to have been tickets of admission to brothels.

Spit Copper or iron rod used as a primitive form of currency in the Mediterranean area. The Greek word *belos* meant a spit, dart or bolt, and from this came the word *obolos* used for a coin worth a 6th of a drachma.

Stamp Money Both postage and revenue (fiscal) stamps have circulated as money during shortages of coins, from the American Civil War onwards. *Encased postage stamps* were used in the USA, 1861–62, before they were superseded by *Postage Currency* notes, but the same expedient was adopted by many countries during and immediately after the First World War. Stamps affixed to special cards have circulated as money in Rhodesia (now Zimbabwe) in 1900, the French colonies and Turkey during the First World War, in Spain during the Civil War (1936–39) and the Philippines during the Japanese occupation (1942–45). Stamps printed on thick card, with an inscription on the reverse signifying their parity with silver coins, were issued in Russia (1917–18) and also in Armenia, the Crimea and the Ukraine (1918–20). During the Second World War Ceylon (now Sri Lanka) and several Indian states issued small money cards with contemporary stamps printed on them.

Steel Refined and tempered from *iron*, and used in chromed or stainless versions as a coinage metal in the 20th century. Zinc-coated steel cents were issued by the USA (1943) but in the form known as *acmonital* (nickel steel) it has been extensively used by Italy since 1939. Other alloys of nickel and steel have been used for coins of the Philippines (1944–45) and Roumania since 1963. Chrome steel was used by France for 5 centime coins in 1961–64. Copper-clad steel is now extensively used for subsidiary coins formerly struck in bronze.

Sterling Word of uncertain origin denoting money of a standard weight and fineness, and hence the more general meaning of recognised worth. The tradi-tionally accepted derivation from the Easterlings, north German merchants who settled in London in the 13th century and produced silver pennies of uniform fineness, is unlikely as the term has been found in documents a century earlier. A more plausible explanation is from Old English *steorling* ("little coin with a star"), alluding to Viking pennies with this device, or even as a diminutive of *stater*. Sterling silver denotes silver of .925 fineness.

Stone Money Primitive currency in the form of large stone discs, used in West Africa in the pre-colonial period, and in the Pacific island of Yap (Caroline Islands, now Micronesia) as recently as 1940.

Striation A pattern of alternate light and dark parallel marks or minute grooves on the surface of a coin or medal. In the latter case it is sometimes done for textural effect, but in coins it may result from faulty *annealing*. Deliberate ridging of the surface, however, was a distinctive feature of Japanese *koban* and *goryoban* coins of 1736–1862.

Styca Name given to the debased silver *sceats* of Northumbria in the 8th century.

Sutlers' Tokens Tokens issued by US Army canteen-keepers for use on military posts and redeemable in merchandise. They were mainly issued in the second half of the 19th century.

Tael Chinese unit of weight corresponding to the European ounce and sometimes referred to as a liang. It was a measure of silver varying between 32 and 39 grams. In the 19th century it served as *money of account*, 100 British or Mexican trade dollars being worth 72 tael. The term has also been loosely applied to the Chinese silver yuan, although this was worth only .72 tael, or 7 mace and 2 candareens (10 candareens = 1 mace; 10 mace = 1 tael).

Thrymsa Early Anglo-Saxon gold coin based on the Merovingian tremissis or third-solidus, current in Kent, London and York about AD 63–75.

Tical Unit of weight in Thailand, first appearing as coins in the form of crudely shaped *bullet money* current from the 14th till the late 19th centuries. When European-style coins were introduced in 1860 the word was retained as a denomination (32 solot = 16 atts = 8 peinung or sio = 4 songpy or sik = 2 fuang= 1 salung or quarter-tical. The currency was decimalised in 1909 (100 satangs = 1 tical), and the tical was superseded by the baht about 1950.

Tin Metallic element, chemical symbol St (from Latin *Stannum*). Because of its unstable nature and tendency to oxidise badly when exposed to the atmosphere, it is unsatisfactory as a coinage metal, but has been used on several occasions, notably in Malaya, Thailand and the East Indies. In was also used for British halfpence and farthings, 1672–92.

Token Any piece of money whose nominal value is greater than its intrinsic value is, strictly speaking, a token or promise. Thus most of the coins issued since 1964 can be regarded in this light, but numismatists reserve the term for a piece of limited validity and circulation, produced by tradesmen, chambers of commerce and other organisations during times of a shortage of government coinage. The term is also loosely applied to metal tickets of admission, such as *communion tokens*, or *jetons* and *counters* intended for games of chance. Tokens with a nominal value may be produced for security reasons to lessen the possibility of theft from milk bottles, vending machines, telephones, parking meters and transport facilities. Tokens exchangeable for goods have been issued by co-operative societies and used in prisons and internment camps in wartime. In addition to the traditional coinage alloys, tokens have been produced in ceramics, plastics, wood, stout card, leather and even rubber, in circular, square or polygonal shapes.

Tombac Type of brass alloy with a high copper content, used in coinage requiring a rich golden colour. It is, in fact, a modern version of the *aurichalcum* used by the Romans. It was used for the Canadian 5-cent coins of 1942–43, while 5- and 10-pfennig coins of Germany have a tombac cladding on a steel core.

Touchpiece Coin kept as a lucky charm, but more specifically the medieval gold angel of England which was worn round the neck as an antidote to scrofula, otherwise known as king's evil, from the belief that the reigning monarch possessed the power of healing by touch. The ceremony of touching for king's evil involved the suspension of an angel round the victim's neck, hence the prevalence of these coins pierced for suspension.

Trade Coins Coins widely used as a medium of international trade, often far beyond the boundaries of the country issuing them. The earliest examples were the Aiginetan turtles and Athenian tetrdrachms of the classical period. In the Middle Ages the English *sterling* was widely prized on account of its silver purity. Arab dinars and Italian florins were popular as gold coins in late-medieval times, while the British gold sovereign has been the preferred gold coin of modern times. The Maria Theresa silver thaler of Austria, with its date frozen at 1782, has been minted widely down to the present time for circulation in the Near and Middle East as a trade coin. Trade dollars were minted by Britain, the USA, the Netherlands and Japan to compete with the Spanish, and later the Mexican, peso or 8-reales coins as a trading medium in the Far East.

Transport Tokens Coin-like pieces of metal, plastic or card, issued by companies and corporations to employees and exchangeable for rides on municipal transport systems, date from the mid-19th century. In more recent times similar tokens have been used in many countries to activate turnstiles in buses, trams and rapid-transit railway systems.

Treasury Note Paper money worth 10 shillings or one pound, issued by the British Treasury on the outbreak of the First World War when *specie* payments were suspended, and continuing till 1928 when the Bank of England took over responsibility for note-issuing. They were popularly known as Bradburys, from the signature of the Treasury official, Sir John Bradbury, engraved on them.

Treasure Trove Articles of precious metal concealed in times of economic or political upheaval and discovered years (often centuries) later are deemed by law to be treasure trove (from the French word *trouve*, found). For further details see *Money and the Law*.

Trial Plate Plate of the same metal as the current coinage against which the fineness and quality of the coins being produced are compared and tested.

Troy Weight System of weights derived from the French town of Troyes whose standard pound was adopted in England in 1526. It continued in Britain till 1879 when it was abolished, with the exception of the troy ounce and its decimal parts and multiples, which were retained for gold, silver, platinum and precious stones. The troy ounce of 480 grains is used by numismatists for weighing coins.

Truncation Stylised cut at the base of a coinage effigy, sometimes containing a die number, engraver's initials or *mintmark*.

Trussel Reverse die in *hammered* coinage, the opposite of the *pile*.

Type Principal motif on a coin or medal, enabling numismatists to identify the issue.

Type Set A set of coins comprising one of each coin in a particular series, regardless of the actual date of issue.

Uncirculated Term used in grading coins to denote specimens in perfect condition, with original mint lustre. In recent years the term "Brilliant Uncirculated" has been adopted (abbreviated as B.Unc. or BU).

Uniface Coin, medal or token with a device on one side only.

Unique Extant in only one known example.

Variety Variation in, or modification of type, effigy, motif or inscription.

Vecture Term (mainly American) for a *transport token*.

Veld Pond (Dutch for "field pound"). Gold coin struck by the Boer guerrillas at Pilgrims Rest in 1902, in imitation of the British sovereign.

Vellon Spanish form of *billon*.

VF Abbreviation for Very Fine, used to describe the state of a coin or medal.

VG Abbreviation for Very Good.

Vignette Strictly speaking the pictorial element of a paper note shading off into the surrounding unprinted paper rather than having a clearly defined border or frame; but nowadays applied generally to the picture portion of a banknote, as opposed to portrait, armorial or numeral elements.

Vis-à-Vis (French for "face to face"). Term describing coins with double portraits of rulers, their profiles or busts facing each other. A good example is the English coinage of Philip and Mary, 1554–48.

Wampum Barter currency of the North American Indians, composed of shells of *Venus mercenaria* strung together to form belts or "fathoms" worth 5 shillings. Wampum were tariffed variously from three to six to the English penny in the American colonies till 1704.

White Gold Alternative term for *electrum*.

Wire Money Primitive currency of the Maldive Islands in the form of lengths of silver wire known as lari, from which the modern currency unit *laree* is derived. The term was also applied to English coins of the 18th century in which the numerals of value were exceptionally thin, resembling wire.

Wooden Coins Thin pieces of wood used as tokens are known from the 19th and 12th centuries in many parts of China and Africa, and as small *Notgeld* from Austria and Germany during the First World War. Wooden nickels is the somewhat contradictory name given to tokens of a commemorative nature, widely popular in the USA since 1930.

Year Set A set of coins issued annually by a mint. It often contains specimens which were not generally released for circulation in that year.

Young Head Profile of Queen Victoria sculpted by William Wyon for the Guildhall Medal of 1837 and subsequently utilised for British coins struck from 1837 to 1860 (copper) and 1887 (silver and gold).

Zinc Metallic element, chemical symbol Zn, widely used, with copper, as a constituent of brass, although it was not isolated till the 18th century. Alloyed with copper to form *tombac*, it was used for Canadian 5-cent coins (1942–43) and, coated on steel, it was used for American cents (1943). Zinc was used for *emergency coinage* in Austria, Belgium, Luxembourg and Germany (1915–18) and in Germany and German-occupied countries during the Second World War. Since then alloys of copper, nickel and zinc have been used for coinage in Eastern Europe, and an alloy of zinc with titanium has been developed in the 1970s as a potential substitute for *bronze* in subsidiary coinage.

MINTMARKS
of the world

The following is a list of the initials and symbols denoting mints. In many cases, notably the Royal Mint, no mintmark was used on either British coins or those struck on behalf of other countries. Conversely many countries have only used one mintmark, that of one or other of the leading private mints.

It should be noted that the mintmarks of the main private mints have been recorded on the coins of the following countries:

H (Heaton, later the Birmingham Mint):
Australia, Bolivia, British Honduras, British North Borneo, British West Africa, Bulgaria, Canada, Ceylon, Chile, Colombia, Costa Rica, Cyprus, Dominican Republic, East Africa, Ecuador, Egypt, El Salvador, Finland, French Indochina, Great Britain, Greece, Guatemala, Guernsey, Haiti, Hong Kong, Iran, Israel, Italy, Jamaica, Jersey, Liberia, Malaya and British Borneo, Mauritius, Mombasa, Mozambique, Newfoundland, Nicaragua, Poland, Roumania, Sarawak, Serbia, Siam, Straits Settlements, Uruguay and Venezuela.

FM (Franklin Mint, Philadelphia): Bahamas, Belize, British Virgin Islands, Cayman Islands, Cook Islands, Guyana, Jamaica, Liberia, Malaysia, Malta, Panama, Papua New Guinea, Philippines, Solomon Islands, Trinidad and Tobago.

PM (Pobjoy Mint, Sutton, Surrey): Ascension, Bosnia, Cook Islands, Gibraltar, Isle of Man, Liberia, Macau, Niue, Philippines, St Helena, Senegal, Seychelles, Tonga and Tristan da Cunha.

ALBANIA
L	London
R	Rome
V	Valona

ARGENTINA
BA	Buenos Aires
Bs	Buenos Aires
B.AS	Buenos Aires
JPP	Jose Policarpo Patino
M	Mendoza
PNP	Pedro Nolasco Pizarro
PP	Pedro Nolasco Pizarro
PTS	Potosi
R	Rioja
RA	Rioja
SE	Santiago del Estero
SoEo	Santiago del Estero
TN	Tucuman

AUSTRALIA
A	Perth
D	Denver
H	Heaton (1912–16)
I	Bombay (1942–43)
I	Calcutta (1916–18)
M	Melbourne
P	Perth
PL	Royal Mint, London
S	Sydney
S	San Francisco (1942–43)
Dot before and after PENNY and I on obverse	Bombay (1942–43)
Dot before and after HALFPENNY and I on obverse	Bombay (1942–43)
Dot before and after PENNY	Bombay (1942–43)
Dot after HALFPENNY	Perth
Dot before SHILLING	Perth (1946)
Dot above scroll on reverse	Sydney (1920)
Dot below scroll on reverse	Melbourne (1919–20)
Dot between designer's initials KG	Perth (1940–41)
Dot after AUSTRALIA	Perth (1952–53)

AUSTRIA
A	Vienna (1765–1872)
AH–AG	Carlsburg, Transylvania (1765–76)
AH–GS	Carlsburg (1776–80)
A–S	Hall, Tyrol (1765–74)
AS–IE	Vienna (1745)
AW	Vienna (1764, 1768)
B	Kremnitz (1765–1857)
B–L	Nagybanya (1765–71)

B–V	Nagybanya (1772–80)
C	Carlsburg (1762–64)
C	Prague (1766–1855)
C–A	Carlsburg (1746–66)
C–A	Vienna (1774–80)
CG–AK	Graz (1767–72)
CG–AR	Graz (1767)
C–K	Vienna (1765–73)
CM	Kremnitz (1779)
CVG–AK	Graz (1767–72)
CVG–AR	Graz (1767)
D	Graz (1765–72), Salzburg (1800–09)
E	Carlsburg (1765–1867)
EC–SK	Vienna (1766)
EvM–D	Kremnitz (1765–74)
EvS–AS	Prague (1765–73)
EvS–IK	Prague (1774–80)
F	Hall (1765–1807)
FH	Hall
G	Graz (1761–63)
G	Gunzburg (1764–79)
G	Nagybanya (1766–1851)
G–K	Graz (1767–72)
G–R	Graz (1746–67)
GTK	Vienna (1761)
H	Hall (1760–80)
H	Gunzburg (1765–1805)
H–A	Hall (1746–65)
H–G	Carlsburg (1765–77)
H–S	Carlsburg (1777–80)
IB–FL	Nagybanya (1765–71)
IB–IV	Nagybanya (1772–80)
IC–FA	Vienna (1774–80)
IC–IA	Vienna (1780)
IC–SK	Vienna (1765–73)
I–K	Graz (1765-67)
I–K	Vienna (1767)
IZV	Vienna (1763–65)
K	Kremnitz (1760–63)
K–B	Kremnitz (1619–1765)
K–D	Kremnitz (1765)
K–M	Kremnitz (1763–65)
M	Milan (1780–1859)
N	Nagybanya (1780)
N–B	Nagybanya (1630–1777, 1849)
O	Oravicza (1783–1816)
P	Prague (1760–63)
P–R	Prague (1746–67)
PS–IK	Prague (1774–80)
S	Hall (1765–80), Schmollnitz (1763–1816)
S–C	Gunzburg (1765–74)
SC–G	Gunzburg (1765)
S–F	Gunzburg (1775–80)
S–G	Gunzburg (1764–65)
S–IE	Vienna (1745)
SK–PD	Kremnitz (1774–80)
TS	Gunzburg (1762–88)

V	Venice (1805–66)
VC–S	Hall (1774–80)
VS–K	Prague (1774–80)
VS–S	Prague (1765–73)
W	Vienna (1748–63)
W–I	Vienna (1746–71)

BAHAMAS
FM	Franklin Mint
JP	John Pinches

BELGIUM
A	Vienna
B	Kremnitz
C	Prague
E	Carlsburg
F	Hall
G	Nagybanya
H	Gunzburg
hand	Antwerp
lion	Bruges

BELIZE (British Honduras)
FM	Franklin Mint
H	Heaton (1912–16)

BOLIVIA
H	Heaton (1892–1953)
P, PTR, PTS	Potosi

BRAZIL
A	Berlin (1913)
B	Bahia (1714–1831)
C	Cuiaba (1823–33)
G	Goias (1823–33)
M	Minas Gerais (1823–28)
P	Pernambuco
R	Rio de Janeiro (1703–1834)
RS	Rio de Janeiro (1869)
SP	Sao Paulo (1825–32)

BRITISH NORTH BORNEO (Sabah)
H	Heaton (1882–1941)

BRITISH WEST AFRICA
G	JR Gaunt, Birmingham
H	Heaton, Birmingham (1911–57)
K	King's Norton
KN	King's Norton
SA	Pretoria

BULGARIA
A	Berlin
BP	Budapest
Heaton	Heaton, Birmingham (1881–1923)
KB	Kormoczbanya
cornucopia	Paris
thunderbolt	Poissy

CANADA

C	Ottawa
H	Heaton (1871–1907)
maple leaf	Ottawa (on coins struck after the year inscribed on them)

CENTRAL AMERICAN REPUBLIC

CR	San Jose (Costa Rica)
G	Guatemala
NG	Guatemala
T	Tegucigalpa (Honduras)

CEYLON

H	Heaton (1912)

CHILE

A	Agustin de Infante y Prado (1768–72)
AJ	The above and Jose Maria de Bobadilla (1800–01)
D	Domingo Eizaguirre
DA	Domingo Eizaguirre and Agustin de Infante (1772–99)
BFF	Francisco Rodriguez Brochero
FJJF	Brochero and Jose Maria de Bobadilla (1803–17)
H	Heaton (1851)
J	Jose Larraneta (1749–67)
So	Santiago
VA	Val Distra

COLOMBIA

A	Paris
B	Bogota
BA	Bogota
B.B	Bogota
H	Heaton (1912)
M	Medellin
NR	Nuevo Reino
NoRo	Nuevo Reino
P	Popayan
PN, Pn	Popayan
SM	Santa Marta

COSTA RICA

CR	San Jose (1825–1947)
HBM	Heaton (1889–93)
S	San Domingo
SD	San Domingo

COURLAND

ICS	Justin Carl Schroder
IFS	Johan Friedrich Schmickert

CYPRUS

H	Heaton (1881–2)

DENMARK

FF	Altona
KM	Copenhagen Altona (1842)
crown	Copenhagen
heart	Copenhagen
orb	Altona (1839–48)

Other letters are the initials of mintmasters and moneyers

DOMINICAN REPUBLIC

HH	Heaton (1888–1919)

EAST AFRICA

A	Ackroyd & Best, Morley
H	Heaton (1910–64)
I	Bombay
K	Kynoch (IMI)
KN	King's Norton
SA	Pretoria

ECUADOR

BIRM^MH	Heaton (1915)
BIRMING-HAM	Heaton (1899–1900, 1928)
D	Denver
H	Heaton (1890, 1909, 1924–5)
HEATON BIRMING-HAM	Heaton (1872–95)
HF	Le Locle
LIMA	Lima
Mo	Mexico
PHILA	Philadelphia
QUITO	Quito
SANTIAGO	Santiago de Chile

EGYPT

H	Heaton (1904–37)

EL SALVADOR

CAM	Central American Mint, San Salvador
H	Heaton (1889–1913)
Mo	Mexico
S	San Francisco

FIJI

S	San Francisco

FINLAND

H	Heaton (1921)
heart	Copenhagen (1922). Since then coins have been struck at Helsinki without a mintmark.

Initials of mintmasters:

S	August Soldan (1864–85)
L	Johan Lihr (1885–1912)
S	Isaac Sundell (1915–47)

L	V. U. Liuhto (1948)	AGP	Cleve, Rhineland (1742–43)
H	Uolevi Helle (1948–58)	AK	Dusseldorf, Julich-Berg (1749–66)
S	Allan Soiniemi (1958–75)	ALS	Berlin (1749)
SH	Soiniemi & Heikki Halvaoja (1967–71)	B	Bayreuth, Franconia (1796–1804)
K	Timo Koivuranta (1977, 1979)	B	Breslau, Silesia (1750–1826)
KN	Koivuranta and Antti Neuvonen (1978)	B	Brunswick, Brunswick (1850–60)
KT	Koivuranta and Erja Tielinen (1982)	B	Brunswick, Westphalia (1809–13)
KM	Koivuranta and Pertti Makinen (1983)	B	Dresden, Saxony (1861–72)
N	Reino Nevalainen (1983)	B	Hannover, Brunswick (1860–71)
		B	Hannover, East Friesland (1823–25)

FRANCE

		B	Hannover, Hannover (1821–66)
A	Paris (1768)	B	Hannover, Germany (1866-78)
AA	Metz (1775–98)	B	Regensburg, Regensburg (1809)
B	Rouen (1786–1857)	B	Vienna, Germany (1938–45)
B	Beaumont le Roger (1943–58)	BH	Frankfurt (1808)
BB	Strasbourg (1743–1870)	B–H	Regensburg, Rhenish Confederation (1802–12)
C	Castelsarrasin (1914, 1942–46)		
CC	Genoa (1805)	C	Cassel, Westphalia (1810–13)
CL	Genoa (1813–14)	C	Clausthal, Brunswick
D	Lyons (1771–1857)	C	Clausthal, Westphalia (1810–11)
G	Geneva (1796–1805)	C	Dresden, Saxony (1779–1804)
H	La Rochelle (1770–1837)	C	Frankfurt, Germany (1866–79)
L	Limoges (1766–1837)	CHI	Berlin (1749–63)
K	Bordeaux (1759–1878)	CLS	Dusseldorf, Julich-Berg (1767–70)
L	Bayonne (1761–1837)	D	Aurich, East Friesland (1750–1806)
M	Toulouse (1766–1837)	D	Dusseldorf, Rhineland (1816–48)
MA	Marseilles (1787–1857)	D	Munich, Germany (1872)
N	Montpellier (1766–93)	E	Dresden, Germany (1872–87)
O	Riom	E	Koenigberg, East Prussia (1750–98)
P	Dijon	E	Muldenhutte, Germany (1887–1953)
Q	Perpignan (1777–1837)	EC	Leipzig, Saxony (1753–63)
R	Royal Mint, London (1815)	EGN	Berlin (1725–49)
R	Orleans (1780–92)	F	Dresden, Saxony (1845–58)
T	Nantes (1739–1835)	F	Magdeburg, Lower Saxony (1740–1806)
U	Turin (1814)	F	Cassel, Hesse-Cassel (1803–07)
V	Troyes	F	Stuttgart, Germany (1872)
W	Lille (1759–1857)	FW	Dresden, Saxony (1734–63)
X	Amiens (1740)	G	Dresden, Saxony (1833–44, 1850–54)
&	Aix en Provence (1775)	G	Glatz, Silesia (1807–09)
9	Rennes	G	Karlsruhe, Germany (1872)
cow	Pau (1746–93)	G	Stettin, Pomerania (1750–1806)
flag	Utrecht (1811–14)	GK	Cleve (1740–55)
crowned R	Rome (1811–14)	GN	Bamberg, Bamberg
thunderbolt	Poissy (1922-24)	H	Darmstadt, Germany (1872–82)
star	Madrid (1916)	H	Dresden, Saxony (1804–12)

In addition, French coins include symbols denoting the privy marks of Engravers General (Chief Engravers since 1880) and Mint Directors.

		HK	Rostock, Rostock (1862–64)
		I	Hamburg, Germany (1872)

GERMANY

The first name gives the location of the mint, and the second the name of the country or state issuing the coins.

		IDB	Dresden, Prussian occupation (1756–59)
		IEC	Dresden, Saxony (1779–1804)
		IF	Leipzig, Saxony (1763–65)
A	Amberg, Bavaria (1763–94)	IGG	Leipzig, Saxony (1716–34, 1813–32)
A	Berlin (1850)	J	Hamburg, Germany (1873)
A	Clausthal, Hannover (1832–49)	J	Paris, Westphalia (1808–09)
AE	Breslau, Silesia (1743–51)	L	Leipzig, Saxony (1761–62)
		MC	Brunswick, Brunswick (1813–14, 1820)
		PM	Dusseldorf, Julich-Berg (1771–83)
		PR	Dusseldorf, Julich-Berg (1783–1804)

S	Dresden, Saxony (1813–32)
S	Hannover, Hannover (1839–44)
S	Schwabach, Franconia (1792–94)
SGH	Dresden, Saxony (1804–12)
ST	Strickling, Blomberg (1820–40)

GREAT BRITAIN

A	Ashby (1645)
B	Nicolas Briot (1631–39)
B	Bridgnorth (1646)
B	Bristol (1696)
Br	Bristol (1643–45)
C	Chester (1696)
CARL	Carlisle (1644–45)
CC	Corfe Castle (1644)
CHST	Chester (1644)
CR	Chester (1644)
E	Southwark (1547–49)
E	Exeter (1696)
E	Edinburgh (1707–13)
E*	Edinburgh (1707–09)
H	Heaton, Birmingham (1874–1919)
HC	Hartlebury Castle (1646)
K	London (1547–49)
KN	King's Norton
N	Norwich (1696)
OX	Oxford (1644–45)
OXON	Oxford (1644)
PC	Pontefract (1648–49)
SC	Scarborough (1644–45)
SOHO	Birmingham (1797–1806)
T	Canterbury (1549)
TC	Bristol (1549)
WS	Bristol (1547–49)
Y	Southwark (1551)
boar	Shrewsbury (1643–44)
book	Aberystwyth (1638–42)
bow	Durham House (1548–49)
castle	Exeter (1644–45)
crown	Aberystwyth Furnace (1648–49)
plume	Shrewsbury (1642)
plume	Oxford (1642–46)
plume	Bristol (1643–46)

Other symbols and marks on the hammered coins of Great Britain are usually referred to as Initial Marks. Complete listings of these marks appear in a number of specialist publications.

GREECE

A	Paris
B	Vienna
BB	Strasbourg
H	Heaton (1921)
K	Bordeaux
KN	King's Norton
owl	Aegina (1828–32)
owl	Athens (1838–55)
thunderbolt	Poissy

GUATEMALA

CG	Guatemala City (1733-76)
G	Guatemala City (1776)
H	Heaton (1894–1901)
NG	Nueva Guatemala (1777)

GUERNSEY

H	Heaton (1855–1949)

HAITI

A	Paris
HEATON	Heaton (1863)

HONDURAS

A	Paris (1869–71)
T	Tegucigalpa (1825–62)

HONG KONG

H	Heaton (1872–1971)
KN	King's Norton

HUNGARY

A	Vienna
B	Kremnitz
BP	Budapest
CA	Vienna
G	Nagybanya
GN	Nagybanya
GYF	Carlsburg
HA	Hall
K	Kremnitz
KB	Kremnitz
NB	Nagybanya
S	Schmollnitz
WI	Vienna

INDIA

B	Bombay (1835-1947)
C	Calcutta (1835-1947)
I	Bombay (1918)
L	Lahore (1943-45)
M	Madras (1869)
P	Pretoria (1943-44)
diamond	Bombay
dot in diamond	Hyderabad
split diamond	Hyderabad
star	Hyderabad

IRAN

H	Heaton (1928–29)

IRAQ

I	Bombay

ISRAEL

H	Heaton (1951–52)
star of David	Jerusalem

ITALY AND STATES

B	Bologna
B/I	Birmingham (1893–4)
FIRENZE	Florence
H	Heaton (1866–67)
KB	Berlin
M	Milan
N	Naples
OM	Strasbourg
R	Rome
T	Turin
V	Venice
ZV	Venice
anchor	Genoa
eagle head	Turin

JAMAICA

C	Ottawa
FM	Franklin Mint
H	Heaton (1882–1916)

JERSEY

H	Heaton (1877)

KENYA

C/M	Calcutta
H	Heaton (1911–64)

LIBERIA

B	Berne
FM	Franklin Mint
H	Heaton (1896–1906)
PM	Pobjoy Mint

LIECHTENSTEIN

A	Vienna
B	Berne
M	Munich

LUXEMBOURG

A	Paris
H	Gunzburg
anchor	Paris
angel	Brussels
caduceus	Utrecht
double eagle	Brussels
sword	Utrecht

MALAYSIA

B	Bombay
FM	Franklin Mint
H	Heaton (1955–61)
I	Calcutta (1941)
I	Bombay (1945)
KN	King's Norton
W	James Watt, Birmingham

MAURITIUS

H	Heaton (1877–90)
SA	Pretoria

MEXICO

A, As	Alamos
C, CN	Culiacan
CA, CH	Chihuahua
Ce	Real del Catorce
D, Do	Durango
Eo	Tlalpam
GA	Guadalajara
GC	Guadelupe y Calvo
Go	Guanajuato
Ho	Hermosillo
M, Mo	Mexico City
Mo	Morelos
MX	Mexico City
O, OA, OKA	Oaxaca
Pi	San Luis Potosi
SLPi	San Luis Potosi
TC	Tierra Caliente
Z, Zs	Zacatecas

MONACO

A	Paris
M	Monte Carlo
clasped hands	Cabanis
thunderbolt	Poissy

MOZAMBIQUE

H	Heaton (1894)
R	Rio

NETHERLANDS AND COLONIES
Austrian Netherlands (1700-93)

H	Amsterdam
S	Utrecht
W	Vienna
hand	Antwerp
head	Brussels
lion	Bruges

Kingdom of the Netherlands

B	Brussels (1821–30)
D	Denver (1943–45)
P	Philadelphia (1941–45)
S	Utrecht (1816–36)
S	San Francisco (1944–45)
Sa	Surabaya
caduceus	Utrecht

NICARAGUA

H	Heaton (1880–1916)
NR	Leon de Nicaragua

NORWAY

hammers	Kongsberg

PANAMA
CHI	Valcambi
FM	Franklin Mint

PERU
AREQ, AREQUIPA	Arequipa
AYACUCHO	Ayacucho
CUZCO, Co	Cuzco
L, LM, LR	Lima
LIMAE	Lima
PASCO	Pasco
Paz, Po	Pasco
P	Lima (1568-70)
P	Philadelphia
S	San Francisco

PHILIPPINES
BSP	Bangko Sentral Pilipinas
D	Denver (1944–45)
FM	Franklin Mint
M, MA	Manila
PM	Pobjoy Mint
S	San Francisco (1903–47)
5 point star	Manila

POLAND
AP	Warsaw (1772–74)
CI	Cracow (1765–68)
EB	Warsaw (1774–92)
EC	Leipzig (1758–63)
FF	Stuttgart (1916–17)
FH	Warsaw (1815–27)
FS	Warsaw (1765–68)
FWoF	Dresden (1734–64)
G	Cracow (1765–72)
H	Heaton (1924)
IB	Warsaw (1811–27)
IGS	Dresden (1716–34)
IP	Warsaw (1834–43)
IS	Warsaw (1768–74)
JGG	Leipzig (1750–53)
JS	Warsaw (1810–11)
KG	Warsaw (1829–34)
MV, MW	Warsaw
arrow	Warsaw (1925–39)
Dot after date	Royal Mint (1925)
8 torches	Paris (1924)

ROUMANIA
B	Bucharest (1879–85)
C	Bucharest (1886)
H	Heaton (1867–1930)
HUGUENIN	Le Locle
J	Hamburg
KN	King's Norton
V	Vienna

W	Watt, Birmingham
thunderbolt	Poissy

RUSSIA
AM	Annensk (1762–96)
BM	Warsaw (1825–55)
bM	St Petersburg (1796)
C–M	Sestroretsk (1762–96)
CM	Souzan (1825–55)
E–M	Ekaterinburg (1762–1810)
KM	Kolpina (1810)
K–M	Kolyvan (1762–1810)
MM, M–M	Moscow (1730–96)
MMD	Moscow (1730–96)
MW	Warsaw (1842–54)
NM	Izhorsk (1811–21)
SP	St Petersburg (1798–1800)
SPB	St Petersburg (1724–1915)
SPM	St Petersburg (1825–55)
T–M	Feodosia (1762–96)

SAN MARINO
M	Milan
R	Rome

SIAM
(Thailand)	H Heaton (1898)

SOUTH AFRICA
SA	Pretoria

SPAIN
B	Burgos
B, BA	Barcelona
Bo	Bilbao
C	Catalonia
C	Cuenca
C	Reus
CA	Zaragoza
G	Granada
GNA	Gerona
LD	Lerida
J, JA	Jubia
M, MD	Madrid
P	Palma de Majorca
PpP, PL, PA	Pamplona
S, S/L	Seville
Sr	Santander
T, To, Tole	Toledo
TOR:SA	Tortosa
V, VA, VAL	Valencia
crowned C	Cadiz
crowned M	Madrid
aqueduct	Segovia
crowned shield	Tarragona
pomegranate	Granada
quartered shield	Palma
scallop	Coruna

SPAIN *continued*
stars:

3 points	Segovia
4 points	Jubia
5 points	Manila
6 points	Madrid
7 points	Seville (1833)
8 points	Barcelona (1838)
wavy lines	Valladolid

SURINAM

P	Philadelphia
S	Sydney
caduceus	Utrecht

SWITZERLAND

A	Paris
AB	Strasbourg
B	Berne
B	Brussels (1874)
BA	Basle
BB	Strasbourg
S	Solothurn

URUGUAY

H	Heaton (1869)

UNITED STATES OF AMERICA

C	Charlotte, North Carolina
Cc	Carson City, Nevada
D	Dahlonega, Georgia (1838–61)
D	Denver, Colorado (1906)
O	New Orleans
P	Philadelphia
S	San Francisco
W	West Point

VENEZUELA

A	Paris
H	Heaton (1852)
HEATON	Heaton (1852–63)

YUGOSLAVIA (including former Serbia)

A	Paris
H	Heaton (1883–84)
KOBHNUA, A.D.	Kovnica
V	Vienna
thunderbolt	Poissy

Matthew Boulton's Soho Manufactory in Birmingham at the beginning of the 19th century.

Coin INSCRIPTIONS

This alphabetical listing is confined to inscriptions found on coins, mainly in the form of mottoes or of a commemorative nature. Names of rulers are, for the most part, excluded. Where the inscription is in a language other than English a translation is given, followed by the name of the issuing country or authority in parentheses.

A Deo et Caesare From God and the Emperor (Frankfurt).

A Domino Factum est Istud et est Mirabile in Oculis Nostris This is the Lord's doing and it is marvellous in our eyes (England, Mary).

A Solo Iehova Sapientia From God alone comes true wisdom (Wittgenstein).

Ab Inimicis Meis Libera Me Deus Free me from enemies (Burgundy).

Ad Legem Conventionis According to the law of the Convention (Furstenberg).

Ad Normam Conventionis According to the standard of the Convention (Prussia).

Ad Palmam Pressa Laeturo Resurgo Pressed to the palm I rise more joyfully (Wittgenstein).

Ad Usam Luxemburgi CC Vallati For the use of the besieged Luxembourgers (Luxembourg siege coins).

Adiuva Nos Deus Salutaris Noster Help us, O God, our Saviour (Lorraine).

Adventus Optimi Principis The coming of the noblest prince (Papacy).

Aes Usibus Aptius Auro Bronze in its uses is more suitable than gold (Brazil).

Aeternum Meditans Decus An ornament intended for all time (Alencon).

Aliis Inserviendo Consumor I spend my life devoted to others (Brunswick-Wolfenbuttel).

Alles Mit Bedacht All with reflection (Brunswick).

Amor Populi Praesidium Regis The love of the people is the king's protection (England, Charles I).

Ang Fra Dom Hib & Aquit (King) of England and France, Lord of Ireland and Aquitaine (England, Edward III).

Anno Regni Primo In the first year of the reign (Britain, edge inscription on crowns).

Apres les Tenebres la Lumiere After the shadows, the light (Geneva).

Archangelus Michael Archangel Michael (Italy, Grimoald IV).

Ardua ad Gloriam Via Struggles are the way to glory (Waldeck).

Arte Mea Bis Iustus Moneta Lud Iust By my art I am twice the just coin of King Louis (France, 1641).

Aspera Oblectant Wild places delight (Nassau-Weilburg).

Aspice Pisas Sup Omnes Specio Behold the coin of Pisa, superior to all (Pisa).

Audiatur Altera Pars Let the other part be heard (Stavelot).

Auf Gott Trawe Ich In God I trust (Brunswick).

Ausen Gefaesen der Kirchen und Burger From the vessels of the Church and citizens (Frankfurt siege, 1796).

Auspicio Regis et Senatus Angliae By authority of the king and parliament of England (East India Company).

Auxilio fortissimo Dei With the strongest help of God (Mecklenburg).

Auxilium de Sanctio Aid from the sanctuary (Papacy).

Auxilium Meum a Dno Qui Fecit Celum e Terram My help comes from God who made heaven and earth (Portugal).

Basilea Basle.

Beata Tranquillatis Blessed tranquillity (Rome, Licinius II).

Beatus Qui Speravit in dom Blessed is he who has hoped in the Lord (Mansfeld).

Benedic Haereditati Tuae Blessings on your inheritance (Savoy).

Benedicta Sit Sancta Trinitas Blessed be the Holy Trinity (Albon).

Benedictio Domini Divites Facit The blessing of the Lord makes the rich (Teschen).

Benedictus Qui Venit in Nomine Domini Blessed is he who comes in the name of the Lord (Flanders).

Beschaw das Ziel Sage Nicht Viel Consider the matter but say little (Quedlinburg).

Besser Land und Lud Verloren als ein Falscher Aid Geschworn Better to lose land and wealth than swear a false oath (Hesse).

Bey Gott ist Rath und That With God is counsel and deed (Mansfeld).

Britanniarum Regina Queen of the Britains (Britain, Victoria).

Britt Omn Rex King of all the Britains (i.e. Britain and the overseas dominions) (Britain, 1902–52).

Cal et Car Com de Fugger in Zin et Norn Sen & Adm Fam Cajetan and Carl, Counts of Fugger in Zinnenberg and Nordendorf, Lords and Administrators of the Family (Empire, Fugger).

Candide et Constanter Sincerely and steadfastly (Hesse-Cassel).

Candide sed Provide Clearly but cautiously (Osterwitz).

Candore et Amore With sincerity and love (Fulda).

Candore et Constantia With sincerity and constancy (Bavaria).

Capit Cath Ecclesia Monasteriensis Chapter of the Cathedral Church of Munster (Munster).

Capit Eccle Metropolit Colon Chapter of the Metropolitan Church of Cologne (Cologne).

Capitulum Regnans Sede Vacante Chapter governing, the See being vacant (Eichstadt).

Carola Magna Ducissa Feliciter Regnante Grand Duchess Charlotte, happily reigning (Luxembourg).

Carolus a Carolo Charles (I) to Charles (II) (England).

Cedunt Prementi Fata The fates yield to him who presses (Ploen, Hese-Cassel).

Charitate et Candore With charity and sincerity (East Frisia).

Charta Magna Bavariae The Great Charter of Bavaria (Bavaria).

Christo Auspice Regno I reign under the auspices of Christ (England, Charles I).

Christus Spes Una Salutis Christ is our one hope of salvation (Cleve).

Chur Mainz Electoral Principality of Mainz (Mainz).

Circumeundo Servat et Ornat It serves and decorates by going around (Sweden).

Civibus Quorum Pietas Coniuratione Die III Mai MDCCXCI Obrutam et Deletam

Libertate Polona Tueri Conabatur Respublica Resurgens To the citizens whose piety the resurgent commonwealth tried to protect Poland overturned and deprived of liberty by the conspiracy of the third day of May 1791 (Poland).

Civitas Lucemborgiensis Millesimum Ovans Expletannum Completing the celebration of a thousand years of the city of Luxembourg (Luxembourg).

Civium Industria Floret Civitas By the industry of its people the state flourishes (Festival of Britain crown, 1951).

Cluniaco Cenobio Petrus et Paulus Peter and Paul from the Abbey of Cluny (Cluny).

Comes Provincie Fili Regis Francie Court of Provence and son of the King of France (Provence).

Communitas et Senatus Bonon City and senate of Bologna (Bologna).

Concordia Fratrum The harmony of the brothers (Iever).

Concordia Patriae Nutrix Peace, the nurse of the fatherland (Waldeck).

Concordia Res Parvae Crescunt Little things increase through harmony (Batavian Republic).

Concordia Res Parvae Crescunt, Discordia Dilabuntur By harmony little things increase, by discord they fall apart (Lowenstein-Wertheim-Virneburg).

Concordia Stabili With lasting peace (Hildesheim).

Confidens Dno Non Movetur He who trusts in God is unmoved (Spanish Netherlands).

Confidentia in Deo et Vigilantia Trust in God and vigilance (Prussian Asiatic Company).

Confoederato Helvetica Swiss Confederation (Switzerland)

Conjuncto Felix Fortunate in his connections (Solms).

Conservator Urbis Suae Saviour of his city (Rome, 4th century).

Consilio et Aequitate With deliberation and justice (Fulda).

Consilio et Virtutis With deliberation and valour (Hesse-Cassel).

Constanter et Sincere Steadfastly and sincerely (Lautern).

Crescite et Multiplicamini Increase and multiply (Maryland).

Cristiana Religio Christian religion (Germany, 11th century).

Crux Benedicat May the cross bless you (Oldenburg).

Cuius Cruore Sanati Sumus By His sacrifice are we healed (Reggio).

Cultores Sui Deus Protegit   God protects His followers (England, Charles I).

Cum Deo et Die   With God and the day (Wurttemberg).

Cum Deo et Jure   With God and the law (Wurttem-berg).

Cum Deo et Labore   With God and work (Wittgenstein).

Cum His Qui Orderant Pacem Eram Pacificus   With those who order peace I was peaceful (Zug).

Curie Bonthon to so Doulo   Protect his servant, o Lord (Byzantine Empire).

Custos Regni Deus   God is the guardian of the kingdom (Naples and Sicily).

Da Gloriam Deo et Eius Genitrici Marie   Give glory to God and His mother Mary (Wurttemberg).

Da Mihi Virtutem Contra Hostes Tuos   Give me valour against mine enemies (Netherlands, Charles V).

Dat Wort is Fleis Gworden   The word is made flesh (Muster).

Date Caesaris Caesari et Quae Sunt Dei Deo   Render unto Caesar the things that are Caesar's and unto God the things that are God's (Stralsund).

De Oficina . . .   From the mint of . . . (France, medieval).

Decreto Reipublicae Nexu Confoederationis Iunctae Die V Xbris MDCCXCII Stanislao Augusto Regnante   By decree of the state in conjunction with the joint federation on the fifth day of December 1792, Stanislaus Augustus ruling (Poland).

Decus et Tutamen   An ornament and a safeguard (Britain, pound).

Deducet Nos Mirabiliter Dextera Tua   Thy right hand will guide us miraculously (Savoy).

Denarium Terrae Mariae   Penny of Maryland (Maryland).

Deo Conservatori Pacis   To God, preserver of peace (Brandenburg-Ansbach).

Deo OM Auspice Suaviter et Fortiter sed Luste nec Sibi sed Suis   Under the auspices of God, greatest and best, pleasantly and bravely but justly, not for himself but for his people (Speyer).

Deo Patriae et Subditio   For God, fatherland and neighbourhood (Mainz).

Der Recht Glaubt In Ewig Lebt   Who believes in right will live in eternity (Linange-Westerburg).

Der Rhein ist Deutschlands Strom Nicht Deutschlands Grenze   The Rhine is Germany's River not Germany's Frontier.

Deum Solum Adorabis   You will venerate God alone (Hesse).

Deus Constituit Regna   God establishes kingdoms (Ni jmegen).

Deus Dat Qui Vult   God gives to him who wishes (Hanau-Munzenberg).

Deus et Dominus   God and Lord (Rome, 3rd century).

Deus in Adiutorium Meum Intende   God stretch out in my assistance (France).

Deus Providebit   God will provide (Lowenstein-Wertheim-Virneburg).

Deus Refugium Meum   God is my refuge (Cleve).

Deus Solatium Meum   God is my comfort (Sweden).

Dextera Domini Exaltavit Me   The right hand of God has raised me up (Modena, Spain).

Dextra Dei Exalta Me   The right hand of God exalts me (Denmark).

Dieu et Mon Droit   God and my right (Britain, George IV).

Dilexit Dns Andream   The Lord delights in St Andrew (Holstein).

Dilexit Dominus Decorem Iustitiae   The Lord is pleased with the beauty of justice (Unterwalden).

Dirige Deus Gressus Meos   O God, direct my steps (Tuscany, Britain, Una £5).

Discerne Causam Meam   Distinguish my cause (Savoy).

Divina Benedictiae et Caesarea Iustitia   Sacrifice of blessings and imperial justice (Coblenz).

Dn Ihs Chs Rex Regnantium   Lord Jesus Christ, King of Kings (Rome, Justinian II).

Dns Ptetor Ms Z Lib'ator Ms   The Lord is my protector and liberator (Scotland, David II).

Dominabitur Gentium et Ipse   He himself will also be lord of the nations (Austrian Netherlands).

Domine Conserva Nos in Pace   O Lord preserve us in peace (Basle, Mulhausen).

Domine Elegisti Lilium Tibi   O Lord Thou hast chosen the lily for Thyself (France, Louis XIV).

Domine ne in Furore Tuo Arguas Me   O Lord, rebuke me not in Thine anger (England, Edward III).

Domine Probasti Me et Congnovisti Me   O Lord Thou hast tested me and recognised me (Mantua).

Domini est Regnum   The Kingdom is the Lord's (Austrian Netherlands).

Dominus Deus Omnipotens Rex   Lord God, almighty King (Viking coins).

Dominus Mihi Adiutor   The Lord is my helper (Spanish Netherlands).

Dominus Providebit   The Lord will provide (Berne).

Dominus Spes Populi Sui   The Lord is the hope of his people (Lucerne).

Donum Dei ex Fodinis Vilmariens   A gift of God from the Vilmar mines (Coblenz).

Duce Deo Fide et Justicia   By faith and justice lead us to God (Ragusa).

Dum Praemor Amplior   I increase while I die prematurely (Savoy).

Dum Spiro Spero   While I live, I hope (Pontefract siege coins).

Dum Totum Compleat Orbem   Until it fills the world (France, Henri II).

Dura Pati Virtus   Valour endures hardships (Saxe-Lauenburg).

Durae Necessitatis   Through force of necessity (Bommel siege, 1599).

Durum Telum Necessitas   Hardship is a weapon of necessity (Minden).

Dux et Gubernatores Reip Genu   Duke and governors of the republic of Genoa (Genoa).

E Pluribus Unum   One out of more (USA).

Eccl S. Barbarae Patronae Fodin Kuttenbergensium Duo Flor Arg Puri   The church of St Barbara, patron of the Kuttensberg mines, two florins of pure silver (Hungary).

Een en Ondelbaer Sterk   One and indivisible (Batavian Republic).

Eendracht Mag Macht   Unity makes strength (Belgium, South African Republic).

Einigkeit Recht und Freiheit   Union, right and freedom (Germany).

Electorus Saxoniae Administrator   Elector and administrator of Saxony (Saxony).

Elimosina   Alms (France, Pepin).

Ep Fris & Ratisb Ad Prum Pp Coad Aug   Bishop of Freising and Regensburg, administrator of Pruem, prince-provost, co-adjutant bishop of Augsburg (Trier).

Equa Libertas Deo Gratia Frat Pax in Virtute Tua et in Domino Confido   I believe in equal liberty by the grace of God, brotherly love in Thy valour and in the Lord (Burgundy).

Equitas Iudicia Tua Dom   Equity and Thy judgments O Lord (Gelderland).

Espoir Me Conforte   Hope comforts me (Mansfeld).

Espreuve Faicto Par Lexpres Commandement du Roy   Proof made by the express commandment of the King (France, piedforts).

Et in Minimis Integer   Faithful even in the smallest things (Olmutz).

Ex Auro Argentes Resurgit   From gold it arises, silver again (Sicily).

Ex Auro Sinico   From Chinese gold (Denmark).

Ex Flammis Orior   I arise from the flames (Hohenlohe-Neuenstein-Ohringen).

Ex Fodinis Bipontio Seelbergensibus   From the Seelberg mines of Zweibrucken (Pfalz-Birkenfeld).

Ex Metallo Novo   From new metal (Spain).

Ex Uno Omnis Nostra Salus   From one is all our salvation (Eichstadt, Mulhouse).

Ex Vasis Argent Cleri Mogunt Pro Aris et Focis   From the silver vessels of the clergy of Mainz for altars and for hearths (Mainz).

Ex Visceribus Fodinse Bieber   From the bowels of the Bieber mine (Hanau-Munzenberg).

Exaltabitur in Gloria   He shall be exalted in glory (England, quarter nobles).

Exemplum Probati Numismatis   An example of a proof coin (France, Louis XIII piedforts).

Exemtae Eccle Passau Episc et SRI Princ   Prince Bishop of the freed church of Passau, prince of the Holy Roman Empire (Passau).

Expectate Veni   Come, o expected one (Roman Britain, Carausius).

Extremum Subidium Campen   Kampen under extreme siege (Kampen, 1578).

Exurgat Deus et Dissipentur Inimici Eius   Let God arise and let His enemies be scattered (England, James I).

Faciam Eos in Gentem Unam   I will make them one nation (England, unites and laurels).

Faith and Truth I will Bear unto You   (UK £5, 1993).

Fata Consiliis Potiora   The fates are more powerful than councils (Hesse-Cassel).

Fata Viam Invenient   The fates will find a way (Gelderland).

Fecit Potentiam in Brachio Suo   He put power in your forearm (Lorraine).

Fecunditas   Fertility (Naples and Sicily).

Fel Temp Reparatio   The restoration of lucky times (Rome, AD 348).

Felicitas Perpetua   Everlasting good fortune (Rome, Constantius II).

Felix coniunctio   Happy Union (Brandenburg-Ansbach).

Fiat Misericordia Tua Dne   Let Thy mercy be O Lord (Gelderland).

Fiat Voluntas Domini Perpetuo   Let the goodwill of the Lord last for ever (Fulda).

Fidei Defensor   Defender of the Faith (Britain).

Fidelitate et Fortitudine   With fidelity and fortitude (Batthanyi).

Fideliter et Constanter   Faithfully and steadfastly (Saxe-Coburg-Gotha).

Fidem Servando Patriam Tuendo   By keeping faith and protecting the fatherland (Savoy).

Filius Augustorum   Son of emperors (Rome, 4th century).

Fisci Iudaici Calumnia Sublata The false accusation of the Jewish tax lifted (Rome, Nerva).

Florent Concordia Regna Through harmony kingdoms flourish (England, Charles I and II).

Fortitudo et Laus Mea Dominu Fortitude and my praise in the Lord (Sardinia).

Free Trade to Africa by Act of Parliment *(Sic)* (Gold Coast).

Friedt Ernehrt Unfriedt Verzehrt Peace nourishes, unrest wastes (Brunswick).

Fulgent Sic Littora Rheni Thus shine the banks of the Rhine (Mannheim).

Fundator Pacis Founder of peace (Rome, Severus).

Gaudium Populi Romani The joy of the Roman people (Rome, 4th century).

Gen C Mar VI Dim Col USC & RAMAI Cons & S Conf M General field marshal, colonel of the only dragoon regiment, present privy councillor of both their sacred imperial and royal apostolic majesties, and state conference minister (Batthanyi).

Gerecht und Beharrlich Just and steadfast (Bavaria).

Germ Hun Boh Rex AAD Loth Ven Sal King of Germany, Hungary and Bohemia, Archduke of Austria, Duke of Lorraine, Venice and Salzburg (Austria).

Germ Jero Rex Loth Bar Mag Het Dux King of Germany, Jerusalem, Lorraine and Bar, Grand Duke of Tuscany (Austrian Netherlands).

Germania Voti Compos Germany sharing the vows (Brandenburg-Ansbach).

Gloria ex Amore Patriae Glory from love of country (Denmark).

Gloria in Excelsis Deo Glory to God in the highest (France, Sweden).

Gloria Novi Saeculi The glory of a new century (Rome, Gratian).

God With Us (England, Commonwealth).

Godt Met Ons God with us (Oudewater).

Gottes Freundt der Pfaffen Feindt God's friend, the Pope's enemy (Brunswick, Christian).

Gratia Dei Sum Id Quod Sum By the grace of God, I am what I am (Navarre).

Gratia Di Rex By the grace of God, king (France, 8th century).

Gratitudo Concivibus Exemplum Posteritati Gratitude to fellow Citizens, an example to posterity (Poland).

Gud och Folket God and the people (Sweden).

Hac Nitimur Hanc Tuemur With this we strive, this we shall defend (Batavian Republic).

Hac Sub Tutela Under this protection (Eichstadt).

Haec Sunt Munera Minerae S Antony Eremitae These are the rewards of the mine of St Antony the hermit (Hildesheim).

Hanc Deus Dedit God has given this (Pontefract siege coins).

Hanc Tuemur Hac Nitimur This we defend, by this we strive (Batavian Republic).

Has Nisi Periturus Mihi Adimat Nemo Let no one remove these (Letters) from me under penalty of death (Commonwealth, edge inscription).

Henricus Rosas Regna Jacobus Henry (united) the roses, James the kingdoms (England and Scotland, James VI and I).

Herculeo Vincta Nodo Bound by a Herculean fetter (Savoy).

Herr Nach Deinem Willen O Lord Thy will be done (Palatinate, Erbach).

Herre Gott Verleich Uns Gnade Lord God grant us grace (Brunswick).

Hic Est Qui Multum Orat Pro Populo Here is he who prays a lot for the people (Paderborn).

Hir Steid te Biscop Here is represented the bishop (Gittelde).

His Ventis Vela Levantur By these winds the sails are raised up (Hesse-Cassel).

Hispaniarum Infans Infante of Spain and its dominions (Spain).

Hispaniarum et Ind Rex King of Spain and the Indies.

Hispaniarum Rex King of Spain (Spain).

Hoc Signo Victor Eris With this sign you will be victor (Rome, Vetranio).

Honeste et Decenter Honestly and decently (Nassau-Idstein).

Honi Soit Qui Mal y Pense Evil to him who evil thinks (Britain, George III).

Honni Soit Qui Mal y Pense (Hesse-Cassel).

Hospitalis et S Sepul Hierusal Hospital and Holy Sepulchre of Jerusalem (Malta).

Hun Boh Gal Rex AA Lo Wi et in Fr Dux King of Hungary, Bohemia and Galicia, Archduke of Austria, Dalmatia, Lodomeria, Wurzburg and Duke in Franconia (Austria).

Hung Boh Lomb et Ven Gal Lod III Rex Aa King of Hungary, Bohemia, Lombardo-Venezia, Galicia, Lodomeria and Illyria, Archduke of Austria (Austria).

Ich Dien I serve (Aberystwyth 2d, UK 2p).

Ich Getrawe Got in Aller Noth I trust in God in all my needs (Hesse-Marburg).

Ich Habe Nur Ein Vaterland und das Heisst Deutschland I have only one fatherland and that is called Germany (Germany).

Ielithes Penniae Penny of Gittelde (Gittelde, 11th century).

Iesus Autem Transiens Per Medium Illorum Ibat But Jesus, passing through the midst of them, went His way (England, Scotland, Anglo-Gallic).

Iesus Rex Noster et Deus Noster Jesus is our king and our God (Florence).

Ihs Xs Rex Regnantium Jesus Christ, King of Kings (Byzantine Empire).

Ihsus Xristus Basileu Baslie Jesus Christ, King of Kings (Byzantine Empire).

Imago Sanch Regis Illustris Castelle Legionis e Toleto The image of Sancho the illustrious king of Castile, Leon and Toledo.

In Casus Per Vigil Omnes In all seasons through vigil (Wertheim).

In Deo Meo Transgrediar Murum In my God I shall pass through walls (Teschen).

In Deo Spes Mea In God is my hope (Gelderland).

In Domino Fiducia Nostra In the Lord is our trust (Iever).

In Equitate Tua Vivificasti Me In thy equity Thou hast vivified me (Gelderland).

In God We Trust (USA).

In Hoc Signo Vinces In this sign shalt thou conquer (Portugal).

In Honore Sci Mavrici Marti In honour of the martyr St Maurice (St Maurice, 8th century).

In Manibus Domini sortes Meae In the hands of the Lord are my fates (Mainz siege, 1688–9).

In Memor Vindicatae Libere ac Relig In memory of the establishment of freedom and religion (Sweden).

In Memoriam Conjunctionis Utriusque Burgraviatus Norice In memory of the union of both burgraviates in peace (Brandenburg-Ansbach).

In Memorian Connub Feliciaes Inter Princ Her Frider Carol et Dub Sax August Louis Frider Rodas D 28 Nov 1780 Celebrati In memory of the most happy marriage between the hereditary prince Friedrich Karl and the Duchess of Saxony Augusta Louisa Frederika, celebrated on 28 Nov 1780 (Schwarzburg-Rudolstadt).

In Memorian Felicisssimi Matrimonii In memory of the most happy marriage (Wied).

In Memoriam Pacis Teschinensis Commemorating the Treaty of Teschen (Brandenburg-Ansbach).

In Nomine Domini Amen In the name of the Lord amen (Zaltbommel).

In Omnem Terram Sonus Eorum In to all the land their shall go sound (Chateau Renault, Papal States).

In Silencio et Spe Fortitudo Mea In silence and hope is my fortitude (Brandenburg-Kustrin).

In Spe et Silentio Fortitudo Mea In hope and silence is my fortitude (Vianen).

In Te Domine Confido In you O Lord I place my trust (Hesse).

In Te Domine Speravi In You, O Lord, I have hoped (Gurk).

In Terra Pax Peace in the land (Papacy).

In Via Virtuti Nulla Via There is no way for virtue on the way. (Veldenz).

Ind Imp, Indiae Imperator, Imperatrix Emperor (Empress) of India (Britain).

India Tibi Cessit India has yielded to thee (Portuguese India).

Infestus Infestis Hostile to the troublesome (Savoy).

Inimicos Eius Induam Confusione As for his enemies, I shall clothe them in shame (Sardinia, England, Edward VI).

Insignia Capituli Brixensis The badge of the chapter of Brixen (Brixen).

Isti Sunt Patres Tui Verique Pastores These are your fathers and true shepherds (Papacy).

Iudicium Melius Posteritatis Erit Posterity's judgment will be better (Paderborn).

Iure et Tempore By right and time (Groningen).

Iusques a Sa Plenitude As far as your plenitude (France, Henri II).

Iuste et Constanter Justly and constantly (Paderborn).

Iustirt Adjusted (Hesse-Cassel).

Iustitia et Concordia Justice and harmony (Zurich).

Iustitia et Mansuetudine By justice and mildness (Bavaria, Cologne).

Iustitia Regnorum Fundamentum Justice is the foundation of kingdoms (Austria).

Iustitia Thronum Firmat Justice strengthens the throne (England, Charles I).

Iustus Non Derelinquitur The just person is not deserted (Brandenburg-Calenberg).

Iustus Ut Palma Florebit The just will flourish like the palm (Portugal).

L Mun Planco Rauracorum Illustratori Vetustissimo To L Municius Plancus the most ancient and celebrated of the Rauraci (Basle).

Landgr in Cleggov Com in Sulz Dux Crum Landgrave of Klettgau, count of Sulz, duke of Krumlau (Schwarzburg-Sonderhausen).

Latina Emeri Munita Latin money of Merida (Suevi).

Lege et Fide By law and faith (Austria).

Lex Tua Veritas Thy law is the truth (Tuscany).

Liberta Eguaglianza Freedom and equality (Venice)

Libertad en la Ley   Freedom within the law (Mexico).

Libertas Carior Auro   Freedom is dearer than gold (St Gall).

Libertas Vita Carior   Freedom is dearer than life (Kulenberg).

Libertas Xpo Firmata   Freedom strengthened by Christ (Genoa).

Liberte, Egalite, Fraternite   Liberty, equality, fraternity (France).

Lucerna Pedibus Meis Verbum Est   Thy word is a lamp unto mine feet (England, Edward VI).

Lumen ad Revelationem Gentium   Light to enlighten the nations (Papacy).

L'Union Fait la Force   The union makes strength (Belgium).

Macula Non Est in Te   There is no sin in Thee (Essen).

Magnus ab Integro Saeculorum Nascitur Ordo   The great order of the centuries is born anew (Bavaria).

Mandavit Dominus Palatie hanc Monetam Fiert   The lord of the Palatine ordained this coin to be made (Balath).

Manibus Ne Laedar Avaris   Lest I be injured by greedy hands (Sweden).

Mar Bran Sac Rom Imp Arcam et Elec Sup Dux Siles   Margrave of Brandenburg, archchamberlain of the Holy Roman Empire and elector, senior duke of Silesia (Prussia).

Maria Mater Domini Xpi   Mary mother of Christ the Lord (Teutonic Knights).

Maria Unxit Pedes Xpisti   Mary washes the feet of Christ (France, Rene d'Anjou).

Mater Castrorum   Mother of fortresses (Rome, Marcus Aurelius).

Matrimonio Conjuncti   Joined in wedlock (Austria).

Me Coniunctio Servat Dum Scinditur Frangor   The relationship serves me while I am being torn to pieces (Lowenstein-Wertheim).

Mediolani Dux   Duke of Milan (Milan).

Mediolani et Man   Duke of Mantua and Milan (Milan).

Memor Ero Tui Iustina Virgo   I shall remember you, o maiden Justina (Venice).

Merces Laborum   Wages of work (Wurzburg).

Mirabilia Fecit   He wrought marvels (Viking coinage).

Misericordia Di Rex   King by the mercy of God (France, Louis II).

Mo Arg Ord Foe Belg D Gel & CZ   Silver coin of the order of the Belgian Federation, duchy of Guelder-land, county of Zutphen (Guelderland).

Moneta Abbatis   Coin of the abbey (German ecclesiastical coins, 13th–14th centuries).

Moneta Argentiae Ord Foed Belgii Holl   Silver coin of the federated union of Belgium and Holland (Batavian Republic).

Mo No Arg Con Foe Belg Pro Hol   New silver coin of the Belgian Federation, province of Holland (Holland).

Mo No Arg Pro Confoe Belg Trai Holl   New silver coin of the confederated Belgian provinces, Utrecht and Holland (Batavian Republic).

Mon Lib Reip Bremens   Coin of the free state of Bremen (Bremen).

Mon Nova Arg Duc Curl Ad Norma Tal Alb   New silver coin of the duchy of Courland, according to the standard of the Albert thaler (Courland).

Mon Nov Castri Imp   New coin of the Imperial free city of . . . (Friedberg).

Moneta Bipont   Coin of Zweibrucken (Pfalz-Birkenfeld-Zweibrucken).

Monet Capit Cathedr Fuld Sede Vacante   Coin of the cathedral chapter of Fulda, the see being vacant (Fulda).

Moneta in Obsidione Tornacensi Cusa   Coin struck during the siege of Tournai (Tournai, 1709).

Moneta Livosesthonica   Coin of Livonia (Estonia).

Moneta Nov Arg Regis Daniae   New silver coin of the king of Denmark (Denmark).

Moneta Nova Ad Norman Conventionis   New coin according to the Convention standard (Orsini-Rosenberg).

Moneta Nova Domini Imperatoris   New coin of the lord emperor (Brunswick, 13th century).

Moneta Nova Lubecensis   New coin of Lubeck.

Moneta Nova Reipublicae Halae Suevicae   New coin of the republic of Hall in Swabia.

Moneta Reipublicae Ratisbonensis   Coin of the republic of Regensburg.

Nach Alt Reichs Schrot und Korn   According to the old empire's grits and grain (Hesse).

Nach dem Conventions Fusse   According to the Convention's basis (German Conventionsthalers).

Nach dem Frankf Schlus   According to the Frankfurt standard (Solms).

Nach dem Schlus der V Staend   According to the standard of the union (Hesse).

Navigare Necesse Est   It is necessary to navigate (Germany).

Nec Aspera Terrent   Nor do difficulties terrify (Brunswick).

Nec Cito Nec Temere   Neither hastily nor rashlly (Cambrai).

Nec Numina Desunt Nor is the divine will absent (Savoy).

Nec Temere Nec Timide Neither rashly nor timidly (Danzig, Lippe).

Necessitas Legem Non Habet Necessity has no law (Magdeburg).

Nemo Me Impune Lacessit No one touches me with impunity (UK, Scottish pound edge inscription).

Nihil Restat Reliqui No relic remains (Ypres).

Nil Ultra Aras Nothing beyond the rocks (Franque-mont).

No Nobis Dne Sed Noi Tuo Da Gloriam Not to us, o Lord but to Thy name be glory given (France, Francis I).

Nobilissimum Dom Ac Com in Lipp & St Most noble lord and count in Lippe and Sternberg (Schaumburg-Lippe).

Nomen Domini Turris Fortissima The name of the Lord is the strongest tower (Frankfurt).

Non Aes Sed Fides Not bronze but trust (Malta).

Non Est Mortale Quod Opto What I desire is not mortal. (Mecklenburg).

Non Mihi Sed Populo Not to me but to the people (Bavaria).

Non Relinquam Vos Orphanos I shall not leave you as orphans (Papacy).

Non Surrexit Major None greater has arisen (Genoa, Malta).

Nullum Simulatum Diuturnum Tandem Nothing that is feigned lasts long (Wittgenstein).

Nummorum Famulus The servant of the coinage (England, tin halfpence and farthings).

Nunquam Retrorsum Never backwards (Brunswick-Wolfenbuttel).

O Crux Ave Spes Unica Hail, o Cross, our only hope (England half-angels, France, Rene d'Anjou).

O Maria Ora Pro Me O Mary pray for me (Bavaria).

Ob Cives Servatos On account of the rescued citizens (Rome, Augustus).

Oculi Domini Super Iustos The eyes of the Lord look down on the just (Neuchatel).

Omnia Auxiliante Maria Mary helping everything (Schwyz).

Omnia Cum Deo Everything with God (Reuss-Greiz).

Omnia cum Deo et Nihil Sine Eo Everthing with God and nothing without Him (Erbach).

Omnis Potestas a Deo Est All power comes from God (Sweden).

Opp & Carn Dux Comm Rittb SCM Cons Int & Compi Mareschal Duke of Troppau and Carniola, count of Rietberg, privy councillor of his sacred imperial majesty, field marshal (Liechtenstein).

Opp & Carn . . . Aur Velleris Eques Duke of Troppau . . . knight of the Golden Fleece (Liechtenstein).

Opportune Conveniently (Savoy).

Optimus Princeps Best prince (Rome, Trajan).

Opulentia Salerno Wealthy Salerno (Siculo-Norman kingdom).

Pace et Iustitia With peace and justice (Spanish Netherlands).

Pacator Orbis Pacifier of the world (Rome, Aurelian).

Palma Sub Pondere Crescit The palm grows under its weight (Waldeck).

Pater Noster Our Father (Flanders, 14th century).

Pater Patriae Farther of his country (Rome, Caligula).

Patria Si Dreptul Meu The country and my right (Roumania).

Patrimon Henr Frid Sorte Divisum The heritage of Heinrich Friedrich divided by lot (Hohenlohe-Langenberg).

Patrimonia Beati Petri The inheritance of the blessed Peter (Papacy).

Patrona Franconiae Patron of Franconia (Wurzburg).

Pax Aeterna Eternal peace (Rome, Marcus Aurelius).

Pax et Abundantia Peace and plenty (Burgundy, Gelderland).

Pax Missa Per Orbem Peace sent throughout the world (England, Anne).

Pax Petrus Peace Peter (Trier, 10th century).

Pax Praevalet Armis May peace prevail by force of arms (Mainz).

Pax Quaeritur Bello Peace is sought by war (Commonwealth, Cromwell).

Pecunia Totum Circumit Orbem Money goes round the whole world (Brazil).

Per Aspera Ad Astra Through difficulties to the stars (Mecklenburg-Schwerin).

Per Angusta ad Augusta Through precarious times to the majestic (Solms-Roedelheim, a pun on the name of the ruler Johan August).

Per Crucem Tuam Salva Nos Christe Redemptor By Thy cross save us, O Christ our Redeemer (England, angels).

Per Crucem Tuam Salva Nos Xpe Redemt By Thy cross save us, O Christ our Redeemer (Portugal, 15th century).

Perdam Babillonis Nomen May the name of Babylon perish (Naples).

Perennitati Iustissimi Regis For the duration of the most just king (France, Louis XIII).

Perennitati Principis Galliae Restitutionis For the duration of the restoration of the prince of the Gauls (France, Henri IV).

Perfer et Obdura Bruxella Carry on and stick it out, Brussels (Brussels siege, 1579–80).

Perpetuus in Nemet Vivar Hereditary count in Nemt-Ujvar (Batthanyi).

Pietate et Constantia By piety and constancy (Fulda).

Pietate et Iustitia By piety and justice (Denmark).

Plebei Urbanae Frumento Constituto Free distribu-tion of grain to the urban working-class established (Rome, Nerva).

Pleidio Wyf Im Gwlad True am I to my country (UK, Welsh pound edge inscription).

Plus Ultra Beyond (the Pillars of Hercules) (Spanish America).

Point du Couronne sans Peine Point of the crown without penalty (Coburg).

Pons Civit Castellana The bridge of the town of Castellana (Papacy).

Populus et Senatus Bonon The people and senate of Bologna (Bologna).

Post Mortem Patris Pro Filio For the son after his father's death (Pontefract siege coins).

Post Tenebras Lux After darkness light (Geneva).

Post Tenebras Spero Lucem After darkness I hope for light (Geneva).

Posui Deum Adiutorem Meum I have made God my helper (England, Ireland, 1351–1603).

Praesidium et Decus Protection and ornament (Bologna).

Prima Sedes Galliarum First see of the Gauls (Lyon).

Primitiae Fodin Kuttenb ab Aerari Iterum Susceptarum First results dug from the Kuttenberg mines in a renewed undertaking (Austria).

Princps Iuventutis Prince of youth (Roman Empire).

Pro Defensione Urbis et Patriae For the defence of city and country (France, Louis XIV).

Pro Deo et Patria For God and the fatherland (Fulda).

Pro Deo et Populo For God and the people (Bavaria).

Pro Ecclesia et Pro Patria For the church and the fatherland (Constance).

Pro Fausio PP Reitur VS For happy returns of the princes of the Two Sicilies (Naples and Sicily).

Pro Lege et Grege For law and the flock (Fulda).

Pro maximo Dei Gloria et Bono Publico For the greatest glory of God and the good of the people (Wurttemberg).

Pro Patria For the fatherland (Wurzburg).

Propitio Deo Secura Ago With God's favour I lead a secure life. (Saxe-Lauenburg).

Protector Literis Literae Nummis Corona et Salus A protection to the letters (on the face of the coin), the letters (on the edge) are a garland and a safeguard to the coinage (Commonwealth, Cromwell broad).

Protege Virgo Pisas Protect Pisa, O Virgin (Pisa).

Provide et Constanter Wisely and firmly (Wurttem-berg).

Providentia et Pactis Through foresight and pacts (Brandenburg-Ansbach).

Providentia Optimi Principis With the foresight of the best prince (Naples and Sicily).

Proxima Fisica Finis Nearest to natural end (Orciano).

Proxima Soli Nearest to the sun (Modena).

Pulcra Virtutis Imago The beautiful image of virtue (Genoa).

Pupillum et Viduam Suscipiat May he support the orphan and the widow (Savoy).

Quae Deus Conjunxit Nemo Separet What God hath joined let no man put asunder (England, James I).

Quem Quadragesies et Semel Patriae Natum Esse Gratulamur Whom we congratulate for the forty-first time for being born for the fatherland (Lippe-Detmold).

Qui Dat Pauperi Non Indigebit Who gives to the poor will never be in need (Munster).

Quid Non Cogit Necessitas To what does Necessity not drive. (Ypres).

Quin Matrimonii Lustrum Celebrant They celebrate their silver wedding (Austria, 1879).

Quocunque Gesseris (Jeceris) Stabit Whichever way you throw it it will stand (Isle of Man).

Quod Deus Vult Hoc Semper Fit What God wishes always occurs. (Saxe-Weimar).

Reconduntur non Retonduntur They are laid up in store, not thundered back (Savoy).

Recta Tueri Defend the right (Austria).

Recte Constanter et Fortiter Rightly, constantly and bravely (Bavaria).

Recte Faciendo Neminem Timeas May you fear no one in doing right. (Solms-Laubach).

Rector Orbis Ruler of the world (Rome, Didius Julianus).

Rectus et Immotus Right and immovable (Hesse).

Redde Cuique Quod Suum Est Render to each that which is his own (England, Henry VIII).

Redeunt antiqui Gaudia Moris There return the joys of ancient custom (Regensburg).

Reg Pr Pol et Lith Saxon Dux   Royal prince of Poland and Lithuania and duke of Saxony (Trier).

Regia Boruss Societas Asiat Embdae   Royal Prussian Asiatic Society of Emden (Prussia).

Regier Mich Her Nach Deinen Wort   Govern me here according to Thy word (Palatinate).

Regnans Capitulum Ecclesiae Cathedralis Ratisbonensis Sede Vacante   Administering the chapter of the cathedral church at Regensburg, the see being vacant (Regensburg).

Regni Utr Sic et Hier   Of the kingdom of the Two Sicilies and of Jerusalem (Naples and Sicily).

Religio Protestantium Leges Angliae Libertas Parliamenti   The religion of the Protestants, the laws of England and the freedom of Parliament (England, Royalists, 1642).

Relinquo Vos Liberos ab Utroque Homine   I leave you as children of each man (San Marino).

Restauracao da Independencia   Restoration of inde-pendence (Portugal, 1990).

Restitutor Exercitus   Restorer of the army (Rome, Aurelian).

Restitutor Galliarum   Restorer of the Gauls (Rome, Gallienus).

Restitutor Generis Humani   Restorer of mankind (Rome, Valerian).

Restitutor Libertatis   Restorer of freedom (Rome, Constantine).

Restitutor Orbis   Restorer of the world (Rome, Valerian).

Restitutor Orientis   Restorer of the east (Rome, Valerian).

Restitutor Saeculi   Restorer of the century (Rome, Valerian).

Restitutor Urbis   Restorer of the city (Rome, Severus).

Rosa Americana Utile Dulci   The American rose, useful and sweet (American colonies).

Rosa Sine Spina   A rose without a thorn (England, Tudor coins).

Rutilans Rosa Sine Spina   A dazzling rose without a thorn (England, Tudor gold coins).

S Annae Fundgruben Ausb Tha in N Oe   Mining thaler of the St Anne mine in Lower Austria (Austria).

S Ap S Leg Nat Germ Primas   Legate of the Holy Apostolic See, born Primate of Germany (Salzburg).

S Carolus Magnus Fundator   Charlemagne founder (Munster).

S. Gertrudis Virgo Prudens Niviella   St Gertrude the wise virgin of Nivelles (Nivelles).

SI Aul Reg Her & P Ge H Post Mag   General hereditary postmaster, supreme of the imperial court of the hereditary kingdom and provinces (Paar).

S. Ian Bapt F. Zachari   St John the Baptist, son of Zachary (Florence).

S. Kilianus Cum Sociis Francorum Apostoli   St Kilian and his companions, apostles to the Franks (Wurzburg).

S. Lambertus Patronus Leodiensis   St Lambert, patron of Liege (Liege).

Sac Nupt Celeb Berol   For the holy matrimony celebrated at Berlin (Brandenburg-Ansbach).

Sac Rom Imp   Holy Roman Empire (German states).

Sac Rom Imp Provisor Iterum   Administrator of the Holy Roman Empire for the second time (Saxony).

Salus Generis Humani   Safety of mankind (Rome, Vindex).

Salus Patriae   Safety of the fatherland (Italy).

Salus Populi   The safety of the people (Spain).

Salus Provinciarum   Safety of the provinces (Rome, Postumus).

Salus Publica Salus Mea   Public safety is my safety (Sweden).

Salus Reipublicae   The safety of the republic (Rome, Theodosius II).

Salus Reipublicae Suprema Lex   The safety of the republic is the supreme law (Poland).

Salvam Fac Rempublicam Tuam   Make your state safe (San Marino).

Sanctus Iohannes Innoce   St John the harmless (Gandersheim).

Sans Changer   Without changing (Isle of Man).

Sans Eclat   Without pomp (Bouchain siege, 1711).

Sapiente Diffidentia   Wise distrust (Teschen).

Scutum Fidei Proteget Eum / Eam   The shield of faith shall protect him / her (England, Edward VI and Elizabeth I).

Secundum Voluntatem Tuam Domine   Your favourable will o Lord (Hesse).

Securitati Publicae   For the public safety (Brandenburg-Ansbach).

Sede Vacante   The see being vacant (Papal states, Vatican and ecclesiastical coinage).

Sena Vetus Alpha et W Principum et Finis   Old Siena alpha and omega, the beginning and the end (Siena).

Senatus Populus QR   Senate and people of Rome (Rome, 1188).

Si Deus Nobiscum Quis Contra Nos   If God is with us who can oppose us (Hesse).

Si Deus Pro Nobis Quis Contra Nos   If God is for us who can oppose us (Roemhild).

Sieh Deine Seeligkeit Steht Fest Ins Vaters Liebe   Behold thy salvation stands surely in thy Father's love (Gotha).

Signis Receptis   When the standards had been recovered (Rome, Augustus).

Signum Crucis   The sign of the cross (Groningen).

Sincere et Constanter   Truthfully and steadfastly (Hesse-Darmstadt).

Sit Nomen Domini Benedictum   Blessed be the name of the Lord (Burgundy, Strasbourg).

St T X Adiuto Reg Iste Domba   Let it be to you, o Christ, the assistant to the king of Dombes (Dombes).

Sit Tibi Xpe Dat q'tu Regis Iste Ducat   May this duchy which Thou rulest be given to Thee, O Christ (Venice, ducat).

Sit Unio Haec Perennis   May this union last for ever (Hohenlohe-Langenberg).

Sola Bona Quae Honesta   The only good things are those which are honest (Brunswick).

Sola Facta Deum Sequor   Through deeds alone I strive to follow God (Milan).

Soli Deo Honor et Gloria   To God alone be honour and glory (Nassau).

Soli Reduci   To him, the only one restored (Naples and Sicily).

Solius Virtutis Flos Perpetuus   The flower of Virtue alone is perpetual (Strasbourg).

Spes Confisa Deo Nunquam Confusa Recedit   Hope entrusted in God never retreats in a disorderly fashion (Lippe).

Spes Nr Deus   God is our hope (Oudenarde siege, 1582).

Spes Rei Publicae   The hope of the republic (Rome, Valens).

Strena ex Argyrocopeo Vallis S Christoph   A New Year's gift from the silver-bearing valley of St Christopher (Wurttemberg, 1625).

Sub His Secura Spes Clupeus Omnibus in Te Sperantibus   Under these hope is safe, a shield for all who reside hope in Thee (Bavaria).

Sub Pondere   Under weight (Fulda).

Sub Protectione Caesarea   Under imperial protection (Soragna).

Sub Tuum Praesidium Confug   We flee to Thy protection (Salzburg).

Sub Umbra Alarum Tuarum   Under the shadow of Thy wings (Iever, Scotland, James V).

Subditorum Salus Felicitas Summa   The safety of the subjects is the highest happiness (Lubeck).

Sufficit Mihi Gratia Tua Domine   Sufficient to me is Thy grace, o Lord (Ploen).

Supra Firmam Petram   Upon a firm rock (Papacy).

Susceptor Noster Deus   God is our defence (Tuscany).

Sydera Favent Industriae   The stars favour industry (Furstenberg).

Sylvarum Culturae Praemium   Prize for the culture of the forest (Brandenburg-Ansbach).

Tali Dicata Signo Mens Fluctuari Nequit   Consecrated by such a sign the mind cannot waver (England, Henry VIII George noble).

Tandem Bona Caus Triumphat   A good cause eventually triumphs (Dillenburg).

Tandem Fortuna Obstetrice   With good luck ultimately as the midwife (Wittgenstein).

Te Stante Virebo   With you at my side I shall be strong (Moravia).

Tene Mensuram et Respice Finem   Hold the measure and look to the end (Burgundy).

Tert Ducat Secular   Tercentenary of the duchy (Wurttemberg).

Thu Recht Schev Niemand   Go with right and fear no one (Saxe-Lauenburg).

Tibi Laus et Gloria   To Thee be praise and glory (Venice).

Timor Domini Fons Vitae   The fear of the Lord is a fountain of life (England, Edward VI shillings).

Tout Avec Dieu   Everything with God (Brunswick, 1626).

Traiectum ad Mosam   The crossing of the Maas (Maastricht).

Transvolat Nubila Virtus   Marriageable virtue soon flies past (Grueyeres).

Travail, Famille, Patrie   Work, family, country (Vichy France).

Triumphator Gent Barb   Victor over the barbarian people (Byzantine Empire, Arcadius).

Tueatur Unita Deus   May God guard these united (Kingdoms) (England, James I; Britain, 1847).

Turck Blegert Wien   Vienna besieged by the Turks (Vienna, 1531).

Tut Mar Gab Pr Vid de Lobk Nat Pr Sab Car et Aug Pr de Lobk   Regency of Maria Gabriela, widow of the prince of Lobkowitz, born princess of Savoy-Carignan, and August prince of Lobkowitz (Lobkowitz).

Tutela Italiae   The guardianship of Italy (Rome, Nerva).

Ubi Vult Spirat   He breathes where he will (Papacy).

Ubique Pax   Peace everywhere (Rome, Gallienus).

Union et Force   Union and strength (France).

Urbe Obsessa   The city under siege (Maastricht).

Urbem Virgo Tuam Serva Protects thy city o virgin (Mary) (Strasbourg).

USC & RAM Cons Int Gen C Mar & Nob Praet H Turmae Capit Privy councillor of both their holy imperial and royal apostolic majesties, general field marshal and captain of the noble praetorian Hungarian squadrons (Eszterhazy).

Vculis Aulae Argenteis Patriae Indigenti Ministravit Auxilia With the silver vessels of the court aid was brought to the needy fatherland (Eichstadt, 1796).

Vehiculatione Italiae Remissa Postal tax of Italy remitted (Rome, Nerva).

Veni Luumen Cordium Come light of hearts (Vatican).

Veni Sancte Spiritus Come Holy Ghost (Vatican).

Verbum Domini Manet in Aeternum The word of the Lord abides forever (Hesse-Darmstadt, Veldenz).

Veritas Lex Tua The truth is your law (Salzburg).

Veritas Temporis Filia Truth is the daughter of time (England and Ireland, Mary Tudor).

Veritate et Labore By truth and work (Wittgenstein).

Veritate et Iustitia By truth and justice (German states).

Victoria Principum The victory of princes (Ostrogoths).

Videant Pauperes et Laetentur Let the poor see and rejoice (Tuscany).

Virgo Maria Protege Civitatem Savonae Virgin Mary Protect the city of Savona (Savona).

Viribus Unitis With united strength (Austria).

Virtute et Fidelitate By virtue and faithfulness (Hesse-Cassel).

Virtute et Prudentia With virtue and prudence (Auersperg).

Virtute Viam Dimetiar I shall mark the way with valour (Waldeck).

Virtutis Gloria Merces Glory is the reward of valour (Holstein-Gottorp).

Vis Unita Concordia Fratrum Fortior United power is the stronger harmony of brothers (Mansfeld).

Visitavit Nos Oriens ex Alto He has visited us arising on high (Luneburg).

Vivit Post Funera He lives after death (Bremen).

Von Gottes Gn Iohan Bischof Zu Strasburg Landtgraf in Elsass By God's grace John, Bishop of Strasbourg, Landgrave in Alsace (Strasbourg).

Vota Optata Romae Fel Vows taken for the luck of Rome (Rome, Maxentius).

Vox de Throno A voice from the throne (Papacy).

Was Got Beschert Bleibet Unerwert What God hath endowed leave undisturbed

Wider macht und List Mein Fels Gott Ist Against might and trickery God is my rock (Hesse-Cassel).

Xpc Vincit Xpc Regnat Christ conquers, Christ reigns (Scotland, Spain).

Xpc Vivet Xpc Regnat Xpc Impat Christ lives, Christ reigns, Christ commands (Cambrai).

Xpe Resurescit Christ lives again (Venice).

Xpistiana Religio Christian religion (Carolingian Empire).

Xps Ihs Elegit me Regem Populo Jesus Christ chose me as king to the people (Norway).

Zelator Fidei Usque ad Montem An upholder of the faith through and through (Portugal).

Zum Besten des Vaterlands To the best of the fatherland (Bamberg).

CARE
of coins

There is no point in going to a great deal of trouble and expense in selecting the best coins you can afford, only to let them deteriorate in value by neglect and mishandling. Unless you give some thought to the proper care of your coins, your collection is unlikely to make a profit for you if and when you come to sell it. Housing your coins is the biggest problem of all, so it is important to give a lot of attention to this.

Storage

The ideal, but admittedly the most expensive, method is the coin cabinet, constructed of air-dried mahogany, walnut or rosewood (*never* oak, cedar or any highly resinous timber likely to cause chemical tarnish). These cabinets have banks of shallow drawers containing trays made of the same wood, with half-drilled holes of various sizes to accommodate the different denominations of coins. Such cabinets are handsome pieces of furniture but, being largely handmade, tend to be rather expensive. Occasionally good specimens can be picked up in secondhand furniture shops, or at the dispersal of house contents by auction, but the best bet is still to purchase a new cabinet, tailored to your own requirements.

The 4-tray Martlet— the smallest in an extensive range from Peter Nichols.

Peter Nichols of 3 Norman Road, St Leonards-on-Sea, East Sussex TN37 6NH (telephone 01424 436682) is a specialist manufacturer of display and storage systems who has also been producing coin and medal cabinets to suit every need for more than a quarter of a century. He can produce a cabinet to fit into a wall safe or some other form of security box. He can match existing work, and thus replicate cabinets which you may already be using, or even produce designs to suit your specific requirements. The only proviso is that the cabinets are made in only one timber—Brazilian mahogany, for reason of chemical balance. A nice touch is that all the products in the Nichols repertoire take their names from Elizabethan mint-marks.

Nichols also offers a custom drilling service for coin trays, either all of the same diameter or in mixed sizes, depending on what you require. Drilling templates are also available on request. Apart from coin cabinets, Peter Nichols manufactures *medal* cabinets in two basic types, the seven-tray Pheon and the fourteen-tray Crozier.

The Crozier—a cabinet for the connoisseur.

The cases for these cabinets are similar in all respects to the coin cabinets, but medal trays are twice the thickness of coin trays. Each tray is made up from solid mahogany mouldings, base and polished mahogany front edges and trimmed with two turned brass knobs. The base of each tray is trimmed with a red felt pad.

Nichols produces a wide range of cabinets from the seven-tray Pheon all the way up to the massive 40-tray specials designed for the British Museum.

All cabinets are fitted with double doors. Nichols also produces the glass-topped Crown display case and the Sceptre display case, fitted with a glazed lid and containing a single tray. The Orb range of display cases are intended for wall mounting and are ideal for a display of campaign medals and decorations.

Prices start at around £30 for a four-tray Martlet coin cabinet and go all the way to the Coronet thirty-tray version at about £300. They are not cheap, but you have the satisfaction of acquiring exquisite examples of the cabinetmaker's craft which would be an elegant addition to any lounge or study.

An excellent compromise is provided by firms such as Abafil of Italy and Lindner of Germany who manufacture coin trays in durable, felt-lined materials with shallow compartments to suit the various sizes of coins. These trays interlock so that they build up into a cabinet of the desired size, and there are also versions designed as carrying cases, which are ideal for transporting coins.

The Mini-Porter, smallest of Abafil's plush Diplomat range.

Collectors Gallery of 6 & 7 Castle Gates, Shrewsbury, SY1 2AE (telephone: 01743 272140, fax: 01743 366041) is the UK agent and distributor for the Abafil series manufactured in Milan. These cases are of stout wooden construction covered with simulated leather and lined with red plush. The Diplomat range is designed primarily for secure transportation, but the Mini-diplomat, at around £40, makes a good static cabinet, and can take up to three standard trays holding a maximum of 241 coins, while the Custom case holds 14 de luxe or 20 standard trays and will house up to 1,500 coins. Even cheaper is the Mignon case holding up to 105 coins, ideally suited for carrying in a briefcase or travel bag.

Lindner Publications of 13 Fore Street, Hayle, Cornwall TR27 4DX (telephone 01726 751914) are well-known for their wide range of philatelic and numismatic accessories, but these include a full array of coin boxes, capsules, carrying cases and trays. The basic Lindner coin box is, in fact, a shallow tray available in a standard version or a smoked glass version. These trays have a crystal clear frame, red felt inserts and holes for various diameters of coins and medals. A novel feature of these trays is the rounded insert which facilitates the removal of coins from their spaces with the minimum of handling. These boxes are designed in such a manner that they interlock and can be built up into banks of trays, each fitted with a draw-handle and sliding in and out easily. Various types of chemically inert plastic capsules and envelopes have been designed for use in combination with plain shallow trays, without holes drilled. Lindner also manufacture a range of luxury cases lined in velvet and Atlas silk with padded covers and gold embossing on the spines, producing a most tasteful and elegant appearance.

Safe Albums of 16 Falcon Business Park, Hogwood Lane, Finchampstead, Berkshire RG11 4QW (telephone 01734 328976) are the UK agents for the German Stapel-Element, a drawer-stacking system with clear plasticiser-free trays that fit into standard bookshelves. The sliding coin compartments, lined with blue velvet, can be angled for display to best advantage. Stackable drawers cost around £12 each, and can be built up to any height desired. A wide range of drawer sizes is available, with compartments suitable for the smallest coins right up to four-compartment trays designed for very large artefacts such as card-cases or cigarette cases. The Mobel-Element cabinet is a superb specialised cabinet constructed of the finest timber with a steel frame and steel grip bars which can be securely locked. It thus combines elegance with security and is the ideal medium for the most valuable coins and medals.

Adding on to the stacking Lindner range is easy.

Safe's cabinet combines elegance with security.

There are also various storage systems, such as Coindex, which operate on the principle of narrow drawers in which the coins are stored in envelopes of chemically-inert plastic. A strip across the top holds a little slip giving a brief description, catalogue number and the price of each coin.

Kwikseal of the USA produce cards with a plastic window: these cards are especially suitable for slabbing coins. The traditional method used by many collectors was to house coins in small, air-dried manila envelopes that could be stored upright in narrow wooden or stout card boxes—knife-boxes were highly regarded as being the right width and depth. The Sydney Museum in Australia, for example, keeps its coins in manila envelopes stored in plastic lunch-boxes which seemed to do the job pretty well!

Coin Albums

When coin collecting became a popular hobby in the 1960s, several firms marketed ranges of coin albums. They had clear plastic sleeves divided into tiny compartments of various sizes and had the merit of being cheap and taking up little room on a bookshelf.

They had several drawbacks, however, not the least being the tendency of the pages to sag with the weight of the coins, or even, in extreme cases, to pull away from the pegs or rings holding them on to the spine. They required very careful handling as the coins could easily fall out of the top row as the pages were turned. The more expensive albums had little flaps that folded over the top of the coin to overcome this problem.

Arguably the worst aspect of these albums was the use of polyvinyl chloride (PVC) in the construction of the sleeves. Collectors soon discovered to their horror that this reacted chemically with their coins, especially those made of silver, causing a rather disgusting yellow slime to adhere to the coins' surface. I shudder to think how many fine collections were ruined as a result,

or of the countless coins that required highly expert treatment in a bid to restore them to as near the original condition as possible.

Fortunately the lesson has been learned and the coin albums now on the market are quite safe. Lindner offer a wide range of albums designed to house coins, medals or banknotes. The old problem about sagging pages is overcome by the use of a multi-ring binding welded to a very stout spine, while the sleeves contain neither Styrol nor PVC and will not affect any metals at all. In addition to pages with pockets of uniform size, the Karat range of albums operates on a slide principle which enables the user to insert vertical strips of different sizes on the same page, so that the coins of one country or series, or perhaps a thematic display of coins from different countries, can be displayed side by side.

Safe Albums offer a wide range of albums in the Coinholder System and Coin-Combi ranges. These, too, offer the choice of fixed pages with uniform-sized pockets, or interchangeable sliding inserts for different sizes side by side.

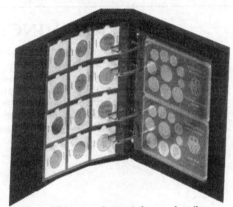

Albums can be carried around easily

Cleaning Coins

This is like matrimony—it should not be embarked on lightly. Indeed, the advice given by the magazine *Punch* in regard to marriage is equally sound in this case—don't do it! It is far better to have a dirty coin than an irretrievably damaged one. Every dealer has horror stories of handling coins that previous owners have cleaned, to their detriment. The worst example I ever saw was a display of coins found by a metal detectorist who "improved" his finds by abrading them in the kind of rotary drum used by lapidarists to polish gemstones. If you really must remove the dirt and grease from coins, it is advisable to practise on coins of little value.

Warm water containing a mild household detergent or washing-up liquid will work wonders in removing surface dirt and grease from most coins, but silver is best washed in a weak solution of ammonia and warm water—one part ammonia to ten parts water. Gold coins can be cleaned with diluted citric acid, such as lemon juice. Copper or bronze coins present more of a problem, but patches of verdigris can usually be removed by careful washing in a 20 per cent solution of sodium sesquicarbonate. Wartime coins made of tin, zinc, iron or steel can be cleaned in a 5 per cent solution of caustic soda containing some aluminium or zinc foil or filings, but they must be rinsed afterwards in clean water and carefully dried. Cotton buds are ideal for gently prising dirt out of coin legends and crevices in the designs. Soft brushes (with animal bristles—*never* nylon or other artificial bristles) designed for cleaning silver are most suitable for gently cleaning coins.

Coins recovered from the soil or the sea bed present special problems, due to chemical reaction between the metals and the salts in the earth or sea water. In such cases, the best advice is to take them to the nearest museum and let the professional experts decide on what can or should be done.

Both Lindner and Safe Albums offer a range of coin-cleaning kits and materials suitable for gold, silver, copper and other base alloys respectively. Safe (living up to their name) also provide a stern warning that rubber gloves should be worn and care taken to avoid breathing fumes or getting splashes of liquid in your eyes or on your skin. Obviously, the whole business of cleaning is a matter that should not be entered into without the utmost care and forethought. I would also recommend collectors to read the excellent paper on cleaning and conservation written by L. R. Green, Higher Conservation Officer at the Department of Coins and Medals in the British Museum, which appears in the new edition of the *Medal Yearbook 1999*.

POLISHING: A WARNING

If cleaning should only be approached with the greatest trepidation, polishing is definitely *out!* Beginners sometimes fall into the appalling error of thinking that a smart rub with Brasso or Duraglit might improve the appearance of their coins. Short of actually punching a hole through it, I cannot imagine a more destructive act. Polishing a coin may improve its superficial appearance for a few days, but such abrasive action will destroy the patina and reduce the fineness of the high points of the surface. Even if a coin is only polished once, it will never be quite the same again, and an expert can tell this a mile off.

CELTIC
coinage of Britain

Celtic coins were the first coins made in Britain. They were issued for a century and a half before the Roman invasion, and possibly a little later in some areas. They were issued by 11 tribal groups or administrative authorities situated southeast of a line from the Humber to the Severn. In this short article Celtic specialist CHRIS RUDD introduces this increasingly popular area.

The earliest coins were uninscribed and often abstract in design. Later ones carried the names of local leaders and tribal centres, and in the southeast became increasingly Roman in style, sometimes copying classical images quite closely.

Most Celtic coins were struck between two dies on flans of gold, silver, billion and bronze. Some were cast in strip moulds in tin-rich bronze alloy called "potin".

Because the Celts wrote no books and left no written records of their activities, little is known about the people and places behind their coins. Who made them? When? Where? And why? These are questions that are still largely unanswered, except in the very vaguest terms. Celtic cataloguers talk about gold quarters, silver units and silver minims. But the truth is we don't even know what the Celts themselves called their coins.

British Celtic coins are among the most fascinating ever fashioned and perhaps the least familiar to the average collector because of their rarity. Like the Celts themselves, Celtic coin designs are wild, free flowing, flamboyant and full of fun. Yes, Celtic moneyers had a great sense of humour!

Celtic coins bear a vast variety of gods and goddesses, armed warriors, chariot wheels, hidden faces, decapitated heads, suns, moons, stars, thunderbolts, floral motifs, magic signs and phallic symbols. Plus a menagerie of antelopes, bears, boars, bulls, cocks, crabs, cranes, dogs, dolphins, ducks, eagles, hares, all kinds of horses (some with wings, some with human heads, many with three tails, a few breathing fire), goats, lions, lizards, owls, rams, rats, ravens, snakes, stags, starfish, worms and wolves. Not to mention dragons, griffins, hippocamps, sphinxes and ram-horned serpents.

Ask any metal detectorist how many Celtic coins he or she has found and you will immediately realise they are rarer than Roman coins in this country—at least a thousand times rarer on average. This is because far fewer Celtic coins were minted, in smaller runs, over a much shorter time span. Though some may have been made as early as 80 BC, the majority of British Celtic coins were struck from 54 BC to AD 43; barely 100 years of production, and most of that seems to have been sporadic.

However, the greater rarity of Celtic coins doesn't mean they are necessarily more costly than other ancient coins: in fact, they are often cheaper. You see, in the coin market, demand determines price. The more collectors that want a coin, the higher its price.

A recent survey revealed "worldwide there may be no more than 150 regular private collectors

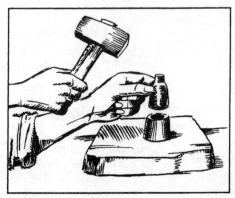

Method that may have been used for striking Celtic coins (drawing by Simon Pressey).

of Celtic coins, buying on average one or more coins per month". Whereas there are literally thousands of people collecting the other major series of ancient and medieval coins. That is why Celtic coins are still comparatively less costly than Greek, Anglo-Saxon and English hammered coins. The Celtic market is smaller, though expanding. For example a very fine Celtic gold stater typically costs half the price of a Greek gold stater or an English gold noble of comparable quality and

rarity. The price differential can be even more dramatic at major international auctions. But the disparity is diminishing as more and more collectors are beginning to appreciate the hitherto unrecognised beauty, scarcity and good value of British Celtic coins. So now could be a good time to start collecting Celtic coins, before their prices begin climbing more steeply.

Thirty years ago collecting British Celtic coins was a rich man's hobby and understanding them

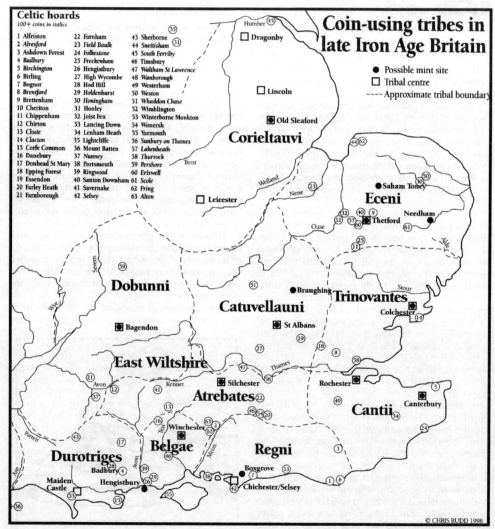

Eleven tribal groups minted coins in late Iron Age Britain, c. 80 BC–AD 45. The boundaries shown here are guesstimates, not actual, and often follow rivers, many of which are still known by their Celtic names.

Silver unit attributed to King Prasutagus of the Eceni, whose death resulted in the revolt of Queen Boudica, AD 60 (drawn four times actual size by Susan White).

was the lonely pursuit of a few scholarly numismatists. Today, thanks to the popularity of metal detecting, Celtic coins are more plentiful and almost everyone can afford to collect them. Most ancient coin dealers sell Celtic coins, some for as little as £20 each, and you will always find a few trays of them at every coin fair.

British Celtic coins are also easier to study today, thanks to the publication of some excellent books on the subject. The Celtic collector's bible is *Celtic Coinage of Britain* by Robert D. Van Arsdell (Spink, 1989)—well researched, well written, well illustrated, always quoted in dealers' catalogues, often controversial when dates are discussed and hopefully to be republished soon in a revised edition. For the dedicated Celtic devotee *British Iron Age Coins in the British Museum* by Richard Hobbs (British Museum Press, 1996) is an invaluable companion volume to Van Arsdell— more cautious, less speculative.

By far the best introductory book is *Celtic Coinage in Britain* by Dr Philip de Jersey (Shire Archaeology, 1996) who manages the Celtic Coin Index, a photographic record of over 23,000 British coins at the Institute of Archaeology, Oxford. In plain language Dr Philip de Jersey explains how Celtic coins and the images they carry can reveal information on the political, economic and social life of the Celts. *Celtic Coinage in Britain* contains clear twice-size photos of over a hundred Celtic coins, some of them rarely seen before. It gives the names, addresses and phone numbers of the museums in England, Scotland and Wales with the best and most accessible collections of Celtic coins.

In short, if you want to know more about British Celtic coins, *Celtic Coinage in Britain* is where you start reading and keep reading. This is the best little book ever written about British Celtic coins and outstanding value for money at £4.99.

How should you start collecting British Celtic coins? First, get a few of the commoner uninscribed types from each of the 11 tribal areas, aiming for the highest grade you can comfortably afford. Then you may wish to get an inscribed coin of each of the main rulers. You would also be well advised to acquire some Gaulish coins at the same time, because many British coins were influenced by Gallic prototypes.

How much do British Celtic coins cost? Very little, considering how scarce they are. Types with legends usually cost more than those without and top quality bronze is frequently more pricey than top quality silver (which may surprise you) because silver is commoner and generally survives better after two-thousand years underground.

Quoting averages can be misleading, but I'll stick my neck out for the benefit of Celtic beginners and say that the average UK retail prices for *very fine* Celtic coins are approximately as follows: silver minims £50–£100, silver units £50–£150, cast potin £40–£80, struck bronze £100–£200, gold quarters £150–£250, gold staters £250–£500. *Fine* specimens cost less than half these prices, *extremely fine* examples (exceptional in the Celtic series) are sometimes more than twice the VF price. The price guide on the blue pages of this YEARBOOK gives a good indication of the prices you could expect to pay, and remember, prices in dealers' catalogues are often higher than at coin fairs, where some of the best Celtic bargains may be found.

Chris Rudd is a well-known dealer who specialises in Celtic coins.

Collecting
ANCIENT
COINS

Ancient coins differ from most other series which are collected in Britain in that
every piece has spent the major part of the last two thousand years in the ground.
As JOHN CUMMINGS, dealer in ancient coins and antiquities explains here, the
effect that burial has had on the surface of the coin determines more than anything
else the value of a particular piece. With more modern coins, the only things which
affect price are rarity and grade. There may be a premium for coins exhibiting
particularly fine tone, or with outstanding pedigrees, but an 1887 crown in "extremely
fine" condition has virtually the same value as every other piece with the same grade
and of the same date. With ancient coins the story is very different.

A large number of different criteria affect the
price of an ancient coin. Factors affecting prices
can be broken down into several categories:

Condition

The most important factor by far in
determining price. Ancient coins were struck by
hand and can exhibit striking faults. Value suffers
if the coin is struck with the designs off-centre, is
weakly struck, or if the flan is irregular in shape.
Many of the Celtic tribes issued coins of varying
fineness and those made from low quality gold or
silver are worth less than similar specimens where
the metal quality is better. Conversely, coins on
exceptional flans, particularly well struck, or with
fine patinas command a premium.

Many ancient coins have suffered during their
stay in the ground. It must be borne in mind that
the prices given in the price guide are for
uncorroded, undamaged examples. A Roman
denarius should be graded using the same criteria
as those used for grading modern coins. The
surfaces must be good, and the coin intact. The
fact that the coin is 2,000 years old is irrelevant as
far as grading is concerned. Coins which are not
perfectly preserved are not without value but the
value for a given grade decreases with the degree
of fault.

Rarity

As with all other series, rare coins usually
command higher prices than common ones

although this is not written in stone. A unique
variety of a small fourth century Roman bronze
coin, even in perfect condition, can be worth much
less than a more worn and common piece from
an earlier part of the empire. In the Celtic series,
there is an almost infinite variety of minor types
and a unique variety of an uninscribed type will
rarely outbid an inscribed issue of a known king.

Historical and local significance

Types which have historical or local interest can
command a price far above their scarcity value.
Denarii of the emperor Tiberius are believed to
have been referred to in the New Testament and
command a far higher price than a less interesting
piece of similar rarity. Similarly, pieces which have
British reverse types such as the "VICT BRIT"
reverse of the third century AD are more
expensive than their scarcity would indicate. The
12 Caesars are ever popular especially in the
American market and this affects prices
throughout the world. In the Celtic series, coins
of Cunobelin or Boudicca are far more popular
than pieces which have no historical interest but
which are far scarcer.

Reverse types

All Roman emperors who survived for a
reasonable time issued coins with many different
reverse types. The most common of these usually
show various Roman gods. When a coin has an
unusual reverse it always enhances the value.

Particularly popular are architectural scenes, animals, references to Judaism, and legionary types.

Artistic merit

Most Celtic tribes issued several distinct series which generally speaking, improved in style up to the time of the Roman invasion. Later issues which exhibit fine "Celtic" style are usually more popular than the more stylised, earlier types.

Typical of the former would be the beautiful gold staters of Tasciovanus and Cunobelin. The Roman coinage is blessed with a large number of bust varieties and these can have a startling effect on price. A common coin with the bust left instead of right can be worth several times the price of a normal example. The coinage of Hadrian has a large number of bust varieties some of which are extremely artistic and these can command a premium.

The coinage used in Britain from the time of the invasion in AD43 was the same as that introduced throughout the Empire by the emperor Augustus around 20 BC. The simple divisions of 2 asses equal to one dupondius, 2 dupondii equal to 1 sestertius, 4 sestertii equal to one denarius and 25 denarii equal to one aureus continued in use until the reformation of the coinage by Caracalla in AD 214.

Aureus (gold)

Denarius (silver)

Sestertius (bronze)

Dupondius (copper)

As (copper)

Introducing
HAMMERED
COINAGE

The hammered currency of medieval Britain is among some of the most interesting coinage in the world. The turbulent history of these islands is reflected in the fascinating changes in size, design, fineness and workmanship, culminating in the many strange examples that emanated from the strife of the Civil War.

The Norman Conquest of England in 1066 and succeeding years had far-reaching effects on all aspects of life. Surprisingly, however, it had little impact on the coinage. William the Conqueror was anxious to emphasise the continuity of his reign, so far as the ordinary people were concerned, and therefore he retained the fabric, size and general design pattern of the silver penny. Almost 70 mints were in operation during this reign, but by the middle of the 12th century the number was reduced to 55 and under Henry II (1154–89) it fell to 30 and latterly to only eleven. By the early 14th century the production of coins had been centralised on London and Canterbury, together with the ecclesiastical mints at York and Canterbury. The silver penny was the principal denomination throughout the Norman period, pieces cut along the lines of the cross on the reverse continuing to serve as halfpence and farthings.

Eight types of penny were struck under William I and five under his son William Rufus, both profiles (left and right) and facing portraits being used in both reigns allied to crosses of various types. Fifteen types were minted under Henry I (1100–35), portraiture having now degenerated to crude caricature, the lines engraved on the coinage dies being built up by means of various punches. Halfpence modelled on the same pattern were also struck, but very sparingly and are very rare.

On Henry's death the succession was contested by his daughter Matilda and his nephew Stephen of Blois. Civil war broke out in 1138 and continued till 1153. Stephen controlled London and its mint, but Matilda and her supporters occupied the West Country and struck their own coins at Bristol. Several of the powerful barons struck their own coins, and there were distinct regional variants of the regal coinage. Of particular interest are the coins struck

Silver pennies of, from left to right, William I, William Rufus, Henry I and Stephen.

from obverse dies with Stephen's portrait erased or defaced, believed to date from 1148 when the usurper was under papal interdict.

Peace was restored in 1153 when it was agreed that Matilda's son Henry should succeed Stephen. On the latter's death the following year, Henry II ascended the throne. Coins of Stephen's last type continued to be minted till 1158, but Henry then took the opportunity to overhaul the coinage which had become irregular and sub-standard during the civil war. The new "Cross Crosslet" coins, usually known as the Tealby coinage (from the hoard of over 5,000 pennies found at Tealby, Lincolnshire in 1807), were produced at 30 mints, but when the recoinage was completed this number was reduced to a dozen. The design of Henry's coins remained virtually the same throughout more than two decades, apart from minor variants. Then, in 1180, a new type, known as the Short Cross coinage, was introduced. This was a vast improvement over the poorly struck Cross Crosslet coins and continued without alteration, not only to the end of the reign of Henry II in 1189, but throughout the reigns of his sons Richard (1189–99) and John (1199–1216) and the first half of the reign of his grandson Henry III (1216–46). Throughout that 66 year period, however, there were minor variations in portraits and lettering which enable numismatists to attribute the HENRICUS coins to specific reigns and periods.

"Tealby" type penny, left, and "Short Cross" penny of Henry II.

The style and workmanship of the Short Cross coinage deteriorated in the reign of Henry III. By the 1220s coin production was confined to the regal mints at London and Canterbury, the sole exception being the ecclesiastical mint maintained by the Abbot of Bury St Edmunds.

Halfpence and farthings were briefly struck in 1221–30, though halfpence are now extremely rare and so far only a solitary farthing has been discovered.

By the middle of this reign the coinage was in a deplorable state, being poorly struck, badly worn and often ruthlessly clipped. In 1247 Henry ordered a new coinage and in this the arms of the cross on the reverse were extended to the rim as a safeguard against clipping. This established a pattern of facing portrait and long cross on obverse and reverse respectively that was to continue till the beginning of the 16th century. Several provincial mints were re-activated to assist with the recoinage but they were all closed down again by 1250, only the regal mints at London and Canterbury and the ecclesiastical mints at Durham and Bury St Edmunds remaining active.

"Long Cross" pennies of Henry III, left, and Edward I.

In 1257 Henry tentatively introduced a gold penny (worth 20 silver pence and twice the weight of a silver penny). The coin was undervalued and soon disappeared from circulation.

The Long Cross coinage of Henry III continued under Edward I till 1279 when the king introduced a new coinage in his own name. The penny continued the style of its predecessors, though much better designed and executed; but new denominations were now added. Henceforward halfpence and farthings became a regular issue and, at the same time, a fourpenny coin known as the groat (from French *gros*) was briefly introduced (minting ceased in 1282 and was not revived till 1351). Due to the centralisation of coin production the name of the moneyer was now generally dropped, although it lingered on a few years at Bury St Edmunds. The provincial mints were again revived in 1299–1302 to recoin the lightweight foreign imitations of pennies which had flooded in from the Continent.

The coinage of Edward II (1307–27) differed only in minor respects from that of his father, and a similar pattern prevailed in the first years of Edward III. In 1335 halfpence and farthings below the sterling fineness were struck. More importantly, further attempts were made to introduce gold coins. In 1344 the florin or double

Pre-Treaty Noble of Edward III which contained reference to France in the legend.

leopard of six shillings was introduced, along with its half and quarter. This coinage was not successful and was soon replaced by a heavier series based on the noble of 80 pence (6s. 8d.), half a mark or one third of a pound. The noble originally weighed 138.5 grains but it was successively reduced to 120 grains, at which weight it continued from 1351. During this reign the protracted conflict with France known as the Hundred Years' War erupted. Edward III, through his mother, claimed the French throne and inscribed this title on his coins. By the Treaty of Bretigny (1361) Edward temporarily gave up his claim and the reference to France

Noble of Edward IV, issued before he was forced to abandon the throne of England.

was dropped from the coins, but when war was renewed in 1369 the title was resumed, and remained on many English coins until the end of the 18th century. The silver coinage followed the pattern of the previous reign, but in 1351 the groat was re-introduced and with it came the twopence or half-groat. Another innovation was the use of mintmarks at the beginning of the inscriptions. Seven types of cross and one crown were employed from 1334 onwards and their sequence enables numismatists to date coins fairly accurately.

The full range of gold (noble, half-noble and quarter-noble) and silver (groat, half-groat, penny, halfpenny and farthing) continued under Richard II (1377–99). Little attempt was made to alter the facing portrait on the silver coins, by now little more than a stylised caricature anyway.

Noble of Henry IV which was reduced in weight due to the shortage of gold.

Under Henry IV (1399–1413) the pattern of previous reigns prevailed, but in 1412 the weights of the coinage were reduced due to a shortage of bullion. The noble was reduced to 108 grains and its sub-divisions lightened proportionately. The penny was reduced by 3 grains, and its multiples and sub-divisions correspondingly reduced. One interesting change was the reduction of the fleur de lis of France from four to three in the heraldic shield on the reverse of the noble; this change corresponded with the alteration in the arms used in France itself. The Calais mint, opened by Edward III in 1363, was closed in 1411. There was no change in the designs used for the coins of Henry V (1413–22) but greater use was now made of mintmarks to distinguish the various periods of production. Coins were by now produced mainly at London, although the episcopal mints at Durham and York were permitted to strike pennies.

The supply of gold dwindled early in the reign of Henry VI and few nobles were struck after 1426. The Calais mint was re-opened in 1424 and struck a large amount of gold before closing finally in 1440. A regal mint briefly operated at York in 1423–24. Mintmarks were now much more widely used and tended to correspond more closely to the annual trials of the Pyx. The series of civil upheavals known as the Wars of the Roses erupted in this period.

In 1461 Henry VI was deposed by the Yorkist Earl of March after he defeated the Lancastrians at Mortimer's Cross. The Yorkists advanced on London where the victor was crowned Edward IV. At first he continued the gold series of his predecessor, issuing nobles and quarter-nobles, but in 1464 the weight of the penny was reduced

Groat of Richard III (1483–85).

to 12 grains and the value of the noble was raised to 100 pence (8s. 4d.). The ryal or rose-noble of 120 grains, together with its half and quarter, was introduced in 1465 and tariffed at ten shillings or half a pound. The need for a coin worth a third of a pound, however, led to the issue of the angel of 80 grains, worth 6s. 8d., but this was initially unsucessful and very few examples are now extant. The angel derived its name from the figure of the Archangel Michael on the obverse; a cross surmounting a shield appeared on the reverse.

In 1470 Edward was forced to flee to Holland and Henry VI was briefly restored. During this brief period (to April 1471) the ryal was discontinued but a substantial issue of angels and half-angels was made both at London and Bristol. Silver coins were struck at York as well as London and Bristol, the issues of the provincial mints being identified by the initials B or E (Eboracum, Latin for York). Edward defeated

the Lancastrians at Tewkesbury and deposed the luckless Henry once more. In his second reign Edward struck only angels and half-angels as well as silver from the groat to halfpenny. In addition to the three existing mints, silver coins were struck at Canterbury, Durham and the archiepiscopal mint at York. Mintmarks were now much more frequent and varied. Coins with a mark of a halved sun and rose are usually assigned to the reign of Edward IV, but they were probably also struck in the nominal reign of Edward V, the twelve-year-old prince held in the Tower of London under the protection of his uncle Richard, Duke of Gloucester. Coins with this mark on the reverse had an obverse mark of a boar's head, Richard's personal emblem. The brief reign of Richard III (1483–5) came to an end with his defeat at Bosworth and the relatively scarce coins of this period followed the pattern of the previous reigns, distinguished by the sequence of mint marks and the inscription RICAD or RICARD.

In the early years of Henry VII's reign the coinage likewise followed the previous patterns, but in 1489 the first of several radical changes was effected, with the introduction of the gold sovereign of 20 shillings showing a full-length portrait of the monarch seated on an elaborate throne. For reverse, this coin depicted a Tudor rose surmounted by a heraldic shield. A similar reverse appeared on the ryal of 10 shillings, but the angel and angelet retained previous motifs. The silver coins at first adhered to the medieval pattern, with the stylised facing portrait and long cross, but at the beginning of the 16th century a large silver coin, the testoon or shilling of 12 pence, was introduced and adopted a realistic profile of the king, allied to a reverse showing a cross surmounted by the royal arms.

First coinage Angel of Henry VIII which retained the traditional 23½ carat fineness.

The same design was also used for the later issue of groat and half groat.

This established a pattern which was to continue till the reign of Charles I. In the reign of Henry VIII, however, the coinage was subject to considerable debasement. This led to the eventual introduction of 22 carat (.916 fine) gold for the crown while the traditional 23 ½ carat gold was retained for the angel and ryal. This dual system continued until the angel was discontinued at the outset of the Civil War in 1642; latterly it had been associated with the ceremony of touching for "King's Evil" or scrofula, a ritual used by the early Stuart monarchs to bolster their belief in the divine right of kings.

Under the Tudors and Stuarts the range and complexity of the gold coinage increased, but it was not until the reign of Edward VI that the silver series was expanded. In 1551 he introduced the silver crown of five shillings, the first English coin to bear a clear date on the obverse. Under Mary dates were extended to the shilling and sixpence.

The mixture of dated and undated coins continued under Elizabeth I, a reign remarkable for the range of denominations—nine gold and eight silver. The latter included the sixpence, threepence, threehalfpence and threefarthings, distinguished by the rose which appeared behind the Queen's head.

The coinage of James I was even more complex, reflecting the king's attempts to unite his dominions. The first issue bore the legend ANG: SCO (England and Scotland), but from 1604 this was altered to MAG: BRIT (Great Britain). This period witnessed new denominations, such as the rose-ryal and spur-ryal, the unite, the Britain crown and the thistle crown, and finally the laurel of 20 shillings and its sub-divisions.

In the reign of Elizabeth experiments began with milled coinage under Eloi Mestrell. These continued sporadically in the 17th century, culminating in the beautiful coins struck by Nicholas Briot (1631–39). A branch mint was established at Aberystwyth in 1637 to refine and coin silver from the Welsh mines. Relations between King and Parliament deteriorated in the reign of Charles I and led to the Civil War (1642). Parliament controlled London but continued to strike coins in the King's name. The Royalists struck coins, both in pre-war and new types, at Shrewsbury, Oxford, Bristol, Worcester, Exeter, Chester, Hereford and other Royalist strongholds, while curious siege pieces were pressed into service at Newark, Pontefract and Scarborough.

After the execution of Charles I in 1649 the Commonwealth was proclaimed under Oliver Cromwell. Gold and silver coins were now inscribed in English instead of Latin. Patterns portraying Cromwell and a crowned shield restored Latin in 1656. Plans for milled coinage were already being considered before the Restoration of the monarchy in 1660. Hammered coinage appeared initially, resuming the style of coins under Charles I, but in 1662 the hand-hammering of coins was abandoned in favour of coins struck on the mill and screw press. The hammered coins of 1660–62 were undated and bore a crown mintmark, the last vestiges of medievalism in British coinage.

The magnificent Rose-Ryal of James I.

Prices section

O N the following pages will be found the up to date
price guide to Celtic and Roman coins used in
Britain, English hammered coins, English milled
and modern coinage, Scottish, Isle of Man, Channel Islands
and Irish coinage and official commemorative medallions.

COIN GRADING

CONDITION is the secret to the value of virtually anything, whether it be antiques, jewellery, horses or second-hand cars—and coins are *certainly* no exception. When collecting coins it is vital to understand the recognised standard British system of grading, i.e. accurately assessing a coin's condition or state of wear. Grading is an art which can only be learned by experience and so often it remains one person's opinion against another's, therefore it is important for the beginner or inexperienced collector to seek assistance from a reputable dealer or knowledgeable numismatist when making major purchases.

The standard grades as used in this Price Guide are as follows:

UNC — **Uncirculated**
A coin that has never been in circulation, although it may show signs of contact with other coins during the minting process.

EF — **Extremely Fine**
A coin in this grade may appear uncirculated to the naked eye but on closer examination will show signs of minor friction on the highest surface.

VF — **Very Fine**
A coin that has had very little use, but shows signs of wear on the high surfaces.

F — **Fine**
A coin that has been in circulation and shows general signs of wear, but with all legends and date clearly visible.

Other grades used in the normal grading system are:

BU — **Brilliant Uncirculated**
As the name implies, a coin retaining its mint lustre.

Fair — A coin extensively worn but still quite recognisable and legends readable.

Poor — A coin very worn and only just recognisable.

Other abbreviations used in the Price Guide are:

Obv — **Obverse**

Rev — **Reverse**

Other abbreviations, mintmarks, etc. can be identified under the appropriate section of this Yearbook.

Coins illustrated in the following listings are indicated with an asterisk (*)

A SIMPLIFIED PRICE GUIDE
TO
ANCIENT COINS USED IN BRITAIN

PART I
CELTIC

The prices given in this section are those that you would expect to pay from a reputable dealer and not the prices at which you could expect to sell coins.

The list below contains most of the commonly available types: a full comprehensive guide is beyond the scope of this book. Prices are for coins with good surfaces which are not weakly struck or struck from worn dies. Examples which are struck from worn or damaged dies can be worth considerably less. Particularly attractive examples of bronze Celtic coins command a very high premium. Where a price is given for an issue of which there are many varieties, the price is for the most common type.

The illustrations are representative examples only and are indicated by an asterisk (*) in the listings.

	F	VF	EF
UNINSCRIBED COINAGE			
GOLD STATERS			
Gallo-Belgic A	£600	£1,350	£5,000
Gallo-Belgic E (Ambiani)	£125	£225	£375
Chute type	£140	£250	£350
Cheriton type			
normally rather "brassy" metal	£185	£325	£650
Corieltauvi (various types)	£150	£300	£500
Norfolk "wolf" type			
fine gold	£200	£400	£700
brassy gold	£125	£250	£400
very debased	£75	£150	£325
*Whaddon Chase types	£150	£275	£550
Wonersh type	£200	£400	£700
Iceni (various types)	£250	£450	£800
Remic type	£200	£350	£550
Dobunni	£250	£450	£800
GOLD QUARTER STATERS			
North Thames types	£150	£225	£350
North Kent types	£150	£225	£350
Iceni	£140	£200	£300
Sussex types	£100	£150	£275
Dobunni	£150	£250	£500
SILVER COINAGE			
North Thames types	£75	£150	£300
South Thames types	£75	£150	£300
Durotriges full stater			
fine silver	£45	£135	£250
*base silver	£30	£65	£165

Uninscribed Whaddon Chase type gold stater

Uninscribed Durotriges base silver stater

	F	VF	EF
Durotriges small silver	£30	£75	£150
Dobunni	£40	£90	£200
(Note—Most examples are base in appearance. Prices for examples with fine surfaces are appreciably higher)			
Corieltauvi	£40	£100	£200
Eceni ("crescent" types)	£30	£65	£125
Eceni ("Norfolk god" types)	£50	£100	£250
Armorican Billon staters	£60	£130	£350

POTIN COINAGE

	F	VF	EF
Thames & South	£30	£45	£100
Kent & N. Thames	£50	£90	£160

BRONZE COINAGE

	F	VF	EF
Durotriges debased stater	£25	£45	£85
*Durotriges cast bronzes	£60	£120	£200
North Thames types. Various issues from:	£40	£90	£400

Durotriges cast bronze

INSCRIBED CELTIC COINAGE

ATTREBATES & REGNI

	F	VF	EF
*Commios			
stater	£500	£1,000	£2,500
Tincomarus			
stater	£400	£800	£1,750
quarter stater	£140	£240	£400
silver unit	£65	£125	£250
silver quarter unit	£150	£275	£500
Eppillus			
quarter stater	£140	£225	£400
silver unit	£65	£135	£275
bronze			Rare
Verica			
stater	£250	£500	£900
quarter stater	£150	£250	£400
silver unit	£50	£90	£200
Epatticus			
stater	£1,000	£2,000	£4,000
*silver unit	£45	£95	£250
silver quarter unit	£50	£100	£265
Caratacos			
silver unit	£155	£300	£450
silver quarter unit	£100	£200	£300

Commios stater

CANTII

	F	VF	EF
Dubnovellaunos			
stater	£275	£550	£850
silver unit	£125	£200	£450
bronze unit	£50	£140	£300
Vosenos			
stater	£1,000	£2,500	£4,500
quarter stater	£260	£550	£1,000
silver unit	£125	£275	£600
bronze unit	£100	£200	£500
Eppillus			
stater	£1,000	£2,000	£4,000
quarter stater	£135	£250	£450
silver unit	£60	£140	£300
bronze unit	£50	£120	£400
Amminus			
silver unit	£150	£300	£600
silver quarter unit	£100	£200	£400
bronze unit	£75	£150	£500

Epatticus silver unit

	F	VF	EF
DUROTRIGES			
Crab			
silver	£150	£300	£600
silver quarter unit	£100	£250	£400
TRINOVANTES			
Addedomaros			
stater	£255	£450	£750
quarter stater	£150	£300	£500
Diras			
stater			Rare
Dubnovellaunos			
stater	£250	£450	£750
quarter stater	£150	£300	£500
*bronze unit	£50	£125	£400

Dubnovellaunos bronze unit

	F	VF	EF
CATUVELLAUNI			
Tasciovanus			
*stater	£225	£425	£1,000
quarter stater	£125	£225	£400
silver unit	£75	£160	£350
bronze unit	£50	£125	£300
bronze half unit	£50	£125	£250
Andoco			
stater	£500	£1,200	£2,500
quarter stater	£200	£400	£750
silver unit	£150	£400	£750
bronze	£75	£200	£350
Cunobelin			
*stater	£200	£450	£1,000
quarter stater	£140	£260	£400
silver unit	£75	£160	£350
bronze unit	£60	£140	£300

Tasciovanos stater

	F	VF	EF
DOBUNNI			
Anted			
stater	£300	£600	£1,200
silver unit	£50	£120	£300
Eisu			
stater	£450	£750	£1,500
silver unit	£50	£120	£300
Inam			
stater			Rare
Catti			
stater	£250	£500	£1,000
Comux			
stater	£750	£1,500	£3,000
Corio			
stater	£250	£500	£900
quarter stater	£200	£350	£600
Boduoc			
stater	£1,000	£2,000	£3,500
silver unit	£200	£500	£850

Cunobelin stater

	F	VF	EF
ECENI			
Duro			
silver unit	£100	£250	£500
Anted			
stater	£425	£1,000	£2,500
silver unit	£25	£60	£175
silver half unit	£40	£90	£160
Ecen			
silver unit	£25	£60	£175
silver half unit	£40	£90	£175

	F	VF	EF
Saemu			
silver unit	£55	£120	£275
Aesu			
silver unit	£55	£120	£275
Prasutagus			
silver unit	£400	£1,000	£1,750
Iat Iso			
silver unit	£150	£400	£1,000
Ale Sca			
silver unit	£350	£750	£1,500
CORIELTAUVI			
Aun Ast			
stater	£250	£550	£900
silver unit	£75	£175	£275
silver half unit	£75	£150	£250
Esup Asu			
stater	£325	£650	£1,200
silver unit	£150	£300	£500
Vep Corf			
stater	£400	£1,000	£2,000
*silver unit	£75	£175	£275
silver half unit	£100	£200	£400
Dumno Tigir Seno			
stater	£750	£1,750	£3,000
silver unit	£100	£175	£450
Volisios Dumnocoveros			
*stater	£300	£700	£1,500
silver unit	£100	£175	£450
silver half unit	£100	£175	£400
Volisios Dumnovellaunos			
stater	£300	£650	£1,200
silver half unit	£150	£325	£650
Volisios Cartivel			
silver half unit	£300	£600	£1,000

Vep Corf silver unit

Volisios Dumnocoveros stater

Illustrations by courtesy of Chris Rudd.

A SIMPLIFIED PRICE GUIDE
TO
ANCIENT COINS USED IN BRITAIN

PART II
ROMAN BRITAIN

In certain cases, especially with large bronze coins, the price for coins in extremely fine condition are _much_ higher than the price for the same coin in very fine condition as early bronze coins are seldom found in hoards and perfect undamaged examples are rarely available.

The illustrations provided are a representative guide to assist with identification only and are indicated by an asterisk (*) in the listings.

	F	VF	EF
Julius Caesar			
aureus	£900	£2,500	£4,000
denarius ("elephant" type)	£90	£200	£375
denarius (with portrait)	£250	£750	£2,200
Mark Anthony			
denarius ("Galley" type)	£50	£100	£300
denarius (with portrait)	£135	£350	£1,750
Augustus			
aureus	£650	£1,850	£3,500
denarius (Caius & Lucius Caesars)	£50	£140	£350
*other types	£55	£175	£600
as	£55	£150	£450
Livia			
Ae as	£85	£275	£750
Tiberius			
aureus	£450	£1,300	£2,500
*denarius	£85	£175	£450
Drusus			
as	£65	£150	£450
Germanicus			
*as	£65	£150	£450
Caligula			
denarius	£300	£650	£1,800
*as	£75	£250	£750
Claudius			
aureus ("DE BRITANN" type)	£850	£2,200	£5,300
denarius similar	£300	£900	£2,000
sestertius	£100	£400	£1,500
as	£50	£100	£275
Nero			
aureus	£475	£1,250	£2,750
sestertius	£185	£350	£2,000
as	£50	£140	£500

Augustus

Germanicus

Caligula

	F	VF	EF
Galba			
denarius	£85	£345	£850
*sestertius	£175	£400	£3,000
as	£70	£155	£650
Otho			
denarius	£220	£500	£1,750
Vitellius			
denarius	£120	£300	£900
sestertius	£260	£750	£4,200
as	£110	£300	£1,750
Vespasian			
aureus	£650	£1,750	£2,800
sestertius	£100	£275	£650
as	£45	£150	£450
Titus			
aureus	£600	£1,650	£2,800
denarius	£50	£150	£300
as	£60	£175	£400
Domitian			
aureus	£600	£1,500	£3,250
denarius	£35	£55	£200
*sestertius	£85	£320	£1,850
as	£50	£100	£450
Nerva			
aureus	£650	£1,750	£3,750
denarius	£55	£145	£375
as	£60	£165	£575
Trajan			
aureus	£500	£1,350	£2,750
denarius	£35	£65	£185
sestertius	£45	£185	£550
as	£35	£85	£350
Hadrian			
aureus	£550	£1,350	£2,750
denarius	£45	£75	£185
as	£50	£120	£325
Sabina			
denarius	£35	£75	£275
*sestertius	£75	£200	£800
as	£45	£150	£375
Aelius			
denarius	£60	£140	£375
sestertius	£100	£250	£1,000
as	£50	£150	£600
Antoninus Pius			
denarius	£20	£50	£150
sestertius	£45	£110	£465
as	£35	£60	£275
Faustina Senior			
denarius	£25	£55	£150
sestertius	£35	£110	£550
as	£25	£65	£275
Marcus Aurelius			
*denarius	£25	£50	£150
sestertius	£45	£125	£550
as	£30	£65	£250
Faustina Junior			
*denarius	£25	£50	£145
sestertius	£35	£110	£520
as	£20	£60	£250
Lucius Verus			
denarius	£25	£65	£175
sestertius	£45	£150	£650
as	£40	£130	£350

Galba

Domitian

Sabina

Marcus Aurelius

Faustina Junior

Commodus

	F	VF	EF
Lucilla			
denarius	£32	£75	£250
sestertius	£40	£135	£550
as	£30	£65	£250
Commodus			
denarius	£25	£55	£150
*sestertius	£40	£150	£650
as	£30	£75	£300
Crispina			
denarius	£35	£80	£250
Pertinax			
*denarius	£200	£600	£1,500
Didius Julianus			
denarius	£450	£900	£2,000
Clodius Albinus			
denarius	£60	£175	£400
sestertius	£80	£300	£1,250
Septimius Severus			
denarius	£20	£40	£90
denarius (VICT BRIT)	£45	£95	£185
sestertius	£65	£220	£650
as	£50	£125	£350
Julia Domna			
denarius	£20	£45	£85
sestertius	£75	£255	£850
as	£45	£125	£450
Caracalla			
*denarius	£25	£45	£95
denarius (VICT BRIT)	£45	£90	£185
sestertius	£80	£200	£700
as	£45	£90	£350
Plautilla			
denarius	£45	£85	£200
Geta			
denarius	£25	£45	£100
denarius (VICT BRIT)	£50	£120	£225
sestertius	£60	£200	£600
as	£50	£125	£350
Macrinus			
denarius	£55	£125	£275
*sestertius	£100	£275	£800
Diadumenian			
*denarius	£120	£225	£450
Elagabalus			
antoninianus	£45	£100	£200
denarius	£25	£45	£120
Julia Paula			
denarius	£55	£135	£275
Aquilla Severa			
denarius	£135	£250	£500
Julia Soaemias			
denarius	£25	£55	£125
Julia Maesa			
denarius	£25	£45	£90
Severus Alexander			
*denarius	£20	£45	£85
sestertius	£30	£60	£220
as	£25	£50	£155
Orblana			
denarius	£100	£225	£500
Julia Mamaea			
denarius	£24	£48	£130

Pertinax

Caracalla

Macrinus

Diadumenian

Severus Alexander

121

	F	VF	EF
Maximinus I			
denarius	£25	£50	£100
*sestertius	£40	£80	£300
as	£40	£80	£250
Maximus			
denarius	£125	£250	£450
sestertius	£70	£140	£400
Balbinus			
denarius	£125	£250	£450
Papienus			
denarius	£125	£250	£450
Gordian III			
antoninianus	£15	£25	£50
denarius	£18	£38	£75
sestertius	£20	£55	£140
Philip I			
antoninianus	£15	£25	£55
*sestertius	£20	£70	£175
Otacilla Severa			
antoninianus	£15	£25	£50
sestertius	£30	£75	£250
Philip II			
antoninianus	£15	£25	£55
Trajan Decius			
antoninianus	£15	£25	£60
Herennius Etruscus			
antoninianus	£20	£50	£125
Hostilian			
antoninianus	£45	£110	£250
Trebonianus Gallus			
antoninianus	£15	£25	£60
Volusian			
antoninianus	£18	£30	£75
Aemillan			
*antoninianus	£50	£125	£250
Valerian I			
antoninianus	£15	£25	£55
Gallienus			
*silver antoninianus	£12	£25	£45
Ae antoninianus	£8	£15	£30
Salonina			
Ae antoninianus	£8	£15	£30
Valerian II			
billon antoninianus	£15	£30	£90
Saloninus			
antoninianus	£15	£35	£120
Macrianus			
billon antoninianus	£35	£80	£160
Quietus			
billon antoninianus	£35	£80	£160
Postumus			
silver antoninianus	£10	£20	£45
*Ae antoninianus	£5	£12	£25
Laelianus			
antoninianus	£150	£275	£475
Marius			
antoninianus	£40	£85	£175
Victorinus			
Ae antoninianus	£5	£14	£30
Claudius II Gothicus			
Ae antoninianus	£5	£14	£30
Tetricus I			
Ae antoninianus	£5	£14	£30

Maximinus

Philip I

Aemillian

Gallienus

Postumus

	F	VF	EF
Tetricus II			
Ae antoninianus	£5	£15	£35
Quintillus			
*Ae antoninianus	£8	£18	£60
Aurelian			
Ae antoninianus	£6	£15	£40
Severina			
*Ae antoninianus	£10	£22	£60
Tacitus			
Ae antoninianus	£8	£20	£55
Florian			
Ae antoninianus	£40	£80	£150
Probus			
Ae antoninianus	£5	£12	£35
Carus			
Ae antoninianus	£10	£22	£65
Numerian			
Ae antoninianus	£10	£22	£65
Carinus			
Ae antoninianus	£10	£22	£65
Diocletian			
Ae follis (London mint)	£15	£35	£75
Ae follis (other mints)	£10	£22	£55
Maximianus			
Ae follis (London mint)	£15	£35	£75
*Ae follis (other mints)	£10	£22	£55
Carausius			
denarius	£250	£750	£1,450
antoninianus	£25	£65	£185
Allectus			
antoninianus	£25	£75	£250
quinarius	£20	£60	£175
Constantius I.			
Ae follis (London mint)	£20	£55	£100
Ae follis (other mints)	£10	£22	£48
Galerius			
Ae follis (London mint)	£15	£35	£75
Ae follis (other mints)	£10	£22	£45
Galeria Valeria			
follis	£30	£65	£175
Severus II			
Ae follis (London mint)	£60	£125	£250
*Ae follis (other mints)	£30	£75	£175
Maximinus II			
Ae follis (London mint)	£20	£45	£85
*Ae follis (other mints)	£10	£22	£45
Maxentius			
follis	£5	£18	£40
Licinius I			
follis	£5	£15	£35
Ae 3	£4	£10	£30
Licinius II			
Ae 3	£6	£15	£40
Constantine I			
follis (London mint)	£10	£24	£50
follis (other mints)	£5	£14	£35
Ae 3	£4	£12	£30
Fausta			
Ae 3 (London mint)	£100	£175	£300
Ae 3 (other mints)	£15	£45	£95
Helena			
*Ae 3 (London mint)	£110	£180	£325
Ae 3 (other mints)	£15	£45	£95

Quintillus

Severina

Maximianus

Severus II

Maximinus II

Helena

123

	F	VF	EF
Theodora			
Ae 4	£7	£15	£45
Crispus			
*Ae 3	£5	£14	£40
Deimatius			
Ae 3/4	£10	£22	£65
Hanniballianus			
Ae 4	£120	£245	£420
Constantine II			
Ae 3	£5	£12	£35
Ae 4	£4	£10	£22
Constans			
*centenionalis	£10	£22	£60
Ae 4	£4	£8	£16
Constantius II			
*siliqua	£25	£55	£120
centenionalis	£8	£18	£45
Ae 4	£4	£8	£16
Magnentius			
double centenionalis	£30	£60	£150
centenionalis	£12	£25	£75
Decentius			
double centenionalis	£40	£80	£200
centenionalis	£15	£35	£100
Constantius Gallus			
centenionalis	£9	£22	£55
Julian II			
*siliqua	£20	£50	£110
Ae 1	£60	£140	£350
Ae 3 (helmeted bust)	£15	£40	£90
Jovian			
Ae 1	£45	£110	£255
Ae 3	£12	£40	£85
Valentinian I			
gold solidus	£155	£285	£550
siliqua	£25	£55	£125
Ae 3	£5	£14	£35
Valens			
gold solidus	£155	£285	£550
*siliqua	£25	£55	£125
Ae 3	£5	£14	£35
Gratian			
*siliqua	£25	£55	£135
Ae 3	£5	£15	£35
Valentinian II			
siliqua	£25	£60	£125
Ae 2	£10	£25	£60
Ae 4	£5	£12	£25
Theodosius I			
siliqua	£25	£60	£125
Magnus Maximus			
solidus	£755	£1,800	£4,200
siliqua	£40	£90	£175
*Ae 2	£20	£65	£130

Ae=bronze; Ae 1, 2, 3, 4=bronze coins in descending order of size.

Illustrations by courtesy of Classical Numismatic Group/Seaby Coins.

Crispus

Constans

Constantius II

Julian II

Valens

Gratian

Magnus Maximus

A SIMPLIFIED PRICE GUIDE
TO
ENGLISH HAMMERED COINS
1066–1663

PART I
1066–1485

INTRODUCTION

In this section we give an approximate price guide that one could expect to pay for the more commonly-located hammered coins in gold and silver. Although coins were struck in England for up to 1,000 years before the Norman Conquest, 1066–1663 provides a useful historical period with which most new collectors can associate.

PRICING

The prices given in the following pages are intended to be used as a "Pocket book guide" to the values of the *most common* coins within any denomination of any one reign. The price quoted is what a collector may expect to pay for such a piece in the condition indicated. For more detailed information we recommend the reader to one of the many specialist publications.

GRADING

The prices quoted are for three different grades of condition: Fine (F), Very Fine (VF) and Extremely Fine (EF). A "Fine" coin is assumed to be a fairly worn, circulated, piece but with all or most of the main features and lettering still clear. "Very Fine" is a middle grade with a small amount of wear and most details fairly clear. For this edition we have included the prices for coins in Extremely Fine condition where appropriate, although very few hammered coins actually turn up in this grade (i.e. nearly mint state with hardly any wear). In some instances the prices quoted are theoretically based and are only included to provide a guide. It is important to note that on all hammered coins the very nature of striking, i.e. individually, by hand, means hammered coinage is rarely a straight grade and when listed by a dealer the overall condition will often be qualified by terms such as: *weak in parts, struck off-centre, cracked or chipped flan, double struck*, etc. When applicable the price should be adjusted accordingly.

HISTORY

Below the heading for each monarch we have given a few historical notes as and when they apply to significant changes in the coinage.

WILLIAM I
(1066–87)

The Norman Conquest had very little immediate effect on the coinage of England. The Anglo-Saxon standard of minting silver pennies was very high and the practise of the moneyer putting his name and mint town on the reverse continued as before, except with William's portrait of course. It is worth noting here that non-realistic, stylised portraits were used until the reign of Henry VII.

There are eight major types of William I penny of which the last, the PAXS type, is by far the commonest.

	F	VF	EF
William I, Penny	£100	£170	£325

WILLIAM II
(1087–1100)

Very little change from his father's reign except that five new types were issued, most of which were much more crudely designed than previous, all are scarce.

	F	VF	EF
William II, Penny	£275	£575	—

HENRY I
(1100–35)

There are fifteen different types of penny for this reign of which the last two are the most common. Most issues are of a very poor standard both in workmanship and metal, the prices reflect a poor quality of issue.

	F	VF	EF
Henry I, Penny	£110	£240	—

STEPHEN
(1135–54)

This is historically a very complicated time for the coinage, mainly due to civil war and a consequential lack of central control in the country which resulted in very poor quality and deliberately damaged pieces. Coins were struck not only in the name of Stephen and his main rival claimant Matilda but also by their supporters. The commonest issue is the "Watford" type; so named, as are many issues, after the area in which a hoard was found.

	F	VF	EF
Stephen, Penny	£115	£275	—

HENRY II
(1154–89)

There were two distinct issues struck during this reign. The first, Cross and Crosslets or "Tealby" coinage (named after Tealby in Lincolnshire), continued to be very poorly made and lasted 20 years. However, in 1180 the new and superior "Short Cross" issue commenced, being issued from only twelve major towns.

	F	VF	EF
Henry II, Penny, Tealby	£50	£130	—
Henry II, Penny, Short Cross	£30	£75	£200

RICHARD I
(1189–1199)

There were no major changes during this reign, in fact pennies continued to be struck with his father Henry's name throughout the reign. The coins struck under Richard tend to be rather crude in style.

	F	VF	EF
Richard I, Penny	£40	£100	£250

JOHN
(1199–1216)

As with his brother before him, there were no major changes during the reign of King John, and pennies with his father's name were struck throughout the reign, although they tended to be somewhat neater in style than those struck during the reign of Richard I.

	F	VF	EF
John, Penny	£30	£65	£135

HENRY III
(1216–72)

The coinage during Henry III's reign continued as before with the short cross issue. However, in 1247 a new long cross design was introduced to prevent clipping. This design was to last in one form or another for many centuries.

	F	VF	EF
Henry III, Penny, Short Cross	£18	£35	£90
Henry III, Penny, Long Cross	£15	£30	£70

EDWARD I
(1272–1307)

After a few years of issuing similar pieces to his father, in 1279 Edward I ordered a major re-coinage. This consisted of well-made pennies, halfpennies and farthings in relatively large quantities, and for a brief period a groat (four pence) was produced. The pennies are amongst the most common of all hammered coins.

	F	VF	EF
Edward I (and Edward II)			
Groat (often damaged)	£900	£2,650	—
Penny	£12	£25	£50
Halfpenny	£20	£50	£135
Farthing	£13	£30	£100

Edward I halfpenny

EDWARD II
(1307–1327)

The coinage of Edward II differs in only a very few minor details from that of Edward I and are of similar value.

EDWARD III
(1327–77)

This was a long reign which saw major changes in the coinage, the most significant being the introduction of a gold coinage (based on the Noble, valued at 6s 8d, and its fractions) and a regular issue of a large silver groat (and half groat). The mints were limited to a few episcopal cities but coins of English type were also struck in the newly-acquired Calais.

	F	VF	EF
Gold			
Noble	£300	£575	£1,150
Half Noble	£200	£375	£800
Quarter Noble	£135	£265	£500
Silver			
Groat	£40	£90	£250
Half Groat	£20	£45	£125
Penny	£15	£35	£95
Half Penny	£15	£35	£80
Farthing	£30	£60	£140

Gold Noble

RICHARD II
(1377–1399)

The denominations continued during this reign much as before. However, coins are quite rare mainly due to the lack of bullion gold and silver going into the mints, mainly because of an inbalance with European weights and fineness.

	F	VF	EF
Gold			
Noble	£500	£1,000	£2,250
Half Noble	£575	£1,200	—
Quarter Noble	£225	£475	£800
Silver			
Groat	£200	£525	—
Half Groat	£150	£400	—
Penny	£45	£135	—
Half Penny	£30	£75	—
Farthing	£115	£225	—

Groat

129

HENRY IV
(1399–1413)

Because of the continuing problems with the scarcity of gold and silver the coinage was reduced in weight in 1412, towards the end of the reign. All coins of this reign are quite scarce.

	F	VF
Gold		
Noble	£850	£1,750
Half Noble	£2,500	£5,000
Quarter Noble	£385	£800
Silver		
Groat	£1,250	£3,250
Half Groat	£475	£1,000
Penny	£175	£550
Half Penny	£140	£275
Farthing	£450	£1,000

Noble

HENRY V
(1413–22)

Monetary reform introduced towards the end of his father's reign in 1412 improved the supply of bullion and hence coins of Henry V are far more common. All of the main denominations continued as before.

	F	VF	EF
Gold			
Noble	£340	£675	£1,400
Half Noble	£375	£750	—
Quarter Noble	£200	£400	£750
Silver			
Groat	£75	£170	—
Half Groat	£65	£165	—
Penny	£25	£65	—
Half Penny	£20	£50	—
Farthing	£120	£280	—

Half Groat

HENRY VI
(1422–61 and again 1470–71)

Although there were no new denominations during these reigns (see Edward IV below), Henry's first reign saw eleven different issues, each for a few years and distinguished by privy marks, i.e. crosses, pellets, annulets, etc.

HENRY VI *continued*

Gold

	F	VF	EF
First reign—			
Noble	£325	£600	£1,100
Half Noble	£225	£435	£850
Quarter Noble	£150	£300	£535
2nd reign—			
Angel	£625	£1,300	£2,750
Half Angel	£1,500	£3,250	—

Silver

	F	VF	EF
Groat	£30	£60	£125
Half Groat	£25	£45	£100
Penny	£20	£40	£95
Half Penny	£18	£35	£90
Farthing	£100	£225	—

Groat

EDWARD IV
(1461–70 and again 1471–83)

The significant changes during these reigns were the replacement of the noble by the rose Ryal (and revalued at 10s) and the introduction of the angel at the old noble value. We also start to see mint-marks or initial marks appearing, usually at the top of the coin, they were used to denote the period of issue for dating purposes and often lasted for 2–3 years.

Gold

	F	VF	EF
Ryal	£325	£625	£1,100
Half Ryal	£280	£540	£950
Quarter Ryal	£185	£425	£700
Angel	£265	£525	£1,000
Half Angel	£240	£500	£950

Silver

	F	VF	EF
Groat	£35	£75	£200
Half Groat	£30	£65	£185
Penny	£20	£60	£150
Half Penny	£25	£65	—
Farthing	£300	£600	—

Gold Ryal

RICHARD III
(1483–85)

The close of the Yorkist Plantagenet and the beginning of the Medieval period come together at this time. There are no new significant numismatic changes but most coins of Richard whilst not really rare, continue to be very popular and priced quite high.

Gold

	F	VF	EF
Angel	£850	£1,750	—
Half Angel			Rare

Silver

	F	VF	EF
Groat	£285	£575	£1,250
Half Groat	£500	£1,000	—
Penny	£125	£300	—
Half Penny	£120	£285	—

Groat

131

PART II: 1485–1663

Among the more significant features of the post-Renaissance period as it affected coinage is the introduction of realistic portraiture during the reign of Henry VII. We also have a much wider and varied number of new and revised denominations, for example eleven different gold denominations of Henry VIII and the same number of silver for Elizabeth I. Here we only mention the introduction or changes in the main denominations, giving a value for all of them, once again listing the commonest type.

HENRY VII
(1485–1509)

The gold sovereign of 20 shillings makes its first appearance in 1489 as does the testoon (later shilling) in about 1500. The silver penny was re-designed to a rather crude likeness of the sovereign.

	F	VF	EF
Gold			
Sovereign	£6,750	£14,000	—
Ryal	£6,500	£16,000	—
Angel	£225	£475	£900
Half Angel	£190	£400	£825
Silver			
Testoon 1/-	£4,600	£9,250	—
Groat	£45	£120	£350
Half Groat	£25	£60	£200
Penny	£20	£65	£150
Half Penny	£20	£60	—
Farthing	£125	£300	—

Profile Groat

Sovereign-style penny

HENRY VIII
(1509–47)

After a long initial period of very little change in the coinage, in 1526 there were many, with an attempt to bring the gold/silver ratio in line with the continental currencies. Some gold coins only lasted a short time and are very rare. The crown (in gold) makes its first appearance. Towards the end of the reign we see large issues of debased silver coins (with a high copper content) bearing the well-known facing portrait of the ageing King. These tend to turn up in poor condition.

Gold			
Sovereign	£1,500	£3,500	—
Half Sovereign	£250	£550	—
Angel	£235	£475	£950
Half Angel	£200	£400	£850
Quarter Angel	£220	£450	—
George Noble	£2,650	£5,750	—
Half George Noble	Rare	Rare	—
Crown of the rose	Rare	Rare	—
Crown of the double rose	£225	£475	£900
Half Crown of the double rose	£200	£400	—
Silver			
Testoon 1/-	£425	£1,250	—
Groat	£50	£110	£275
Half Groat	£25	£65	£185
Penny	£25	£65	£140
Half Penny	£20	£55	—
Farthing	£250	£600	—

Facing Groat

Crown of the double rose

EDWARD VI
(1547–53)

Some of the coins struck in the first few years of this short reign could really be called Henry VIII posthumous issues as there is continuity in both name and style from his father's last issue. However, overlapping this period are portrait issues of the boy King, particularly shillings (usually poor quality coins). This period also sees the first dated English coin (shown in Roman numerals). In 1551 however, a new coinage was introduced with a restored silver quality from the Crown (dated 1551) down to the new sixpence and threepence.

	F	VF	EF
Gold			
Sovereign (30s)	£1,750	£3,650	—
Half Sovereign	£400	£900	—
Crown	£650	£1,300	—
Half Crown	£600	£1,200	—
Angel	£3,250	£7,500	—
Half Angel	—	—	—
Sovereign (20s)	£1,000	£2,250	—
Silver			
Crown	£300	£650	—
Half Crown	£220	£550	—
Shilling	£60	£165	£425
Sixpence	£70	£200	—
Groat	£425	£1,000	—
Threepence	£140	£375	—
Half Groat	£185	£500	—
Penny	£45	£115	—
Half Penny	£160	£375	—
Farthing	£600	—	—

Base Shilling, obverse

Fine Shilling

MARY
(1553–54)

The early coins of Mary's sole reign are limited and continue to use the same denominations as Edward, except that the gold Ryal was reintroduced.

	F	VF
Gold		
Sovereign (30s)	£1,900	£4,200
Ryal	£7,000	—
Angel	£575	£1,150
Half Angel	£1,700	£3,800
Silver		
Groat	£70	£200
Half Groat	£500	£1,400
Penny	£300	£850

Groat

PHILIP & MARY
(1554–58)

After a very short reign alone, Mary married Philip of Spain and they technically ruled jointly (although not for very long in practise) until her death. After her marriage we see both her and Philip on the shillings and sixpences.

	F	VF
Gold		
Angel	£1,600	£3,550
Half Angel	£4,750	—
Silver		
Shilling	£160	£500
Sixpence	£160	£525
Groat	£70	£250
Half Groat	£275	£700
Penny	£50	£165

Shilling

ELIZABETH I
(1558–1603)

As might be expected with a long reign there are a number of significant changes in the coinage which include several new denominations—so many in silver that every value from the shilling downwards was marked and dated to distinguish them. Early on we have old base Edward VI shillings countermarked to a new reduced value (not priced here). Also due to a lack of small change and the expense of making a miniscule farthing we have a new threehalfpence and threefarthings. Finally we see the beginnings of a milled (machine produced) coinage for a brief period from 1561–71.

	F	VF	EF
Gold			
Sovereign (30s)	£1,600	£3,400	—
Ryal (15s)	£3,000	£7,250	—
Angel	£300	£600	—
Half Angel	£275	£600	—
Quarter Angel	£240	£500	—
Pound (20s)	£700	£1,500	£3,000
Half Pound	£375	£850	—
Crown	£350	£750	—
Half Crown	£350	£750	—
Silver			
Crown	£475	£1,150	£3,000
Half Crown	£325	£700	—
Shilling	£60	£160	£300
Sixpence	£35	£90	£200
Groat	£30	£75	£150
Threepence	£20	£65	£140
Half Groat	£18	£45	—
Threehalfpence	£25	£75	—
Penny	£15	£50	£120
Threefarthings	£45	£125	—
Half Penny	£20	£50	£100

Shilling

Milled Sixpence

JAMES I
(1603–25)

Although the size of the gold coinage remains much the same as Elizabeth's reign, the name and weight or value of the denominations have several changes, i.e. Pound = Sovereign = Unite = Laurel. A new four shilling gold coin (thistle crown) was introduced. A number of the silver coins now have their value in Roman numerals on the coin. Relatively few angels were made from this period onwards and they are usually found pierced.

Gold

	F	VF	EF
Sovereign (20s)	£675	£1,400	—
Unite	£250	£500	£950
Double crown/half unite	£200	£435	£850
Crown	£140	£300	£650
Thistle Crown	£150	£325	£635
Half Crown	£130	£235	—
Rose Ryal (30s)	£875	£1,900	—
Spur Ryal (15s)	£1,700	£4,250	—
Angel (pierced)	£250	£550	—
Half Angel (Unpierced)	£1,300	£3,000	—
Laurel	£230	£450	£925
Half Laurel	£175	£370	£825
Quarter Laurel	£130	£240	£450

Silver

	F	VF	EF
Crown	£250	£550	—
Half Crown	£115	£275	—
Shilling	£40	£140	—
Sixpence	£35	£125	—
Half Groat	£15	£35	£75
Penny	£15	£30	£65
Half Penny	£15	£28	£55

Half Groat

Shilling

CHARLES I
(1625–49)

This reign is probably the most difficult to simplify as there are so many different issues and whole books have been produced on this period alone. From the beginning of the King's reign and throughout the Civil War, a number of mints operated for varying lengths of time, producing both regular and irregular issues. The Tower mint was taken over by Parliament in 1642 but before this a small quantity of milled coinage was produced alongside the regular hammered issues. The Court then moved to Oxford from where, for the next three years, large quantities of gold and silver were struck (including rare triple unites and large silver pounds). The most prolific of the provincial mints were those situated at Aberystwyth, York, Oxford, Shrewsbury, Bristol, Exeter, Truro, Chester and Worcester as well as some smaller mints mainly situated in the West Country. Among the more interesting coins of the period are the pieces struck on unusually-shaped flans at Newark and Pontefract whilst those towns were under siege. As many of the coins struck during the Civil War were crudely struck on hastily gathered bullion and plate, they provide a fascinating area of study. The prices indicated below are the minimum for the commonest examples of each denomination irrespective of town of origin.

	F	VF	EF
Gold			
Triple Unite (£3)	£2,200	£5,000	—
Unite	£230	£450	—
Double crown/Half unite	£200	£400	—
Crown	£130	£275	—
Angel (pierced)	£325	£700	—
Silver			
Pound (20 shillings)	£950	£2,300	—
Half Pound	£350	£800	—
Crown	£170	£425	—
Half Crown	£35	£110	—
Shilling	£30	£90	£300
Sixpence	£30	£115	£275
Groat	£30	£70	£160
Threepence	£30	£65	£150
Half Groat	£15	£35	£85
Penny	£12	£28	£75
Half Penny	£12	£30	£55

Many of the coins of Charles' reign, particularly those produced during the Civil War, are poorly struck. However, the sixpence shown above is a superb example with a good portrait.

The siege coins of Newark, Pontefract and Scarborough are keenly sought.

THE COMMONWEALTH
(1649–60)

After the execution of Charles I, Parliament changed the design of the coinage. They are simple non portrait pieces with an English legend.

	F	VF	EF
Gold			
Unite	£450	£925	£1,700
Double crown/Half unite	£375	£750	£1,500
Crown	£350	£625	£1,250
Silver			
Crown	£350	£650	£1,200
Half Crown	£125	£325	£800
Shilling	£80	£180	£450
Sixpence	£75	£170	£425
Half Groat	£25	£60	£125
Penny	£25	£50	£120
Half Penny	£25	£50	£95

Unite

CHARLES II
(1660–85)

Although milled coins had been produced for Oliver Cromwell in 1656–58, after the Restoration of the monarchy hammered coins continued to be produced until 1663, when the machinery was ready to manufacture large quantities of good milled pieces.

	F	VF	EF
Gold			
Unite	£600	£1,200	—
Double crown/Half unite	£450	£900	—
Crown	£500	£1,050	—
Silver			
Half Crown	£110	£350	—
Shilling	£70	£180	—
Sixpence	£60	£175	—
Fourpence	£20	£50	£90
Threepence	£25	£50	£90
Twopence	£12	£28	£60
Penny	£25	£50	£100

Halfcrown

A COMPREHENSIVE PRICE GUIDE
TO THE COINS OF

THE
UNITED KINGDOM
1656–1998

including

ENGLAND
SCOTLAND
ISLE OF MAN
GUERNSEY, JERSEY, ALDERNEY

and

IRELAND

When referring to this price guide one must bear a number of important points in mind. The points listed here have been taken into consideration during the preparation of this guide and we hope that the prices given will provide a true reflection of the market at the time of going to press. Nevertheless, the publishers can accept no liability for the accuracy of the prices quoted.

1. "As struck" examples with flaws will be worth less than the indicated price.
2. Any coin in superb state will command a higher price.
3. These prices refer strictly to the British market, and do not reflect outside opinions.
4. Some prices given for coins not seen in recent years are estimates based on a knowledge of   the market.
5. In the case of coins of high rarity, prices are not generally given.
6. In the listing, "—" indicates, where applicable, one of the following:
    a. Metal or bullion value only
    b. Not usually found in this grade
    c. Not collected in this condition
7. Proof coins are listed in FDC under the UNC column.
8. All prices are quoted in £ sterling, exclusive of VAT (where applicable).

FIVE GUINEAS

	F	VF	EF

CHARLES II (1660–85)

	F	VF	EF
1668 First bust	£850	£1950	£7000
1668 — Elephant	£850	£1950	£7500
1669 —	£850	£2050	—
1669 — Elephant	£1500	—	—
*1670 —	£850	£1700	£7000
1671 —	£850	£2050	—
1672 —	£850	£1950	£7000
1673 —	£850	£1950	£7000
1674 —	£850	£1950	£7500
1675 —	£850	£1950	£7000
1675 — Elephant	£1500	—	—
1675 — Elephant & Castle		Extremely rare	
1676 —	£900	£100	—
1676 — Elephant & Castle	£850	£2050	—
1677 —	£850	£2050	—
1677/5 —		Extremely rare	
1677 — Elephant & Castle	£900	£2050	—
1678 —	£850	£1950	£6500
1678 — Elephant & Castle	£1000	£2200	—
1678 Second bust	£1000	£2200	—
1679 —	£850	£1950	£6500
1680 —	£850	£1950	£7000
1680 — Elephant & Castle		Extremely rare	
1681 —	£850	£1950	£6500
1681 — Elephant & Castle	£1000	£2200	—
1682 —	£850	£1950	£6500
1682 — Elephant & Castle	£850	£1950	—
1683 —	£850	£1950	£6500
1683 — Elephant & Castle	£1000	£2200	—
1684 —	£850	£1700	£6500

JAMES II (1685–88)

	F	VF	EF
1686	£850	£1750	£6000
1687	£1000	£2000	£6500
1687 Elephant & Castle	£850	£1600	£6000
1688	£1000	£2000	£6500
1688 Elephant & Castle	£1000	£2000	£6500

WILLIAM AND MARY (1688–94)

	F	VF	EF
*1691	£850	£1750	£5000
1691 Elephant & Castle	£1000	£1850	£5250
1692	£850	£1750	£5000
1692 Elephant & Castle	£1250	£2000	£5500
1693	£850	£1750	£5000
1693 Elephant & Castle	£1250	£2000	£5750
1694	£850	£1750	£5000
1694 Elephant & Castle	£1250	£2000	£5500

WILLIAM III (1694–1702)

	F	VF	EF
1699 First bust	£850	£1750	£4500
1699 — Elephant & Castle	£1000	£2000	£4500
1700 —	£850	£1750	£4500
1701 Second bust "fine work"	£1000	£2250	£5000

ANNE (1702–14)

Pre-Union with Scotland

	F	VF	EF
1703 VIGO below bust		Extremely rare	

	F	VF	EF
*1705	£1250	£2500	£6750
1706	£1200	£2250	£6250
Post-Union later shields			
1706	£900	£1500	£5000
1709 Broader shields	£950	£1650	£5250
1711 Broader bust	£900	£1500	£5000
1713 —	£950	£1650	£5250
1714 —	£900	£1500	£5000

GEORGE I (1714–27)

	F	VF	EF
1716	£1100	£2500	£7000
1717	£1100	£2750	£7500
1720	£1100	£2500	£7000
1726	£1100	£2500	£7000

GEORGE II (1727–60)

	F	VF	EF
1729 Young head	£850	£1500	£4000
1729 — E.I.C. below head	£850	£1500	£4000
1731 —	£900	£1550	£4500
1735 —	£900	£1550	£4500
1738 —	£850	£1500	£4250
1741 —	£750	£1500	£4000
1746 Old head, LIMA	£900	£1600	£4500
1748 —	£750	£1500	£4000
1753 —	£750	£1500	£4000

GEORGE III (1760–1820)

	F	VF	EF
1770 Patterns	—	—	£35000
1773	—	—	£35000
1777	—	—	£35000

The Great Fire of London, 1666.

TWO GUINEAS

	F	VF	EF

CHARLES II (1660–85)

	F	VF	EF
1664 First bust	£400	£1350	—
*1664 — Elephant	£375	£900	£4500
1665 —		Extremely rare	
1669 —		Extremely rare	
1671 —	£500	£1600	—
1675 Second bust	£400	£1450	—
1676 —	£375	£1200	—
1676 — Elephant & Castle	£375	£1100	—
1677 —	£375	£1050	£4500
1677 — Elephant & Castle		Extremely rare	
1678 —	£375	£1050	—
1678 — Elephant		Extremely rare	
1678 — Elephant & Castle	£400	£1200	—
1679 —	£400	£1200	—
1680 —	£500	£1600	—
1681 —	£375	£1100	£4000
1682 — Elephant & Castle	£400	£1200	—
1683 —	£375	£1300	£4000
1683 — Elephant & Castle	£700	—	—
1684 —	£400	£1300	—
1684 — Elephant & Castle	£500	£1600	—

JAMES II (1685–88)

	F	VF	EF
1687	£450	£1100	£4000
*1688/7	£500	£1350	£4500

WILLIAM AND MARY (1688–94)

	F	VF	EF
1691 Elephant & Castle		Extremely rare	
1693	£450	£1100	£3500
1693 Elephant & Castle	£500	£1200	£3750
1694	£450	£1100	£3500
1694 Elephant & Castle	£500	£1375	£3750

WILLIAM III (1694–1702)

	F	VF	EF
1701 "fine work"	£550	£1750	£450

ANNE (1702–14)

	F	VF	EF
1709	£400	£900	£350
1711	£400	£900	£300
1713	£400	£900	£350
1714	£400	£1000	£375

GEORGE I (1714–27)

	F	VF	EF
1717	£400	£1100	£400
1720	£450	£1200	£450
*1726	£400	£1100	£400

	F	VF	EF

GEORGE II (1727–60)

	F	VF	EF
1734 Young head	£750	£2000	—
1735 —	£350	£750	£2500
*1738 —	£275	£600	£1600
1739 —	£275	£700	£1750
1739 Intermediate head	£275	£600	£1500
1740 —	£275	£625	£1750
1748 Old head	£300	£700	£2000
1753 —	£450	£1250	—

GEORGE III (1760–1820)

	F	VF	EF
1768 Patterns only	—	—	£12000
1773 Patterns only	—	—	£12000
1777 Patterns only	—	—	£12000

GUINEAS

CHARLES II (1660–85)

	F	VF	EF
1663 First bust	£550	£1600	—
1663 — Elephant below	£500	£1600	—
1664 Second bust	£400	£1200	—
1664 — Elephant		Extremely rare	
1664 Third bust	£250	£800	£3250
1664 — Elephant	£300	£950	£3950
1665 —	£250	£700	£3250
1665 — Elephant	£325	£950	£4000
1666 —	£250	£800	£3250
1667 —	£250	£800	£3250
1668 —	£250	£775	£3250
1668 — Elephant		Extremely rare	
1669 —	£325	£1050	—
*1670 —	£250	£700	£3250
1671 —	£250	£700	£3250
1672 —	£325	£1100	—
1672 Fourth bust	£200	£600	£3000
1673 Third bust	£400	£1400	—
1673 Fourth bust	£250	£700	£3000
1674 —	£250	£1100	—
1674 — Elephant & Castle	£2500	—	—
1675 —	£250	£700	£3250
*1675 — Elephant & Castle	£325	£1200	—
1676 —	£200	£600	£2750
1676 — Elephant & Castle	£300	£950	£3000
1677 —	£180	£600	£2750
1677 — Elephant		Extremely rare	
1677 — Elephant & Castle	£300	£950	£3250
1678 —	£180	£600	£2750
1678 — Elephant	£2500	—	—
1678 — Elephant & Castle	£400	£1300	—
1679 —	£175	£500	£2750

	F	VF	EF
1679 — Elephant & Castle	£325	£1200	—
1680 —	£175	£575	£2750
1680 — Elephant & Castle	£500	£1300	—
1681 —	£250	£700	£3000
1681 — Elephant & Castle	£300	£1100	—
1682 —	£250	£700	£3000
1682 — Elephant & Castle	£300	£1100	£2750
1683 —	£200	£600	£2750
1683 — Elephant & Castle	£450	£1300	£3000
1684 —	£250	£700	£3300
1684 — Elephant & Castle	£300	£800	£3000

JAMES II (1685–1688)

	F	VF	EF
1685 First bust	£225	£500	£2500
*1685 — Elephant & Castle	£250	£600	£2750
1686 —	£275	£600	£3000
1686 — Elephant & Castle		Extremely rare	
1686 Second bust	£225	£550	£2500
1686 — Elephant & Castle	£300	£800	£3000
1687 —	£225	£550	£2500
1687 —Elephant & Castle	£250	£600	£2500
*1688 —	£225	£550	£2500
1688 — Elephant & Castle	£250	£600	£2500

WILLIAM AND MARY (1688–94)

	F	VF	EF
1689	£225	£600	£2500
1689 Elephant & Castle	£250	£600	£2500
1690	£300	£650	£2500
1690 Elephant & Castle	£450	£850	£3250
1691	£325	£700	£2750
1691 Elephant & Castle	£325	£700	£2750
1692	£325	£700	£2750
1692 Elephant	£450	£1000	£3500
1692 Elephant & Castle	£350	£750	£2750
1693	£325	£700	£2750
1693 Elephant		Extremely rare	
1693 Elephant & Castle		Extremely rare	
1694	£275	£600	£2500
1694 Elephant & Castle	£350	£750	£2750

WILLIAM III (1694–1702)

	F	VF	EF
1695 First bust	£180	£450	£2000
1695 — Elephant & Castle	£350	£650	£2500
1696 —	£200	£450	£2000
1696 — Elephant & Castle		Extremely rare	
1697 —	£200	£450	£2000
1697 Second bust	£200	£450	£2000
1697 — Elephant & Castle	£650	£1500	—
1698 —	£200	£450	£2000
1698 — Elephant & Castle	£350	£650	£2500
1699 —	£300	£600	£2250
1699 — Elephant & Castle		Extremely rare	
1700 —	£200	£450	£2000
1700 — Elephant & Castle	£650	£1500	—
1701 —	£200	£450	£2000
1701 — Elephant & Castle		Extremely rare	
1701 Third bust "fine work"	£400	£1000	£2500

	F	VF	EF

ANNE (1702–1714)

	F	VF	EF
1702 (Pre-Union) First bust	£275	£750	£2750
1703 — VIGO below	£4000	£8000	—
1705 —	£275	£750	£2750
1706 —	£275	£750	£2750
1707 —	£275	£750	£2750
1707 — (Post-Union)	£175	£500	£2000
1707 — Elephant & Castle	£850	£1500	—
1707 Second bust	£650	—	.
1708 First bust		Extremely rare	
1708 Second bust	£175	£400	£1650
1708 — Elephant & Castle	£700	£1250	£3250
1709 —	£175	£425	£1750
1709 — Elephant & Castle	£700	£1250	£3250
1710 Third bust	£160	£350	£1600
1711 —	£160	£350	£1600
1712 —	£160	£350	£1600
*1713 —	£160	£325	£1500
1714 —	£160	£325	£1500

GEORGE I (1714–27)

	F	VF	EF
1714 First bust (Prince Elector)	£600	£1000	£3000
1715 Second bust	£180	£350	£1650
1715 Third bust	£180	£350	£1650
1716 —	£180	£350	£1650
1716 Fourth bust	£180	£350	£1650
1717 —	£180	£350	£1650
1718 —		Extremely rare	
1719 —	£180	£350	£1650
1720 —	£180	£350	£1650
1721 —	£180	£350	£1650
1721 — Elephant & Castle		Extremely rare	
1722 —	£180	£350	£1650
1722 — Elephant & Castle		Extremely rare	
1723 —	£180	£350	£1850
1723 Fifth bust	£180	£350	£1850
1724 —	£180	£350	£1850
1725 —	£180	£350	£1850
1726 —	£180	£350	£1650
1726 — Elephant & Castle	£600	£1500	—
1727 —	£250	£500	£2000

GEORGE II (1727–60)

	F	VF	EF
1727 First young head, early large shield	£500	£900	£2500
1727 — Larger lettering, early small shield	£350	£700	£2000
1728 — —	£350	£550	£2000
1729 — 2nd Young Head E.I.C. below	£300	£600	£2250
1730 —	£200	£450	£2000
1731 —	£180	£375	£2000
1731 — E.I.C below	£300	£450	£2500
1732 —	£180	£375	£2000
1732 — E.I.C	£250	£450	£2250
1732 — Larger lettering obverse	£225	£300	£1600
1732 — E.I.C	£300	£900	£2500
1733 — —	£180	£350	£1750
1734 — —	£180	£350	£1750
1735 — —	£180	£350	£1750
1736 — —	£180	£350	£1750
1737 — —	£180	£350	£1750

	F	VF	EF
1738 — —	£180	£350	£1500
1739 Intermediate head	£180	£375	£1500
1739 — E.I.C	£200	£450	£2250
1740 —	£180	£325	£1500
1741/39 —		Extremely rare	
1743 —		Extremely rare	
1745 — (GEORGIUS) Larger lettering obv.	£220	£400	£2000
1745 — LIMA	£400	£1250	£3250
1746 — (GEORGIVS) Larger lettering obv.	£180	£325	£1500
1747 Old head, large lettering	£180	£325	£1250
1748 —	£180	£325	£1250
1749 —	£180	£325	£1250
1750 —	£180	£325	£1250
1751 — small lettering	£180	£325	£1250
1753 —	£180	£325	£1250
1755 —	£180	£325	£1250
1756 —	£180	£325	£1250
1758 —	£180	£325	£1250
1759 —	£180	£325	£1250
1760 —	£180	£325	£1250

GEORGE III (1760–1820)

1761 First head	£350	£850	£2400
1763 Second head	£300	£750	£2000
1764 —	£200	£500	£1500
1765 Third head	£150	£350	£850
1766 —	£130	£300	£750
1767 —	£175	£400	£900
1768 —	£130	£300	£750
1769 —	£130	£300	£750
1770 —	£175	£400	£900
*1771 —	£130	£300	£750
1772 —	£130	£300	£750
1773 —	£130	£250	£650
1774 Fourth head	£90	£160	£400
1775 —	£90	£160	£400
1776 —	£90	£160	£400
1777 —	£90	£160	£400
1778 —	£90	£175	£500
1779 —	£90	£160	£400
1781 —	£90	£160	£400
1782 —	£90	£160	£400
1783 —	£75	£160	£400
1784 —	£90	£160	£400
1785 —	£90	£160	£400
1786 —	£90	£160	£400
1787 Fifth head "Spade" rev	£80	£125	£200
1788 —	£80	£125	£250
1789 —	£80	£125	£250
1790 —	£80	£125	£250
1791 —	£80	£125	£250
1792 —	£80	£125	£250
1793 —	£80	£125	£250
1794 —	£80	£125	£250
1795 —	£100	£175	£350
1796 —	£120	£200	£500
1797 —	£85	£130	£260
*1798 —	£80	£120	£230
1799 —	£90	£175	£400
*1813 Sixth head, "Military" rev	£150	£400	£850

(*Beware of Counterfiets)

HALF GUINEAS

	F	VF	EF

CHARLES II (1660–85)

	F	VF	EF
1669 First bust	£250	£500	£2500
*1670 —	£160	£450	£2000
1671 —	£350	£900	—
1672 —	£350	£900	—
1672 Second bust	£160	£450	£2000
1673 —	£400	£1100	—
1674 —	£400	£1100	—
1675 —		Extremely rare	
1676 —	£160	£400	—
1676 — Elephant & Castle		Extremely rare	
1677 —	£180	£425	£1750
1677 — Elephant & Castle	£400	£1100	—
1678 —	£180	£500	£2000
1678 — Elephant & Castle	£350	£900	—
1679 —	£160	£400	£1750
1680 —	£400	£1100	—
1680 — Elephant & Castle		Extremely rare	
1681 —	£400	£1100	—
1682 —	£250	£575	£2000
1682 — Elephant & Castle	£450	£1350	—
1683 — —		Extremely rare	
1684 —	£160	£325	£1750
1684 — Elephant & Castle	£350	£700	£2750

JAMES II (1685–88)

	F	VF	EF
1686	£240	£500	£2500
1686 Elephant & Castle	£450	£1250	£4000
1687	£325	£600	£2750
1688	£250	£500	£2500

WILLIAM AND MARY (1688–94)

	F	VF	EF
1689 First busts	£300	£575	£2000
1690 Second busts	£350	£600	£2000
1691 —	£400	£700	£2000
1691 — Elephant & Castle	£300	£575	£2000
1692 —	£325	£600	£2250
*1692 — Elephant		Extremely rare	
1692 — Elephant & Castle	£300	£575	£2000
1693 —		Extremely rare	
1694 —	£250	£550	£1850

WILLIAM III (1694–1702)

	F	VF	EF
1695	£125	£350	£1500
1695 Elephant & Castle	£400	£800	£2250
1696 —	£200	£500	£2000
1697 Larger Harp rev.	£250	£600	£2000
1698	£125	£400	£1500
1698 Elephant & Castle	£350	£700	£2250
*1699		Extremely rare	
1700	£125	£400	£1800
1701	£125	£400	£1800

	F	VF	EF

ANNE (1702–14)

	F	VF	EF
1702 (Pre-Union)	£250	£600	£2500
1703 VIGO below bust	£2000	£4000	—
1705	£250	£600	£2500
1707 (Post-Union)	£150	£350	£1250
1708	£150	£350	£1500
1709	£130	£300	£1250
1710	£130	£250	£1000
*1711	£130	£250	£1150
1712	£130	£300	£1250
1713	£130	£250	£1000
1714	£130	£250	£1000

GEORGE I (1714–27)

	F	VF	EF
1715 First bust	£130	£275	£1100
*1718 —	£130	£250	£1000
1719 —	£130	£250	£1000
1720 —	£250	£600	—
1721 —		Extremely rare	
1721 — Elephant & Castle		Extremely rare	
1722 —	£130	£275	£1350
1723 —		Extremely rare	
1724 —	£250	£500	£1850
1725 Second bust	£130	£250	£1000
1726 —	£130	£250	£1000
1727 —	£160	£350	£1000

GEORGE II (1727–60)

	F	VF	EF
1728 Young head	£175	£350	£1500
1729 —	£175	£350	£1500
1729 — E.I.C.	£250	£600	—
1730 —		Extremely rare	
1730 — E.I.C.	£325	£850	—
1731 —	£200	£400	£1750
1731 — E.I.C.		Extremely rare	
1732 —	£150	£350	£1500
1732 — E.I.C.		Extremely rare	
1733 —		Extremely rare	
1734 —	£150	£350	£1500
1735 —		Extremely rare	
1736 —	£150	£350	£1500
*1737 —		Extremely rare	
1738 —	£130	£325	£1500
1739 —	£130	£325	£1500
1739 — E.I.C.		Extremely rare	
1740 Intermediate head	£175	£400	£1500
1743 —		Extremely rare	
1745 —	£175	£350	£1500
1745 — LIMA	£600	£1500	—
1746 —	£130	£300	£1250
1747 Old head	£150	£350	£1250
1748 —	£130	£300	£1000
1749 —		Extremely rare	
*1750 —	£150	£300	£1000
1751 —	£130	£250	£1000
1752 —	£130	£350	£1000
1753 —	£130	£250	£850
1755 —	£130	£250	£850

	F	VF	EF
1756 —	£130	£250	£850
1758 —	£130	£250	£850
1759 —	£110	£200	£850
1760 —	£110	£200	£850

GEORGE III (1760–1820)

	F	VF	EF
1762 First head	£200	£400	£1100
1763 —	£275	£550	£1500
1764 Second head	£150	£275	£500
1765 —	£225	£450	£1250
1766 —	£175	£300	£750
1768 —	£175	£300	£750
*1769 —	£150	£275	£600
1772 —		Extremely rare	
1773 —	£175	£300	£750
1774 —	£250	£500	£1500
1774 Third head		Extremely rare	
1775 —	£250	£500	£1500
1775 Fourth head	£75	£135	£300
1776 —	£75	£135	£300
1777 —	£75	£135	£300
1778 —	£90	£150	£350
1779 —	£100	£175	£400
1781 —	£90	£150	£350
1783 —	£300	£750	—
1784 —	£75	£135	£300
1785 —	£70	£155	£300
1786 —	£70	£155	£300
1787 Fifth head, "Spade" rev.	£55	£100	£200
1788 —	£55	£100	£200
1789 —	£55	£100	£200
1790 —	£55	£100	£200
1791 —	£55	£100	£200
1792 —		Extremely Rare	
1793 —	£55	£100	£200
1794 —	£55	£100	£200
1795 —	£75	£125	£300
1796 —	£55	£100	£200
1797 —	£55	£100	£200
1798 —	£55	£100	£200
1800 —	£125	£275	£750
1801 Sixth head, Shield in Garter rev.	£50	£90	£175
1802 —	£50	£90	£175
1803 —	£50	£90	£175
1804 Seventh head	£50	£90	£175
1805		Extremely Rare	
1806 —	£50	£90	£175
1808 —	£50	£90	£175
1899 —	£50	£90	£175
1810 —	£50	£90	£175
1811 —	£75	£110	£275
1813 —	£60	£115	£260

THIRD GUINEAS

GEORGE III (1760–1820)

DATE	F	VF	EF
*1797 First head, date in legend	£35	£65	£140
1798 — —	£35	£65	£140
1799 — —	£50	£90	£210
1800 — —	£35	£65	£140
1801 Date under crown	£35	£65	£140
1802 —	£35	£65	£140
1803 —	£35	£65	£140
1804 Second head	£35	£65	£150
1806 —	£35	£65	£150
1808 —	£35	£65	£150
1809 —	£35	£65	£150
*1810 —	£35	£65	£150
1811 —	£100	£300	£700
1813 —	£45	£90	£180

QUARTER GUINEAS

GEORGE I (1714–27)

	F	VF	EF
1718	£55	£110	£225

GEORGE III (1760–1820)

	F	VF	EF
*1762	£45	£100	£225

FIVE POUNDS

DATE	Mintage	F	VF	EF	UNC
GEORGE III (1760–1820)					
1820 (pattern only)	—			Extremely rare	
GEORGE IV (1820–30)					
*1826 proof only	—	—	—	£6,000	£10,000
VICTORIA (1837–1901)					
1839 Proof Only	—	—	—	£16,000	£20,000
1887	53,844	£325	£450	£625	£800
1887 Proof	797	—	—	—	£2,000
1887 S on ground on rev. (Sydney Mint)				Excessively rare	
1893	20,405	£400	£550	£800	£1,200
1893 Proof	773	—	—	—	£2,500
EDWARD VII (1902–10)					
1902	34,910	—	£375	£500	£700
1902 Matt proof	8,066	—	—	—	£700

DATE	MINTAGE	F	VF	EF	UNC

GEORGE V (1911–36)

1911 Proof only	2,812	—	—	—	£1,400

GEORGE VI (1937–52)

*1937 Proof only	5,501	—	—	—	£700

Later issues are listed in the Decimal section.

TWO POUNDS

GEORGE III (1760–1820)

1820 (pattern only)	—		—	—	Extremely rare

GEORGE IV (1820–30)

1823 St George reverse	—	£200	£375	£700	£1500
1826 Proof only, shield reverse	—	—	—	£2750	£4000

WILLIAM IV (1830–37)

1831 Proof only	225	—	—	£2800	£5000

VICTORIA (1837–1901)

1887	91,345	£150	£210	£290	£425
1887 Proof	797	—	—	—	£850
1887 S on ground of rev. (Sydney Mint)				Excessively rare	
1893	52,212	£220	£320	£475	£625
1893 Proof	773	—	—	—	£1000

EDWARD VII (1902–10)

1902	45,807	£140	£170	£260	£325
1902 Matt proof	8,066	—	—	—	£350

GEORGE V (1911–36)

1911 Proof only	2,812	—	—	—	£650

GEORGE VI (1937–52)

*1937 Proof only	5,501	—	—	—	£360

Later issues are listed in the Decimal section.

SOVEREIGNS

DATE	MINTAGE	F	VF	EF	UNC

GEORGE III (1760–1820)

DATE	MINTAGE	F	VF	EF	UNC
1817	3,235,239	£80	£165	£400	£650
1818	2,347,230	£80	£165	£400	£650
1819	3,574		Exceedingly rare		
1820	931,994	£80	£165	£450	£700

GEORGE IV (1820–30)

DATE	MINTAGE	F	VF	EF	UNC
1821 First bust, St George reverse	9,405,114	£80	£150	£450	£850
1821 — Proof	incl. above	—	—	£1500	£2500
1822 —	5,356,787	£85	£150	£450	£850
1823 —	616,770	£125	£325	£1200	—
1824 —	3,767,904	£85	£150	£450	£850
1825 —	4,200,343	£150	£400	£1200	—
1825 Second bust, shield reverse	incl. above	£85	£130	£400	£750
1826 —	5,724,046	£85	£130	£400	£750
*1826 — Proof	—	—	—	£1500	£2500
1827 —	2,266,629	£85	£130	£400	£750
1828 —	386,182	£500	£1250	£2500	—
1829 —	2,444,652	£85	£130	£400	£750
1830 —	2,387,881	£85	£130	£400	£750

WILLIAM IV (1830–37)

DATE	MINTAGE	F	VF	EF	UNC
1831	598,547	£85	£150	£450	£900
*1831 Proof	—	—	—	£1750	£2750
1832	3,737,065	£85	£135	£450	£850
1833	1,225,269	£85	£135	£450	£800
1835	723,441	£90	£150	£450	£850
1836	1,714,349	£85	£150	£450	£850
1837	1,172,984	£85	£135	£450	£800

VICTORIA (1837–1901)

Many of the gold coins struck at the colonial mints found their way into circulation in Britain, for the sake of completeness these coins are listed here. These can easily be identified by a tiny initial letter for the appropriate mint which can be found below the base of the reverse shield or, in the case of the St George reverse, below the bust on the obverse of the Young Head issues, or on the "ground" below the horse's hoof on the later issues.

YOUNG HEAD ISSUES

Shield reverse
(Note—Shield back sovereigns in Fine/VF condition, common dates, are normally traded as bullion + a percentage)

DATE	MINTAGE	F	VF	EF	UNC
1838	2,718,694	—	£85	£200	£500
1839	503,695	—	£350	£850	£2000
*1839 Proof	—	—	—	—	£2000
1841	124,054	£550	£1100	£2000	—
1842	4,865,375	—	£70	£125	£225
1843	5,981,968	—	£70	£125	£225
1843 "Narrow shield" variety	incl. above	£275	£600	£1500	—
1844	3,000,445	—	£70	£125	£225
1845	3,800,845	—	£70	£125	£225
1846	3,802,947	—	£70	£125	£250

DATE	MINTAGE	F	VF	EF	UNC
1847	4,667,126	—	£70	£125	£225
1848	2,246,701	—	£70	£150	£300
1849	1,755,399	—	£70	£150	£300
1850	1,402,039	—	£70	£125	£250
1851	4,013,624	—	£70	£125	£225
1852	8,053,435	—	£70	£125	£225
1853	10,597,993	—	£70	£125	£225
1853 Proof	—	—	—	—	£3500
1854	3,589,611	—	£70	£125	£225
1855	8,448,482	—	£70	£125	£225
1856	4,806,160	—	£70	£125	£225
1857	4,495,748	—	£70	£125	£225
1858	803,234	—	£80	£175	£450
1859	1,547,603	—	£70	£135	£300
1859 "Ansell" (additional line on lower part of hair ribbon)	—	£160	£320	£1200	—
1860	2,555,958	—	£70	£200	£500
1861	7,624,736	—	£70	£125	£225
1862	7,836,413	—	£70	£125	£225
1863	5,921,669	—	£70	£125	£225
1863 with Die number	incl. above	—	£70	£100	£200
1864 —	8,656,352	—	£70	£100	£200
1865 —	1,450,238	—	£70	£100	£200
1866 —	4,047,288	—	£70	£100	£200
1868 —	1,653,384	—	£70	£100	£200
1869 —	6,441,322	—	£70	£100	£200
1870 —	2,189,960	—	£70	£100	£200
1871 —	8,767,250	—	£70	£100	£200
1872 —	8,767,250	—	£70	£100	£200
1872 no Die number	incl. above	—	£70	£125	£225
1873 with Die number	2,368,215	—	£70	£125	£225
1874 —	520,713	£750	—	—	—

M below (Melbourne Mint)

1872	748,180	—	£80	£180	£350
1873	—		Extremely rare		
1874	1,373,298	—	£80	£160	£325
1879			Extremely rare		
1880	3,053,454	£300	£800	£3000	—
1881	2,325,303	£80	£140	£400	£900
1882	2,465,781	—	£80	£180	£350
1883	2,050,450	£100	£200	£600	—
1884	2,942,630	—	£80	£160	£325
1885	2,967,143	—	£80	£160	£325
1886	2,902,131	£500	£1300	£3000	—
1887	1,916,424	£325	£750	£2000	£3000

S below (Sydney Mint)

1871	2,814,000	—	£70	£140	—
1872	1,815,000	—	£70	£140	—
1873	1,478,000	—	£70	£140	—
1875	2,122,000	—	£70	£140	—
1877	1,590,000	—	£70	£140	—
1878	1,259,000	—	£75	£150	—
1879	1,366,000	—	£70	£140	—
1880	1,459,000	—	£70	£140	—
1881	1,360,000	—	£75	£180	—
1882	1,298,000	—	£70	£140	—
1883	1,108,000	—	£75	£180	—
1884	1,595,000	—	£70	£140	—
1885	1,486,000	—	£70	£140	—
1886	1,667,000	—	£70	£140	—
1887	1,000,000	—	£80	£180	£350

DATE	MINTAGE	F	VF	EF	UNC
St George & Dragon reverse					
1871	incl. above	—	£65	£80	£150
1872	incl. above	—	£65	£80	£150
1873	incl. above	—	£65	£80	£150
1874	incl. above	—	£65	£75	£150
1876	3,318,866	—	£65	£75	£150
1878	1,091,275	—	£65	£80	£200
1879	20,013	£100	£300	£750	—
1880	3,650,080	—	£65	£75	£150
1884	2,942,630	—	£65	£75	£150
1885	2,967,143	—	£65	£75	£150
M below (Melbourne Mint)					
1872	incl. above	—	£65	£100	£160
1873	752,199	—	£65	£100	£150
1874	incl. above	—	£65	£100	£150
1875	incl. above	—	£65	£100	£150
1876	2,124,445	—	£65	£100	£160
1877	1,487,316	—	£65	£100	£150
1878	2,171,457	—	£65	£100	£150
1879	2,740,594	—	£65	£100	£150
1880	incl. above	—	£65	£100	£150
1881	incl. above	—	£65	£100	£150
1882	incl. above	—	£65	£100	£150
1883	incl. above	—	£65	£100	£150
1884	incl. above	—	£65	£100	£150
1885	incl. above	—	£65	£100	£150
1886	incl. above	—	£65	£100	£150
1887	incl. above	—	£65	£100	£150
S below (Sydney Mint)					
1871	incl. above	—	£80	£110	£175
1872	incl. above	—	£65	£110	£175
1873	incl. above	—	£65	£110	£175
1874	1,899,000	—	£65	£100	£150
1875	inc above	—	£65	£100	£150
1876	1,613,000	—	£65	£100	£150
1877	—		Extremely rare		
1879	incl. above	—	£65	£100	£150
1880	incl. above	—	£65	£100	£150
1881	incl. above	—	£65	£100	£150
1882	incl. above	—	£65	£100	£150
1883	incl. above	—	£65	£100	£150
1884	incl. above	—	£65	£100	£150
1885	incl. above	—	£65	£100	£150
1886	incl. above	—	£65	£100	£150
1887	incl. above	—	£65	£100	£150
JUBILEE HEAD ISSUES					
*1887	1,111,280	—	—	£70	£80
1887 Proof	797	—	—	—	£700
1888	2,717,424	—	—	£65	£80
1889	7,257,455	—	—	£65	£80
1890	6,529.887	—	—	£65	£80
1891	6,329,476	—	—	£65	£80
1892	7,104,720	—	—	£65	£80
M below (Melbourne Mint)					
1887	940,000	£70	£100	£200	—
1888	2,830,612	£60	£70	£110	—
1889	2,732,590	£60	£70	£110	—
1890	2,473,537	£60	£70	£110	—
1891	2,749,592	£60	£70	£110	—
1892	3,488,750	£60	£70	£110	—
1893	1,649,352	£60	£70	£110	—

DATE	MINTAGE	F	VF	EF	UNC
S below (Sydney Mint)					
1887	1,002,000	£60	£100	£110	£150
1888	2,187,000	—	£75	£100	—
1889	3,262,000	—	£75	£100	—
1890	2,808,000	—	£75	£100	
1891	2,596,000	—	£75	£100	—
1892	2,837,000	—	£75	£100	—
1893	1,498,000	—	£75	£100	—
OLD HEAD ISSUES					
*1893	6,898,260	—	—	£65	£80
1893 Proof	773	—	—	—	£650
1894	3,782,611	—	—	£65	£80
1895	2,285,317	—	—	£65	£80
1896	3,334,065	—	—	£65	£80
1898	4,361,347	—	—	£65	£80
1899	7,515,978	—	—	£65	£80
1900	10,846,741	—	—	£65	£80
1901	1,578,948	—	—	£65	£80
M below (Melbourne Mint)					
1893	1,914,000	—	—	£100	—
1894	4,166,874	—	—	£100	—
1895	4,165,869	—	—	£100	—
1896	4,456,932	—	—	£100	—
1897	5,130,565	—	—	£100	—
1898	5,509,138	—	—	£100	—
1899	5,579,157	—	—	£100	—
1900	4,305,904	—	—	£100	—
1901	3,987,701	—	—	£100	—
P below (Perth Mint)					
1899	690,992	£60	£80	£130	—
1900	1,886,089	—	—	£100	£150
1901	2,889,333	—	—	£100	£150
S below (Sydney Mint)					
1893	1,346,000	—	—	£80	£110
1894	3,067,000	—	—	£80	£110
1895	2,758,000	—	—	£80	£110
1896	2,544,000	—	—	£100	£150
1897	2,532,000	—	—	£80	£110
1898	2,548,000	—	—	£80	£110
1899	3,259,000	—	—	£80	£110
1900	3,586,000	—	—	£80	£110
1901	3,012,000	—	—	£80	£110

EDWARD VII (1902–10)

DATE	MINTAGE	F	VF	EF	UNC
*1902	4,737,796	—	—	—	£75
1902 Matt proof	15,123	—	—	—	£150
1903	8,888,627	—	—	—	£75
1904	10,041,369	—	—	—	£75
1905	5,910,403	—	—	—	£75
1906	10,466,981	—	—	—	£75
1907	18,458,663	—	—	—	£75
1908	11,729,006	—	—	—	£75
1909	12,157,099	—	—	—	£75
1910	22,379,624	—	—	—	£75
C below (Ottawa Mint)					
1908 Satin finish Proof only	636		Extremely rare		
1909	16,273	£75	£100	£250	—
1910	28,012	£75	£100	£250	—

DATE	MINTAGE	F	VF	EF	UNC
M below (Melbourne Mint)					
1902	4,267,157	—	—	£90	£130
1903	3,521,780	—	—	£90	£130
1904	3,743,897	—	—	£90	£130
1905	3,633,838	—	—	£90	£130
1906	3,657,853	—	—	£90	£130
1907	3,332,691	—	—	£90	£130
1908	3,080,148	—	—	£90	£130
1909	3,029,538	—	—	£90	£130
1910	3,054,547	—	—	£90	£130
P below (Perth Mint)					
1902	3,289,122	—	—	£90	£130
1903	4,674,783	—	—	£90	£130
1904	4,506,756	—	—	£90	£130
1905	4,876,193	—	—	£90	£130
1906	4,829,817	—	—	£90	£130
1907	4,972,289	—	—	£90	£130
1908	4,875,617	—	—	£90	£130
1909	4,524,241	—	—	£90	£130
1910	4,690,625	—	—	£90	£130
S below (Sydney Mint)					
1902	2,813,000	—	—	£90	£130
1902 Proof	incl. above		Extremely rare		
1903	2,806,000	—	—	£90	£130
1904	2,986,000	—	—	£90	£130
1905	2,778,000	—	—	£90	£130
1906	2,792,000	—	—	£90	£130
1907	2,539,000	—	—	£90	£130
1908	2,017,000	—	—	£90	£130
1909	2,057,000	—	—	£90	£130
1910	2,135,000	—	—	£90	£130

GEORGE V (1911–36)

(Extra care should be exercised when purchasing as good quality forgeries exist of virtually all dates and mintmarks)

DATE	MINTAGE	F	VF	EF	UNC
1911	30,044,105	—	—	—	£70
1911 Proof	3,764	—	—	—	£275
1912	30,317,921	—	—	—	£70
1913	24,539,672	—	—	—	£70
1914	11,501,117	—	—	—	£70
1915	20,295,280	—	—	—	£70
1916	1,554,120	—	—	—	£75
1917	1,014,714		Extremely rare		
1925	4,406,431	—	—	—	£70
C below (Ottawa Mint)					
1911	256,946	—	£70	£100	£150
1913	3,715	£100	£120	£500	—
1914	14,891	£100	£180	£300	—
1916	6,111		Extremely rare		
1917	58,845	—	£70	£110	—
1918	106,516	—	£70	£110	—
1919	135,889	—	£70	£110	—
I below (Bombay Mint)					
1918	1,295,372	—	—	£80	—
M below (Melbourne Mint)					
1911	2,851,451	—	—	£80	£110
1912	2,469,257	—	—	£80	£110
1913	2,323,180	—	—	£80	£110
1914	2,012,029	—	—	£80	£110
1915	1,637,839	—	—	£80	£110

DATE	MINTAGE	F	VF	EF	UNC
1916	1,273,643	—	—	£80	£110
1917	934,469	—	—	£80	£110
1918	4,969,493	—	—	£80	£110
1919	514,257	—	—	£90	£125
1920	530,266	£200	£600	£1000	—
1921	240,121	—	—	£4000	—
1922	608,306	£300	£800	£3000	—
1923	510,870	—	—	£100	£140
1924	278,140	—	—	£100	£140
1925	3,311,622	—	—	£90	£110
1926	211,107	—	—	£90	£110
1928	413,208	£200	£500	£600	—
1929	436,719	£100	£275	£800	—
1930	77,547	—	£80	£140	—
1931	57,779	£75	£120	£275	—

P below (Perth Mint)

DATE	MINTAGE	F	VF	EF	UNC
1911	4,373,165	—	—	£90	£110
1912	4,278,144	—	—	£90	£110
1913	4,635,287	—	—	£90	£110
1914	4,815,996	—	—	£90	£110
1915	4,373,596	—	—	£90	£110
1916	4,096,771	—	—	£90	£110
1917	4,110,286	—	—	£90	£110
1918	3,812,884	—	—	£90	£110
1919	2,995,216	—	—	£90	£110
1920	2,421,196	—	—	£90	£110
1921	2,134,360	—	—	£90	£110
1922	2,298,884	—	—	£90	£110
1923	2,124,154	—	—	£90	£110
1924	1,464,416	—	—	£90	£110
1925	1,837,901	—	—	£90	£120
1926	1,313,578	—	—	£90	£140
1927	1,383,544	—	—	£90	£140
1928	1,333,417	—	—	£100	£120
1929	1,606,625	—	—	£85	£100
1930	1,915,352	—	—	£85	£100
1931	1,173,568	—	—	£85	£100

S below (Sydney Mint)

DATE	MINTAGE	F	VF	EF	UNC
1911	2,519,000	—	—	£75	£100
1912	2,227,000	—	—	£75	£100
1913	2,249,000	—	—	£75	£100
1914	1,774,000	—	—	£75	£100
1915	1,346,000	—	—	£75	£100
1916	1,242,000	—	—	£75	£100
1917	1,666,000	—	—	£75	£100
1918	3,716,000	—	—	£75	£100
1919	1,835,000	—	—	£75	£100
1920	—		Excessively rare		
1921	839,000	—	£500	£1200	—
1922	578,000		Extremely rare		
1923	416,000		Extremely rare		
1924	394,000	—	£400	£800	—
1925	5,632,000	—	—	£90	£110
1926	1,031,050		Extremely rare		

SA below (Pretoria Mint)

DATE	MINTAGE	F	VF	EF	UNC
1923	719		Extremely rare		
1923 Proof	655	—	—	—	£760
1924	3,184		Extremely rare		
1925	6,086,264	—	£60	£80	£95
1926	11,107,611	—	£60	£80	£95
1927	16,379,704	—	£60	£80	£95
1928	18,235,057	—	£60	£80	£95

DATE	MINTAGE	F	VF	EF	UNC
1929	12,024,107	—	—	£80	£100
1930	10,027,756	—	—	£80	£100
1931	8,511,792	—	—	£80	£100
1932	1,066,680	—	—	£90	£130

GEORGE VI (1937–52)

*1937 Proof only	5,501	—	—	—	£300

ELIZABETH II (1952–   )

Pre Decimal Issues

1957	2,072,000	—	—	—	£65
1958	8,700,140	—	—	—	£60
1959	1,358,228	—	—	—	£65
1962	3,000,000	—	—	—	£60
1963	7,400,000	—	—	—	£60
1964	3,000,000	—	—	—	£60
1965	3,800,000	—	—	—	£60
1966	7,050,000	—	—	—	£60
1967	5,000,000	—	—	—	£60
1968	4,203,000	—	—	—	£60

Later issues are included in the Decimal section.

HALF SOVEREIGNS

GEORGE III (1760–1820)

1817	2,080,197	£50	£80	£150	£325
1818	1,030,286	£50	£80	£150	£325
1820	35,043	£50	£80	£150	£325

GEORGE IV (1820–30)

1821 First bust, ornate shield reverse	231,288	£150	£400	£1500	£2250
1821 — Proof	unrecorded	—	—	£2000	£3000
1823 First bust, Plain shield rev.	224,280	£70	£150	£400	£650
1824 —	591,538	£70	£150	£425	£650
1825 —	761,150	£70	£150	£425	£650
1826 bare head, shield with full legend reverse	344,830	£65	£125	£400	£600
1826 — Proof	unrecorded	—	—	£750	£1000
1827 —	492,014	£70	£150	£400	£650
1828 —	1,224,754	£65	£125	£400	£650

WILLIAM IV (1830–37)

1831 Proof only	uncrecorded	—	—	£750	£1250
1834	133,899	£75	£150	£450	£800
1835	772,554	£65	£125	£400	£750
1836	146,865	£75	£150	£450	£850
1836 obverse from 6d die	incl. above	£450	£1000	£2500	—
1837	160,207	£65	£125	£400	£750

VICTORIA (1837–1901)

YOUNG HEAD ISSUES
Shield reverse

1838	273,341	—	£60	£200	£450
1839 Proof only	1,230	—	—	—	£900
1841	508,835	—	£65	£250	£500
1842	2,223,352	—	£60	£150	£300
1843	1,251,762	—	£65	£250	£500
1844	1,127,007	—	£60	£150	£300
1845	887,526	£50	£150	£350	£525
1846	1,063,928	—	£60	£150	£325
1847	982,636	—	£60	£150	£325
1848	410,595	—	£60	£150	£325
1849	845,112	—	£60	£150	£325
1850	179,595	£50	£150	£375	£600
1851	773,573	—	£60	£150	£300
1852	1,377,671	—	£60	£165	£325
1853	2,708,796	—	£60	£150	£300
1853 Proof	unrecorded	—	—	—	£2750
1854	1,125,144		Extremely rare		
1855	1,120,362	—	£60	£150	£300
1856	2,391,909	—	£60	£150	£300
1857	728,223	—	£60	£165	£325
1858	855,578	—	£60	£150	£300
1859	2,203,813	—	£60	£150	£300
1860	1,131,500	—	£60	£150	£300
1861	1,130,867	—	£60	£150	£300
1862	unrecorded	£350	—	—	—
1863	1,571,574	—	£60	£150	£300
1863 with Die number	incl. above	—	£60	£150	£325
1864 —	1,758,490	—	£60	£150	£300
1865 —	1,834,750	—	£60	£150	£300
1866 —	2,058,776	—	£60	£150	£300
1867 —	992,795	—	£60	£150	£300
1869 —	1,861,764	—	£60	£150	£300
1870 —	1,159,544	—	£55	£125	£225
1871 —	2,062,970	—	£55	£125	£225
1872 —	3,248,627	—	£55	£125	£225
1873 —	1,927,050	—	£55	£125	£225
1874 —	1,884,432	—	£55	£125	£225
1875 —	516,240	—	£55	£125	£225
1876 —	2,785,187	—	£55	£125	£225
1877 —	2,197,482	—	£55	£110	£175
1878 —	2,081,941	—	£55	£110	£175
1879 —	35,201	—	£55	£110	£175
1880 —	1,009,049	—	£55	£110	£175
1880 no Die number	incl. above	—	£55	£125	£225
1883 —	2,870,457	—	£55	£110	£175
1884 —	1,113,756	—	£55	£110	£175
1885 —	4,468,871	—	£55	£110	£175
M below (Melbourne Mint)					
1873	165,034	£80	£150	£450	—
1877	80,016	£60	£100	£450	—
1881	42,009	£100	£200	£600	—
1882	107,522	£80	£150	£500	—
1884	48,009	£100	£200	£600	—
1885	11,003	£150	£350	£1500	—
1886	38,008	£90	£150	£650	—
1887	64,013	£140	£300	£1000	—
S below (Sydney Mint)					
1871	unrecorded	£60	£100	£400	—
1872	356,000	£70	£120	£400	—

Date	Mintage	F	VF	EF	UNC
1875	*unrecorded*	£70	£120	£400	—
1879	94,000	£70	£120	£400	—
1880	80,000	£70	£120	£400	—
1881	62,000	£100	£175	£700	—
1882	52,000	£150	£250	£1000	—
1883	220,000	£60	£100	£400	—
1886	82,000	£60	£100	£350	—
1887	134,000	£60	£100	£350	—

JUBILEE HEAD ISSUES

Date	Mintage	F	VF	EF	UNC
1887	871,770	—	—	£55	£75
1887 Proof ....,.............	797	—	—	—	£400
1890	2.266,023	—	—	£55	£90
1891	1,079,286	—	—	£55	£90
1892	13,680,486	—	—	£55	£85
1893	4,426,625	—	—	£60	£100

M below (Melbourne Mint)

Date	Mintage	F	VF	EF	UNC
1887	*incl. above*	£50	£90	£250	£450
1893	110,024	£60	£100	£325	—

S below (Sydney Mint)

Date	Mintage	F	VF	EF	UNC
1887	*incl. above*	£50	£80	£200	£375
1889	64,000	£60	£100	£300	—
1891	154,000	£60	£100	£325	—

OLD HEAD ISSUES

Date	Mintage	F	VF	EF	UNC
1893	*incl. above*	—	—	£50	£60
1893 Proof	773	—	—	—	£500
1894	3,794,591	—	—	£50	£75
1895	2,869,183	—	—	£50	£75
1896	2,946,605	—	—	£50	£75
1897	3,568,156	—	—	£50	£75
1898	2,868,527	—	—	£50	£75
1899	3,361,881	—	—	£50	£75
1900	4,307,372	—	—	£50	£75
1901	2,037,664	—	—	£50	£75

M below (Melbourne Mint)

Date	Mintage	F	VF	EF	UNC
1893	*unrecorded*		Extremely rare		
1896—	218,946	£45	£90	£300	—
1899—	97,221	£50	£90	£300	—
1900—	112,920	£50	£90	£300	—

P below (Perth Mint)

Date	Mintage	F	VF	EF	UNC
1899 "P"			Extremely rare		
1900	119,376	£60	£100	£450	—

S below (Sydney Mint)

Date	Mintage	F	VF	EF	UNC
1893	250,000	£50	£90	£300	—
1897—	*unrecorded*	£50	£90	£300	—
1900—	260,00	£50	£90	£300	—

EDWARD VII (1902–10)

Date	Mintage	F	VF	EF	UNC
1902	4,244,457	—	—	£45	£55
1902 Matt proof	15,123	—	—	—	£100
1903	2,522,057	—	—	£45	£55
1904	1,717,440	—	—	£45	£55
1905	3,023,993	—	—	£45	£55
1906	4,245,437	—	—	£45	£55
1907	4,233,421	—	—	£45	£55
1908	3,996,992	—	—	£45	£55
1909	4,010,715	—	—	£45	£55
1910	5,023,881	—	—	£45	£55

DATE		F	VF	EF	UNC
M below (Melbourne Mint)					
1906	82,042	—	£50	£80	£175
1907	405,034	—	£50	£80	£175
1908	incl. above	—	£50	£80	£175
1909	186,094	—	£50	£80	£175
P below (Perth Mint)					
1904	60,030	£100	£175	£600	—
1908	24,668	£100	£175	£600	—
1909	44,022	£70	£140	£400	—
S below (Sydney Mint)					
1902	84,000	—	£55	£110	£200
1903	231,000	—	£55	£110	£180
1906	308,00	—	£55	£110	£180
1908	538,000	—	£55	£110	£160
1910	474,000	—	£55	£110	£160

GEORGE V (1911–36)

1911	6,104,106	—	—	£45	£55
1911 Proof	3,764	—	—	—	£175
1912	6,224,316	—	—	£45	£55
1913	6,094,290	—	—	£45	£55
1914	7,251,124	—	—	£45	£55
1915	2,042,747	—	—	£45	£55
M below (Melbourne Mint)					
1915	125,664	—	—	£90	£140
P below (Perth Mint)					
1911	130,373	—	—	£70	£100
1915	136,219	—	—	£70	£100
1918	unrecorded	£175	£350	£550	—
S below (Sydney Mint)					
1911	252,000	—	—	£70	£110
1912—	278,000	—	—	£70	£110
1914—	322,000	—	—	£70	£110
1915—	892,000	—	—	£70	£110
1916—	448,000	—	—	£70	£110
SA below (Pretoria Mint)					
1923 Proof only	655	—	—	—	£450
1925—	946,615	—	—	£60	£75
1926—	806,540	—	—	£60	£75

GEORGE VI (1937–52)

1937 Proof only	5,501	—	—	—	£160

Later issues are included in the Decimal section.

161

CROWNS

DATE	F	VF	EF	UNC

OLIVER CROMWELL

	F	VF	EF	UNC
1658 8 over 7 (always)	£550	£925	£1750	—
1658 Dutch Copy		Extremely rare		
1658 Patterns. In Various Metals		Extremely rare		

CHARLES II (1660–85)

	F	VF	EF	UNC
1662 First bust, rose (2 varieties)	£55	£220	£2000	—
1662 — no rose (2 varieties)	£55	£220	£2000	—
1663 —	£55	£220	£2000	—
1664 Second bust	£55	£300	£2500	—
1665 —	£150	£450	—	—
*1666 —	£70	£300	£2500	—
1666 — Elephant below bust	£175	£500	£3500	—
1667 —	£55	£220	£2000	—
1668 —	£55	£220	£2000	—
1669 —	£125	£300	£2250	—
1670 —	£55	£220	£1850	—
1671	£55	£220	£1850	—
1671 Third Bust	£55	£220	£1700	—
1672 —	£55	£220	£1700	—
1673 —	£55	£220	£1700	—
1674 —		Extremely rare		
1675 —	£175	—	—	—
1675/3	£160	£600	—	—
1676 —	£55	£220	£1650	—
1677 —	£55	£220	£1650	—
1678/7	£70	£300	—	—
1679 —	£55	£220	£1650	—
1679 Fourth bust	£55	£220	£1800	—
1680 Third bust	£55	£220	£1850	—
1680 Fourth bust	£55	£220	£1850	—
1681 —	£55	£220	£1850	—
1681 — Elephant & Castle below bust	£500	£1000	—	—
1682/1 —	£55	£275	£1850	—
1683 —	£60	£300	£1850	—
1684 —	£90	£450	—	—

JAMES II (1685–88)

	F	VF	EF	UNC
1686 First bust	£80	£275	£1250	—
1686 — No stops on obv	£100	£300	—	—
1687 Second bust	£70	£250	£800	—
*1688 —	£70	£250	£800	—

WILLIAM AND MARY (1688–94)

	F	VF	EF	UNC
1691	£150	£450	£1850	—
1692	£150	£425	£1800	—
1692 2 over upside down 2	£150	£425	£1800	—

WILLIAM III (1694–1702)

	F	VF	EF	UNC
1695 First bust	£45	£150	£475	—
1696 — GEI for DEI	£70	£220	—	—
1696 —	£40	£140	£475	—
1696 Second bust		Only one known		
1696 Third bust	£45	£150	£550	—
1697 —	£150	£650	£800	—
1700 Third bust variety edge year Duodecimo	£70	£175	£550	—
1700 — edge year Duodecimo Tertio	£70	£175	£550	—

DATE	F	VF	EF	UNC

ANNE (1702–14)

	F	VF	EF	UNC
1703 First bust, VIGO	£130	£350	£1200	—
1705 — Plumes in angles on rev.	£250	£600	£2000	—
1706 — Roses & Plumes in angles on rev .	£140	£325	£950	—
1707 — Roses & Plumes in angles on rev .	£140	£325	£950	—
1707 Second bust, E below	£70	£210	£700	—
1707 — Plain	£70	£210	£750	—
1708 — E below	£75	£225	£700	—
1708 — Plain	£70	£210	£750	—
1708 — Plumes in angles on rev.	£125	£350	£1100	—
*1713 Third bust, Roses & Plumes rev	£150	£400	£1100	—

GEORGE I (1714–27)

	F	VF	EF	UNC
1716	£175	£400	£1400	—
1718	£175	£400	£1550	—
1720	£175	£425	£1550	—
1723 SSC in angles on rev(South Sea Co.)	£175	£400	£1100	—
1726	£210	£475	£1800	—

GEORGE II (1727–60)

	F	VF	EF	UNC
1732 Young head, Plain Proof	—	—	£3000	
1732 — Roses & Plumes in angles on rev .	£150	£325	£800	—
1734 —	£150	£325	£800	—
1735 —	£150	£325	£800	—
1736 —	£165	£350	£900	—
1739 — Roses in angles on rev	£140	£300	£650	—
1741 —	£140	£300	£650	—
1743 Old head, Roses in angles on rev	£125	£300	£700	—
*1746 — LIMA below bust	£125	£300	£700	—
1746 — Plain Proof	—	—	£1750	—
1750 — Plain	£170	£350	£900	—
1751 —	£200	£400	£1000	—

GEORGE III (1760–1820)

	F	VF	EF	UNC
Dollar with oval counterstamp	£75	£160	£400	—
Dollar with octagonal counterstamp	£90	£175	£425	—
1804 Bank of England Dollar, Britannia rev.	£50	£100	£250	—
1818 LVIII	£16	£60	£200	£450
1818 LIX	£16	£60	£200	£450
1819 LIX	£16	£60	£200	£450
1819 LX	£16	£60	£200	£450
1820 LX	£16	£60	£200	£450
1820 LX 20 over 19	£20	£75	£250	—

GEORGE IV (1820–30)

	F	VF	EF	UNC
1821 First bust, St George rev. SECUNDO on edge	£18	£70	£250	£650
1821 — — Proof	—	—	—	£2000
1821 — — Proof TERTIO (error edge)	—	—	—	£3000
1822 — — SECUNDO	£18	£80	£350	£900
1822 — — TERTIO	£18	£70	£300	£750
1823 — — Proof only	Extremely rare			
1826 Second bust, shield rev, SEPTIMO Proof only	—	—	£1750	£2250

WILLIAM IV (1830–37)

	F	VF	EF	UNC
1831 Proof only W.W. on truncation	—	—	£2500	£4500
1831 Proof Only W. WYON on truncation	—	—	£3000	£5250
1834 Proof only	—	—	—	—

DATE	MINTAGE	F	VF	EF	UNC

VICTORIA (1837–1901)

YOUNG HEAD ISSUES

DATE	MINTAGE	F	VF	EF	UNC
1839 Proof Only	—	—	—	—	£2500
1844 (two edge varieties)	94,248	£25	£120	£500	£1800
1845	159,192	£25	£120	£500	£1800
1847	140,976	£30	£130	£550	£2000
1847 "Gothic" Proof only UNDECIMO edge	8,000	£225	£400	£625	£1100
1847 Plain edge, Proof only	—	—	—	£800	£1400
1853 D. SEPTIMO edge, Proof only	460	—	—	—	£5000
1853 Plain edge, Proof only	—	—	£2200	—	£5000

JUBILEE HEAD ISSUES

DATE	MINTAGE	F	VF	EF	UNC
*1887	173,581	£10	£18	£40	£60
1887 Proof	1,084	—	—	—	£300
1888	131,899	£10	£22	£50	£100
1889	1,807,224	£10	£18	£32	£65
1890	997,862	£10	£20	£45	£90
1891	556,394	£10	£20	£45	£90
1892	451,334	£10	£20	£50	£100

OLD HEAD ISSUES (Regnal date on edge in Roman numerals)

DATE	MINTAGE	F	VF	EF	UNC
1893 LVI	497,845	£12	£20	£65	£125
1893 LVII	incl. above	£14	£35	£150	£350
1893 Proof	1,312	—	—	—	£350
1894 LVII	144,906	£12	£25	£65	£135
1894 LVIII	incl. above	£12	£25	£65	£135
1895 LVIII	252,862	£12	£30	£75	£135
1895 LIX	incl. above	£12	£30	£75	£135
1896 LIX	317,599	£14	£30	£125	£300
1896 LX	incl. above	£12	£30	£75	£135
1897 LX	262,118	£12	£30	£75	£135
1897 LXI	incl. above	£12	£30	£75	£135
1898 LXI	166,150	£14	£35	£90	£200
1898 LXII	incl. above	£12	£30	£75	£150
1899 LXII	166,300	£12	£30	£75	£150
1899 LXIII	incl. above	£12	£30	£75	£150
1900 LXIII	353,356	£12	£30	£65	£135
1900 LXIV	incl. above	£12	£30	£65	£125

EDWARD VII (1901–10)

DATE	MINTAGE	F	VF	EF	UNC
1902	256,020	£20	£35	£80	£120
1902 "Matt Proof"	15,123	—	—	—	£110

GEORGE V (1910–36)

DATE	MINTAGE	F	VF	EF	UNC
1927 Proof only	15,030	—	£50	£80	£120
1928	9,034	£35	£60	£95	£140
1929	4,994	£40	£60	£100	£150
1930	4,847	£40	£60	£100	£160
1931	4,056	£40	£60	£100	£150
1932	2,395	£70	£125	£200	£320
1933	7,132	£35	£60	£100	£140
*1934	932	£300	£500	£1000	£1500
1935 Jubilee issue	714,769	£7	£10	£15	£22
1935 Specimen	—	—	—	—	£30
1935 Proof Raised Edge inscription	2,500	—	—	—	£200
1936	2,473	£60	£120	£200	£300

GEORGE VI (1936–52)

DATE	MINTAGE	F	VF	EF	UNC
1937 Coronation	418,699	£9	£12	£15	£25
1937 Proof	26,402	—	—	—	£30
1951 Festival of Britain, Proof-like	1,983,540	—	—	£2	£5

DATE	MINTAGE	F	VF	EF	UNC

ELIZABETH II (1952–   )

Pre-Decimal issues (Five Shillings)

1953	5,962,621	—	—	—	£6
1953 Proof	40,000	—	—	—	£15
1960	1,024,038	—	—	—	£6
1960 Polished dies	70,000	—	—	—	£7
1965	19,640,000	—	—	—	£1

Later issues are listed in the Decimal section.

DOUBLE FLORINS

VICTORIA (1837–1901)

1887 Roman I	483,347	£9	£16	£30	£50
1887 Roman I Proof	incl. above	—	—	—	£200
1887 Arabic 1	incl. above	£9	£16	£30	£50
1887 Arabic 1 Proof	incl. above	—	—	—	£175
1888	243,340	£10	£20	£40	£65
1888 Second I in VICTORIA an inverted 1	incl. above	£15	£30	£60	£140
1889	1,185,111	£10	£18	£30	£55
1889 inverted 1	incl. above	£15	£28	£60	£140
1890	782,146	£10	£25	£45	£95

Patterns were also produced in 1911, 1914 and 1950 and are all extremely rare.

HALFCROWNS

OLIVER CROMWELL

1656			Extremely rare	
1658	£280	£500	£900	—
1658 Proof in Gold			Extremely rare	

CHARLES II (1660–1685)

1663 First bust	£50	£300	£1250	—
1664 Second bust	£55	£350	£1750	—
1666 Third bust	£300	—	—	—
1666 — Elephant	£140	£450	£2500	—
1667/4 —			Extremely rare	
1668/4 —	£60	—	—	—
1669 —	£110	£400	—	—
1670 —	£40	£120	£850	—
1671 —	£40	£120	£850	—
1672 —	£40	£140	£850	—
1672 Fourth bust	£50	£175	£1000	—
1673 —	£40	£120	£850	—
1673 — Plumes both sides			Extremely rare	
1673 — Plume below bust	£800	—	—	—
1674 —	£60	£175	—	—
1675 —	£40	£140	£850	—
1676 —	£40	£120	£750	—
1677 —	£40	£120	£750	—
1678 —	£100	£300	—	—
1679 —	£40	£130	£750	—
1680 —	£100	£250	—	—
1681 —	£60	£149	£850	—
1681 — Elephant & Castle	£600	—	—	—
1682 —	£60	£180	£1350	—

DATE	MINTAGE	F	VF	EF	UNC
1683 —		£60	£160	£850	—
1683 — Plume below bust			Extremely rare		
1684/3 —		£100	£300	£1500	—

JAMES II (1685–1688)

		F	VF	EF	UNC
1685 First bust		£60	£175	£600	—
1686 —		£60	£175	£600	—
1687 —		£65	£175	£650	—
1687 Second bust		£60	£175	£700	—
1688 —		£60	£175	£700	—

WILLIAM AND MARY (1688–1694)

		F	VF	EF	UNC
1689 First busts; first shield		£50	£110	£400	—
1689 — second shield		£50	£110	£400	—
1690 — —		£50	£160	£550	—
1690 — — variety GRETIA for GRATIA		£110	£285	—	—
1691 Second busts		£65	£150	£450	—
1692 —		£65	£150	£450	—
1693 —		£65	£150	£400	—

WILLIAM III (1694–1702)

		F	VF	EF	UNC
1696 First bust, large shields, early harp		£25	£70	£230	—
1696 — — — B (Bristol) below bust		£28	£90	£325	—
1696 — — — C (Chester)		£30	£100	£400	—
1696 — — — E (Exeter)		£30	£100	£450	—
1696 — — — N (Norwich)		£50	£150	—	—
1696 — — — y (York)		£30	£110	£325	—
1696 — ordinary harp		£65	£175	—	—
1696 — — — C		£65	£175	—	—
1696 — — — E		£65	£175	—	—
1696 — — — N		£75	£275	—	—
1696 — Small shields, ordinary harp		£28	£100	£260	—
1696 — — — B		£30	£120	£450	—
1696 — — — C		£35	£150	£500	—
1696 — — — E		£50	£150	—	—
1696 — — — N		£30	£120	£450	—
1696 — — — y		£30	£120	£450	—
1696 Second bust			Only one known		
1697 First bust, large shields, ordinary harp		£28	£90	£225	
1697 — — — B		£30	£100	£325	
1697 — — — C		£30	£110	£350	
1697 — — — E		£30	£120	£325	—
1697 — — — N		£30	£120	£350	—
1697 — — — y		£30	£120	£325	—
1698 —		£30	£100	£240	
1699 —		£50	£150	£450	—
1700 —		£40	£110	£300	—
1701 —		£45	£120	£350	—
1701 — Elephant & Castle		£500	—	—	—
1701 — Plumes in angles on rev.		£60	£220	£575	—

ANNE (1702–1714)

		F	VF	EF	UNC
1703 Plain (pre-Union)		£110	£375	—	—
1703 VIGO below bust		£55	£120	£400	—
1704 Plumes in angles on rev.		£70	£140	£500	—
1705 —		£40	£140	£500	—
1706 Roses & Plumes in angles on rev.		£40	£110	£370	—
*1707 —		£35	£100	£350	—
1707 Plain (post-Union)		£30	£80	£250	—
1707 E below bust		£30	£80	£350	—
1708 Plain		£28	£75	£250	—
1708 E below bust		£28	£80	£350	—

DATE	MINTAGE	F	VF	EF	UNC
1708 Plumes in angles on rev.		£30	£90	£400	—
1709 Plain		£30	£80	£250	—
1709 E below bust		£65	£150	—	—
1710 Roses & Plumes in angles on rev.		£35	£90	£350	—
1712 —		£35	£90	£350	—
1713 Plain		£35	£90	£400	—
1713 Roses & Plumes in angles on rev.		£35	£90	£350	—
1714 —		£35	£90	£350	—

GEORGE I (1714–1727)

1715 Roses & Plumes in angles on rev.		£90	£275	£750	—
1717 —		£90	£275	£750	—
*1720 —		£90	£275	£750	—
1723 SSC in angles on rev.		£90	£275	£700	—
1726 Small Roses & Plumes in angles on rev..		£800	£1750	—	—

GEORGE II (1727–1760)

1731 Young head, Plain, proof only		—	—	£1850	—
1731 — Roses & Plumes in angles on rev.		£55	£125	£400	—
1732 — —		£55	£125	£400	—
1734 — —		£55	£125	£400	—
1735 — —		£55	£135	£400	—
1736 — —		£55	£135	£400	—
1739 — Roses in angles on rev.		£45	£115	£325	—
1741 — —		£45	£115	£325	—
1743 Old head, Roses in angles on rev.		£35	£70	£200	—
1745 — —		£35	£70	£200	—
1745 — LIMA below bust		£28	£55	£175	—
1746 — —		£28	£55	£175	—
1746 — Plain, Proof		—	—	—	£750
1750 — —		£50	£175	£500	—
1751 — —		£60	£200	£600	—

GEORGE III (1760–1820)

1816 "Bull head"	—	£8	£35	£90	£165
1817 —	8,092,656	£8	£35	£90	£170
1817 "Small head"	incl. above	£8	£35	£95	£185
1818 —	2,905,056	£8	£35	£95	£185
1819 —	4,790,016	£8	£35	£95	£185
1820 —	2,396,592	£12	£45	£125	£260

GEORGE IV (1820–30)

1820 First bust, first reverse	incl. above	£10	£35	£110	£220
1821 — —	1,435,104	£10	£35	£110	£220
1821 — — Proof	incl. above	—	—	—	£650
1823 —	2,003,760	£250	£500	£1750	—
1823 — Second reverse	incl. above	£10	£35	£100	£220
1824 — —	465,696	£15	£45	£140	£260
1824 Second bust, third reverse .	incl. above		Extremely rare		
*1825 — —	2,258,784	£10	£30	£100	£220
1826 — —	2,189,088	£10	£30	£100	£220
1826 — — Proof	incl. above	—	—	£325	£450
1828 — —	49,890	£30	£60	£150	£320
1829 —	508,464	£25	£50	£140	£280

WILLIAM IV (1830–37)

1831	—		Extremely rare		
1831 Proof (W.W. in script & block)	—	—	—	£350	£600
1834 W.W. in block	993,168	£10	£45	£150	£275
1834 W.W. in script	incl. above	£10	£40	£120	£240
1835	281,952	£10	£45	£150	£260
*1836	1,588,752	£10	£35	£120	£240
1837	150,526	£10	£45	£160	£275

DATE	MINTAGE	F	VF	EF	UNC

VICTORIA (1837–1901)

YOUNG HEAD ISSUES

1839 (two varieties)	—	£400	£800	£2000	—
1839 Proof	—	—	—	—	£1000
1840	386,496	£25	£90	£175	£275
1841	42,768	£250	£500	£1500	£2200
1842	486,288	£20	£50	£160	£250
1843	454,608	£50	£130	£550	£850
*1844	1,999,008	£15	£35	£130	£240
1845	2,231,856	£15	£35	£130	£240
1846	1,539,668	£15	£40	£130	£275
1848 Plain 8	367,488	£35	£100	£400	£700
1848/6	incl. above	£30	£80	£300	£600
1849	261,360	£25	£60	£240	£425
1850	484,613	£25	£60	£250	£325
1853 Proof only	—	—	—	—	£1800
1874	2,188,599	£12	£28	£80	£150
1875	1,113,483	£12	£28	£80	£150
1876	633,221	£12	£28	£80	£150
1877	447,059	£12	£28	£80	£150
1878	1,466,323	£12	£28	£80	£150
1879	901,356	£16	£30	£110	£185
1880	1,346,350	£12	£28	£80	£130
1881	2,301,495	£12	£28	£80	£130
1882	808,227	£12	£28	£80	£130
1883	2,982,779	£12	£28	£80	£130
1884	1,569,175	£12	£28	£80	£130
1885	1,628,438	£12	£28	£80	£130
1886	891,767	£12	£28	£80	£130
1887	1,438,046	£12	£28	£80	£140

JUBILEE HEAD ISSUES

1887	incl. above	£5	£8	£15	£35
1887 Proof	1,084	—	—	—	£125
1888	1,428,787	£8	£12	£30	£50
1889	4,811,954	£8	£12	£30	£50
1890	3,228,111	£8	£12	£35	£55
1891	2,284,632	£8	£15	£45	£75
1892	1,710,946	£8	£12	£35	£55

OLD HEAD ISSUES

1893	1,792,600	£5	£12	£30	£50
1893 Proof	1,312	—	—	—	135
1894	1,524,960	£10	£20	£50	£75
1895	1,772,662	£8	£15	£40	£70
1896	2,148,505	£5	£12	£35	£65
1897	1,678,643	£5	£12	£35	£60
1898	1,870,055	£5	£12	£35	£60
1899	2,865,872	£5	£12	£35	£55
1900	4,479,128	£5	£12	£35	£55
1901	1,516,570	£5	£12	£35	£55

EDWARD VII (1901–10)

1902	1,316,008	£5	£15	£45	£60
1902 "Matt Proof"	15,123	—	—	—	£60
*1903	274,840	£45	£120	£380	£800
1904	709,652	£40	£110	£350	£575
1905	166,008	£110	£300	£750	£1200
1906	2,886,206	£8	£25	£75	£130
1907	3,693,930	£8	£25	£80	£150
1908	1,758,889	£10	£30	£120	£200
1909	3,051,592	£8	£25	£80	£155
1910	2,557,685	£8	£25	£65	£125

GEORGE V (1910–36)

First issue

1911	2,914,573	£5	£10	£30	£55
1911 Proof	6,007	—	—	—	£75
1912	4,700,789	£4	£9	£30	£60
1913	4,090,169	£4	£10	£40	£75
1914	18,333,003	£3	£8	£20	£32

George V first type reverse

DATE	MINTAGE	F	VF	EF	UNC
1915	32,433,066	£3	£8	£16	£30
1916	29,530,020	£3	£8	£16	£30
1917	11,172,052	£3	£8	£18	£30
1918	29,079,592	£3	£8	£16	£30
1919	10,266,737	£3	£10	£20	£35
Second issue—*debased silver*					
1920	17,982,077	£2	£7	£15	£35
1921	23,677,889	£2	£7	£16	£35
1922	16,396,724	£2	£7	£16	£35
1923	26,308,526	£6	£7	£15	£25
1924	5,866,294	£6	£12	£30	£60
1925	1,413,461	£8	£25	£100	£195
1926	4,473,516	£3	£10	£25	£60
Third issue —*Modified effigy*					
1926	*incl. above*	£4	£10	£25	£60
1927	6,837,872	£3	£8	£20	£40
Fourth issue—*New shield reverse*					
1927 Proof	15,000	—	—	—	£35
1928	18,762,727	£2	£5	£12	£22
1929	17,632,636	£2	£5	£12	£22
1930	809,051	£5	£35	£85	£180
1931	11,264,468	£2	£5	£12	£20
1932	4,793,643	£2	£5	£16	£50
£4521933	10,311,494	£2	£5	£12	£28
1934	2,422,399	£3	£8	£30	£60
1935	7,022,216	£2	£5	£12	£16
1936	7,039,423	£2	£5	£10	£15

GEORGE VI (1936–52)

1937	9,106,440	—	£2	£4	£10
1937 Proof	26,402	—	—	—	£12
1938	6,426,478	£1	£3	£10	£17
1939	15,478,635	—	£1	£3	£8
1940	17,948,439	—	£1	£3	£6
1941	15,773,984	—	£1	£3	£6
1942	31,220,090	—	£1	£3	£6
1943	15,462,875	—	£1	£3	£6
1944	15,255,165	—	£1	£3	£6
1945	19,849,242	—	£1	£3	£6
1946	22,724,873	—	£1	£3	£6
Cupro-nickel					
1947	21,911,484	—	£1	£2	£4
1948	71,164,703	—	£1	£2	£4
1949	28,272,512	—	£1	£2	£6
1950	28,335,500	—	£1	£2	£6
1950 Proof	17,513	—	£1	£2	£9
1951	9,003,520	—	£1	£2	£6
1951 Proof	20,000	—	—	—	£9
1952				Only one known	

ELIZABETH II (1952–   )

1953	4,333,214	—	—	£1	£3
1953 Proof	40,000	—	—	—	£5
1954	11,614,953	—	£1	£3	£15
1955	23,628,726	—	—	£1	£4
1956	33,934,909	—	—	£1	£4
1957	34,200,563	—	—	£1	£4
1958	15,745,668	£1	£1	£3	£15
1959	9,028,844	—	£1	£5	£18
1960	19,929,191	—	—	£1	£2
1961	25,887,897	—	—	—	£1
1962	24,013,312	—	—	—	£1
1963	17,625,200	—	—	—	£1
1964	5,973,600	—	—	—	£1
1965	9,778,440	—	—	—	£1
1966	13,375,200	—	—	—	£1
1967	33,058,400	—	—	—	—

FLORINS

DATE	MINTAGE	F	VF	EF	UNC

VICTORIA (1837–1901)

YOUNG (CROWNED) HEAD ISSUES
"Godless" type (without D.G.—"Dei Gratia")

DATE	MINTAGE	F	VF	EF	UNC
*1849	413,820	£8	£25	£75	£140

"Gothic" type i.e. date in roman numerals in obverse legend
"brit." in legend. No die no.

DATE	MINTAGE	F	VF	EF	UNC
1851 mdccccli Proof	1,540		Extremely rare		
1852 mdccclii	1,014,552	£10	£35	£90	£160
1853 mdcccliii	3,919,950	£10	£35	£90	£160
1853 — Proof	incl. above	—	—	—	£1200
1854 mdcccliv	550,413	£500	—	—	—
1855 mdccclv	831,017	£10	£35	£90	£160
1856 mdccclvi	2,201,760	£10	£35	£90	£160
1857 mdccclvii	1,671,120	£10	£35	£90	£160
1858 mdccclviiii	2,239,380	£10	£35	£90	£160
1859 mdccclix	2,568,060	£10	£35	£90	£160
1860 mdccclx	1,475,100	£14	£40	£130	£240
1862 mdccclxii	594,000	£50	£150	£425	£750
1863 mdccclxiii	938,520	£110	£275	£800	£1200

"brit" in legend. Die no. below bust

DATE	MINTAGE	F	VF	EF	UNC
1864 mdccclxiv	1,861,200	£10	£35	£90	£160
1865 mdccclxv	1,580,044	£10	£35	£95	£160
1866 mdccclxvi	914,760	£10	£35	£95	£165
*1867 mdccclxvii	423,720	£20	£50	£220	£375
1867—only 42 arcs in border	incl. above		Extremely rare		

"britt" in legend. Die no. below bust

DATE	MINTAGE	F	VF	EF	UNC
1868 mdccclxviii	896,940	£10	£35	£90	£150
1869 mdccclxix	297,000	£12	£35	£110	£220
1870 mdccclxx	1,080,648	£10	£30	£90	£150
1871 mdccclxxi	3,425,605	£10	£30	£90	£140
1872 mdccclxxii	7,199,690	£10	£30	£90	£140
1873 mdccclxxiii	5,921,839	£10	£30	£90	£140
1874 mdccclxxiv	1,642,630	£10	£30	£90	£140
1875 mdccclxxv	1,117,030	£10	£30	£90	£140
1876 mdccclxxvi	580,034	£10	£30	£90	£150
1877 mdccclxxvii	682,292	£10	£30	£90	£140
1877 — 48 arcs in border no W.W.	incl. above	£12	£40	£110	£220
1877 — 42 arcs	incl. above	£12	£40	£110	£220
1877 — — no die number	incl. above		Extremely rare		
1878 mdccclxxviii with die number	1,786,680	£12	£35	£120	£185
1879 mdccclxxix no die no	1,512,247		Extremely rare		
1879 — 48 arcs in border	incl. above	£12	£35	£120	£185
1879 — no die number	incl. above		Extremely rare		
1879 — 38 arcs, no W.W.	incl. above	£12	£45	£125	£200
1880 mdccclxxx Younger portrait	—		Extremely rare		
1880 — 34 arcs, Older portrait	2,167,170	£10	£35	£90	£150
1881 mdccclxxxi — —	2,570,337	£10	£35	£90	£140
1883 mdccclxxxiii — —	3,555,667	£10	£35	£90	£140
1884 mdccclxxxiv — —	1,447,379	£10	£35	£90	£140
1885 mdccclxxxv — —	1,758,210	£10	£35	£90	£140
1886 mdccclxxxvi — —	591,773	£10	£35	£90	£140
1887 mdccclxxxvii — —	1,776,903	£12	£50	£150	£270
1887 — 46 Arcs	incl. above	£18	£60	£175	£300

JUBILEE HEAD ISSUES

DATE	MINTAGE	F	VF	EF	UNC
1887	incl. above	£3	£6	£15	£28
1887 Proof	1,084	—	—	—	£90
1888	1,547,540	£4	£8	£25	£45

"Godless" florin

"Gothic" florin

DATE	MINTAGE	F	VF	EF	UNC
1889	2,973,561	£4	£10	£25	£45
1890	1,684,737	£7	£20	£60	£110
1891	836,438	£12	£35	£100	£165
1892	283,401	£20	£55	£140	£270

VICTORIA—OLD HEAD ISSUES

1893	1,666,103	£3	£11	£25	£40
1893 Proof	1,312	—	—	—	£100
1894	1,952,842	£5	£18	£40	£70
1895	2,182,968	£4	£16	£40	£65
1896	2,944,416	£4	£14	£30	£50
1897	1,699,921	£4	£14	£30	£50
1898	3,061,343	£4	£14	£30	£50
1899	3,966,953	£4	£14	£30	£50
*1900	5,528,630	£4	£14	£30	£50
1901	2,648,870	£4	£14	£30	£50

EDWARD VII (1901–10)

*1902	2,189,575	£5	£12	£30	£55
1902 "Matt Proof"	15,123	—	—	—	£50
1903	1,995,298	£7	£25	£70	£140
1904	2,769,932	£7	£25	£70	£150
1905	1,187,596	£22	£60	£220	£475
1906	6,910,128	£7	£25	£65	£120
1907	5,947,895	£7	£25	£65	£120
1908	3,280,010	£8	£30	£100	£200
1909	3,482,829	£7	£25	£90	£160
1910	5,650,713	£6	£20	£55	£90

GEORGE V (1910–36)

First issue

1911	5,951,284	£3	£8	£20	£50
1911 Proof	6,007	—	—	—	£60
1912	8,571,731	£3	£10	£28	£60
1913	4,545,278	£4	£15	£30	£70
1914	21,252,701	£2	£12	£20	£35
1915	12,367,939	£2	£12	£20	£35
1916	21,064,337	£2	£12	£20	£35
1917	11,181,617	£2	£10	£20	£40
1918	29,211,792	£2	£12	£20	£35
1919	9,469,292	£3	£14	£28	£50

Second issue —debased silver

1920	15,387,833	£2	£12	£32	£55
1921	34,863,895	£2	£12	£28	£45
1922	23,861,044	£2	£12	£28	£45
1923	21,546,533	£2	£10	£20	£35
1924	4,582,372	£2	£10	£35	£65
1925	1,404,136	£8	£30	£90	£170
1926	5,125,410	£4	£12	£35	£65

Fourth issue—new reverse

1927 Proof only	101,497	—	—	—	£35
1928	11,087,186	£2	£4	£12	£22
1929	16,397,279	£2	£4	£10	£20
1930	5,753,568	£2	£5	£12	£28
1931	6,556,331	£2	£5	£10	£25
1932	717,041	£6	£15	£80	£150
1933	8,685,303	£1	£3	£10	£28
1935	7,540,546	£1	£2	£8	£15
*1936	9,897,448	£1	£2	£8	£14

DATE	MINTAGE	F	VF	EF	UNC

GEORGE VI (1936–52)

DATE	MINTAGE	F	VF	EF	UNC
1937	13,006,781	—	£1	£3	£6
1937 Proof	26,402	—	—	—	£8
1938	7,909,388	£1	£2	£8	£16
1939	20,850,607	£1	£2	£3	£5
1940	18,700,338	£1	£2	£3	£5
1941	24,451,079	£1	£2	£3	£5
1942	39,895,243	£1	£2	£3	£5
1943	26,711,987	£1	£2	£3	£5
*1944	27,560,005	£1	£2	£3	£5
1945	25,858,049	£1	£2	£3	£5
1946	22,300,254	£1	£2	£3	£5
1947	22,910,085	—	—	£1	£3
1948	67,553,636	—	—	£1	£3
1949	28,614,939	—	—	£1	£5
1950	24,357,490	—	—	£2	£7
1950 Proof	17,513	—	—	£1	£8
1951	27,411,747	—	—	£2	£7
1951 Proof	20,000	—	—	£1	£8

ELIZABETH II (1952–   )

DATE	MINTAGE	F	VF	EF	UNC
1953	11,958,710	—	—	—	£2
1953 Proof	40,000	—	—	—	£5
1954	13,085,422	—	—	£5	£15
1955	25,887,253	—	—	£1	£3
1956	47,824,500	—	—	£1	£3
1957	33,071,282	—	—	£4	£15
1958	9,564,580	—	—	£3	£12
1959	14,080,319	—	—	£4	£15
1960	13,831,782	—	—	£1	£2
1961	37,735,315	—	—	£1	£2
1962	35,147,903	—	—	£1	£2
1963	26,471,000	—	—	£1	£2
1964	16,539,000	—	—	£1	£2
1965	48,163,000	—	—	—	£1
1966	83,999,000	—	—	—	£1
1967	39,718,000	—	—	—	£1

SHILLINGS

OLIVER CROMWELL

1658		£275	£450	£800	—
1658 Dutch Copy			Extremely rare		

CHARLES II (1660–85)

*1663 First bust	£45	£110	£400	—
1663 First bust variety	£45	£110	£400	—
1666 — Elephant below bust	£200	£550	£1500	—
1666 "Guinea" head, elephant	£500	£950	—	—
1666 Second bust		Extremely rare		
1669/6 First bust variety		Extremely rare		
1668 Second bust	£40	£115	£400	—
1669 —		Extremely rare		
1670 —	£65	£200	£550	—
1671 —	£75	£250	£675	—
1671 — Plume below, plume in centre rev.	£150	£320	£1000	—
1672 —	£50	£150	£475	—
1673 —	£75	£250	£675	—
1673 — Plume below, plume in centre rev.	£160	£320	£1150	—
1674 —	£75	£250	£675	—
1674 — Plume below, plume in centre rev.	£150	£350	£1000	—
1674 — Plume rev. only	£160	£350	£1000	—

DATE	F	VF	EF	UNC
1674 Third bust	£225	£575	—	—
1675 Second bust	£90	£275	—	—
1675 — Plume below, plume in centre rev.	£160	£350	£1000	—
1675 Third bust	£175	£450	—	—
1676 Second bust	£50	£150	£400	—
1676 — Plume below, plume in centre rev.	£160	£350	£1000	—
1677 —	£60	£150	£450	—
1677 — Plume below	£175	£375	£1000	—
1678 —	£65	£200	£600	—
1679 —	£55	£150	£450	—
1679 — Plume below, plume in centre rev.	£180	£375	£1000	—
1679 — Plume below	£180	£400	£1000	—
1680 —	£225	—	—	—
1680 — Plume below, plume in centre rev.	£180	£400	£1000	—
1681 —	£75	£250	£800	—
1681 — Elephant & Castle	£750	—	—	—
1682 —	£200	£600	—	—
1683 —	£600	—	—	—
1683 Fourth bust	£90	£275	£750	—
1684 —	£80	£275	£700	—

William III First bust

JAMES II (1685–88)

	F	VF	EF	UNC
1685	£70	£175	£450	—
1685 Plume rev		Extremely Rare		
1686	£70	£175	£475	—
1687	£70	£190	£475	—
1688	£75	£200	£500	—

William III Second bust

WILLIAM & MARY (1688–94)

	F	VF	EF	UNC
1692	£75	£200	£525	—
1693	£75	£200	£525	—

WILLIAM III (1694–1702)

*Many of William's shillings carry privy marks or initials below the bust as follows:
B: Bristol. C: Chester. E: Exeter. N: Norwich. Y or y: York.*

William III Third bust

	F	VF	EF	UNC
1695 First bust	£22	£60	£160	—
1696 —	£20	£50	£150	—
1696 — B below bust	£24	£60	£175	—
1696 — C	£25	£70	£200	—
1696 — E	£25	£70	£200	—
1696 — N	£25	£70	£200	—
1696 — y	£25	£70	£200	—
1696 — Y	£30	£80	£250	—
1696 Second bust		Only one known		
1696 Third bust C below	£75	£175	£500	—
1696 — Y	£300	—	—	—
1697 First bust	£20	£50	£150	—
1697 — B	£25	£65	£200	—
1697 — C	£25	£65	£200	—
1697 — E	£25	£65	£200	—
1697 — N	£25	£65	£200	—
1697 — y	£25	£65	£200	—
1697 — Y	£25	£65	£225	—
1697 Third bust	£20	£50	£150	—
1697 — B	£25	£70	£225	—
1697 — C	£25	£65	£200	—
1697 — E	£25	£70	£225	—
1697 — N	£25	£70	£225	—
1697 — y	£25	£70	£225	—
1697 Third bust variety	£22	£55	£150	—
1697 — B	£25	£70	£240	—
1697 — C	£40	£150	—	—
1698 —	£40	£80	£250	—
1698 — Plumes in angles of rev.	£60	£225	£550	—

William III Fourth bust

William III Fifth bust

DATE	F	VF	EF	UNC
1698 Fourth bust "Flaming hair"	£70	£230	£700	—
1699 —	£70	£200	£750	—
1699 Fifth bust	£60	£120	£425	—
1699 — Plumes in angles on rev.	£60	£170	£500	—
1699 — Roses in angles on rev.	£60	£180	£550	—
1700 —	£35	£75	£190	—
1700 — Plume below bust	£750	—	—	—
1701 —	£50	£115	£260	—
1701 — Plumes in angles on rev.	£70	£175	£450	—

ANNE (1702–14)

	F	VF	EF	UNC
1702 First bust (pre-Union with Scotland)	£30	£75	£225	—
1702 — Plumes in angles on rev.	£30	£80	£250	—
*1702 — VIGO below bust	£30	£75	£200	—
1703 Second bust, VIGO below	£30	£75	£200	—
1704 — Plain	£70	£175	—	—
1704 — Plumes in angles on rev.	£35	£110	£350	—
1705 — Plain	£30	£110	£300	—
1705 — Plumes in angles on rev.	£30	£110	£300	—
1705 — Roses & Plumes in angles on rev.	£30	£110	£300	—
1707 —	£30	£110	£300	—
1707 Second bust (post-Union) E below bust ...	£25	£55	£200	—
1707 — E* below bust	£60	£140	£400	—
1707 Third bust, Plain	£25	£55	£130	—
1707 — Plumes in angles on rev.	£35	£90	—	—
1707 — E below bust	£22	£55	£200	—
1707 "Edinburgh" bust, E* below		Extremely Rare		
1708 Second bust, E below	£25	£55	£250	—
1708 — E below bust	£30	£100	£300	—
1708 — Roses & Plumes in angles on rev.	£70	£200	£425	—
1708 Third bust, Plain	£25	£50	£145	—
1708 — Plumes in angles on rev.	£35	£90	£250	—
1708 — E below bust	£35	£110	£250	—
1708 — Roses & Plumes in angles on rev.	£30	£90	£250	—
1708 "Edinburgh" bust, E* below	£35	£100	£300	—
1709 Third bust, Plain	£22	£55	£155	—
1709 "Edinburgh" bust, E* below	£35	£100	£300	—
1709 — E no star (filled in die?)	£60	£150	£300	—
1710 Third bust, Roses & Plumes in angles	£28	£70	£225	—
1710 Fourth bust, Roses & Plumes in angles ...	£28	£75	£225	—
1711 Third bust, Plain	£60	£120	£325	—
1711 Fourth bust, Plain	£20	£40	£125	—
1712 —Roses & Plumes in angles on rev.	£25	£60	£170	—
1713 — —	£25	£60	£170	—
1714 — —	£25	£60	£170	—

GEORGE I (1714–27)

	F	VF	EF	UNC
*1715 First bust, Roses & Plumes in angles on rev.	£25	£65	£225	—
1716 — —	£60	£150	£400	—
1717 — —	£30	£75	£225	—
1718 — —	£30	£70	£190	—
1719 — —	£70	£150	£450	—
1720 — —	£30	£75	£190	—
1720 — Plain	£20	£65	£180	—
1721 — Roses & Plumes in angles on rev.	£40	£100	£300	—
1721 — Plain	£100	£225	£700	—
1722 — Roses & Plumes in angles on rev.	£50	£140	£450	—
1723 — —	£50	£130	£425	—
1723 — SSC in angles of rev.	£15	£35	£120	—
1723 Second bust, SSC in angles on rev.	£25	£70	£260	—
1723 First bust, SSC rev., Arms of France at date	£60	£120	£425	—
1723 Second bust, Roses & Plumes in angles .	£40	£110	£350	—
1723 — WCC (Welsh Copper Co) below bust ..	£200	£475	£1800	—
1724 — Roses & Plumes in angles on rev.	£35	£90	£250	—
1724 — WCC below bust	£220	£500	£2000	—
1725 — Roses & Plumes in angles on rev.	£35	£100	£270	—
1725 — WCC below bust	£220	£500	£2000	—
1726 — —.	£22-0	£500	£2000	—

DATE	MINTAGE	F	VF	EF	UNC
1726 — Roses & Plumes in angles on rev.		£200	£700	—	—
1727 — —				Extremely rare	
1727 — — no stops on obv.				Extremely rare	

GEORGE II (1727–60)

	MINTAGE	F	VF	EF	UNC
1727 Young head, Plumes in angles on rev.		£30	£100	£300	—
1727 — Roses & Plumes in angles on rev.		£30	£95	£250	—
1728 — —		£30	£90	£300	—
1728 — Plain		£35	£100	£350	—
1729 — Roses & Plumes in angles on rev.		£30	£90	£250	—
1731		£30	£70	£175	—
1731 — Plumes in angles on rev.		£40	125	£375	—
1732 — Roses & Plumes in angles on rev.		£30	£70	£175	—
1734 — —		£30	£70	£175	—
1735 — —		£30	£70	£175	—
1736 — —		£30	£70	£175	—
1737 — —		£30	£70	£160	—
*1739 — Roses in angles on rev.		£25	£65	£160	—
1741 — —		£25	£65	£160	—
1743 Old head, Roses in angles on rev.		£18	£45	£140	—
1745 — —		£18	£45	£140	—
1745 — — LIMA beow bust		£15	£35	£110	—
1746 — — —		£30	£100	£350	—
1746 — Plain, Proof		—	—	£425	—
*1747 — Roses in angles on rev.		£18	£45	£145	—
1750 — Plain		£15	£45	£160	—
1751 — —		£25	£60	£175	—
1758 — —		£8	£25	£75	—

George II Young head

GEORGE III (1760–1820)

	MINTAGE	F	VF	EF	UNC
*1763 "Northumberland" bust		£140	£290	£475	—
1787 rev. no semée of hearts in 4th shield		£6	£15	£45	—
1787 rev. with semée of hearts		£6	£14	£45	—
1798 "Dorrien Magens" bust		—	—	£3500	—

NEW COINAGE—shield in garter reverse

	MINTAGE	F	VF	EF	UNC
1816	—	£4	£12	£35	£70
1817	3,031,360	£4	£12	£35	£70
1818	1,342,440	£6	£16	£55	£85
1819	7,595,280	£4	£12	£35	£70
1820	7,975,440	£4	£12	£35	£70

GEORGE IV (1820–30)

George II Old head

	MINTAGE	F	VF	EF	UNC
1821 First bust, first reverse	2,463,120	£8	£25	£80	£140
1821 — — Proof	incl. above	—	—	—	£400
1823 — Second reverse	693,000	£20	£50	£150	£225
1824 — —	4,158,000	£8	£25	£70	£130
1825 — —	2,459,160	£15	£28	£70	£130
1825 Second bust, third reverse .	incl. above	£2	£10	£45	£95
1826 — —	6,351,840	£2	£10	£45	£95
1826 — — Proof	incl. above	—	—	—	£175
1827 — —	574,200	£18	£40	£90	£150
1829 — —	879,120	£15	£30	£80	£150

WILLIAM IV (1830–37)

	MINTAGE	F	VF	EF	UNC
1831 Proof only	—	—	—	£140	£245
1834	3,223,440	£6	£20	£60	£130
1835	1,449,360	£6	£20	£65	£140
1836	3,567,960	£6	£20	£55	£130
1837	478,160	£7	£20	£80	£200

VICTORIA (1837–1901)

YOUNG HEAD ISSUES
First head

	MINTAGE	F	VF	EF	UNC
1838 WW on truncation	1,956,240	£6	£20	£60	£120
1839 —	5,666,760	£6	£20	£60	£120

George III "Northumberland" shilling

175

DATE	MINTAGE	F	VF	EF	UNC
Second head					
1839 WW on truncation, Proof only	incl. above	—	—	—	£250
1839 no WW	incl. above	£6	£20	£65	£120
1840	1,639,440	£7	£20	£80	£180
1841	875,160	£6	£20	£80	£130
1842	2,094,840	£6	£20	£60	£120
1843	1,465,200	£6	£22	£80	£140
1844	4,466,880	£6	£20	£60	£120
1845	4,082,760	£6	£20	£60	£120
1846	4,031,280	£6	£20	£50	£100
1848 last 8 of date over 6	1,041,480	£25	£45	£135	£275
1849	845,480	£8	£30	£70	£140
1850	685,080	£150	£300	£800	£1400
1851	470,071	£25	£100	£250	£350
1852	1,306,574	£6	£20	£60	£100
1853	4,256,188	£6	£20	£60	£100
1853 Proof	incl. above	—	—	—	£400
1854	552,414	£60	£130	£270	£525
1855	1,368,400	£6	£20	£60	£100
1856	3,168,000	£6	£20	£60	£100
1857	2,562,120	£6	£20	£60	£100
1858	3,108,600	£6	£20	£60	£100
1859	4,561,920	£6	£18	£60	£90
1860	1,671,120	£6	£20	£65	£110
1861	1,382,040	£7	£25	£75	£140
1862	954,320	£35	£80	£200	£350
1863	859,320	£70	£140	£275	£450
Die no. added above date up to 1879					
1864	4,518,360	£5	£20	£50	£90
1865	5,619,240	£5	£20	£50	£90
1866	4,984,600	£5	£20	£50	£90
1867	2,166,120	£5	£20	£50	£90
Third head—with die no.					
1867	incl. above	£20	£50	£125	£200
1868	3,330,360	£5	£18	£50	£85
1869	736,560	£5	£18	£50	£85
1870	1,467,471	£5	£18	£50	£85
1871	4,910,010	£5	£15	£45	£80
1872	8,897,781	£5	£15	£45	£80
1873	6,489,598	£5	£15	£45	£80
1874	5,503,747	£5	£15	£45	£80
1875	4,353,983	£5	£15	£45	£80
1876	1,057,487	£5	£15	£45	£90
1877	2,989,703	£5	£15	£45	£80
1878	3,127,131	£5	£15	£45	£80
1879	3,611,507	£6	£30	£60	£125
Fourth head—no die no					
1879 no Die no.	incl. above	£5	£15	£50	£10
1880	4,842,786	£5	£15	£40	£70
1881	5,255,332	£5	£15	£40	£70
1882	1,611,786	£7	£20	£90	£160
1883	7,281,450	£4	£15	£40	£60
1884	3,923,993	£4	£15	£40	£60
1885	3,336,526	£4	£15	£40	£60
1886	2,086,819	£4	£15	£40	£60
1887	4,034,133	£5	£15	£50	£100
JUBILEE HEAD ISSUES					
1887	incl. above	£2	£4	£8	£18
1887 Proof	1,084	—	—	—	£60
1888	4,526,856	£2	£7	£15	£35
1889	7,039,628	£12	£40	£150	—
1889 Large bust (until 1892)	incl. above	£2	£7	£28	£50
1890	8,794,042	£2	£7	£28	£50
*1891	5,665,348	£2	£7	£28	£50
1892	4,591,622	£2	£7	£28	£50
OLD HEAD ISSUES					
1893	7,039,074	£3	£7	£16	£40
1893 Proof	1,312	—	—	—	£75
1894	5,953,152	£5	£15	£40	£70
1895	8,880,651	£4	£12	£28	£50
1896	9,264,551	£4	£10	£28	£45

Victoria Small Jubilee head

Victoria Large Jubilee head

DATE	MINTAGE	F	VF	EF	UNC
1897	6,270,364	£3	£9	£30	£45
*1898	9,768,703	£3	£9	£30	£45
1899	10,965,382	£3	£9	£30	£50
1900	10,937,590	£3	£9	£30	£40
1901	3,426,294	£3	£9	£30	£40

EDWARD VII (1901–10)

1902	7,809,481	£3	£6	£15	£35
1902	13,123	—	—	—	£20
1903	2,061,823	£5	£25	£65	£175
1904	2,040,161	£5	£25	£65	£175
1905	488,390	£32	£110	£375	£750
1906	10,791,025	£2	£7	£25	£45
1907	14,083,418	£3	£8	£30	£70
1908	3,806,969	£5	£18	£65	£130
1909	5,664,982	£3	£12	£50	£100
*1910	26,547,236	£2	£5	£20	£35

GEORGE V (1910–36)

First issue

1911	20,065,901	£1.50	£5	£15	£30
1911 Proof	6,007	—	—	—	£35
*1912	15,594,009	£1.50	£5	£20	£40
1913	9,011,509	£2	£7	£25	£55
1914	23,415,843	£1	£4	£15	£30
1915	39,279,024	£1	£4	£15	£30
1916	35,862,015	£1	£4	£15	£30
1917	22,202,608	£1	£4	£15	£30
1918	34,915,934	£1	£4	£15	£30
1919	10,823,824	£1	£5	£15	£35

Second issue —debased silver

1920	22,825,142	—	£2	£15	£30
1921	22,648,763	—	£2	£15	£30
1922	27,215,738	—	£2	£15	£30
1923	14,575,243	—	£2	£15	£25
1924	9,250,095	£2	£5	£20	£55
1925	5,418,764	£2	£5	£20	£60
1926	22,516,453	—	£3	£15	£35

George V First obverse

Third issue—Modified bust

1926	incl. above	—	£3	£18	£30
1927 —	9,247,344	£1	£3	£18	£30

Fourth issue —large lion and crown on rev., date in legend

1927	incl. above	£1	£2	£15	£30
1927 Proof	15,000	—	—	—	£25
1928	18,136,778	—	£2	£10	£25
1929	19,343,006	—	£2	£12	£25
1930	3,172,092	—	£2	£10	£35
1931	6,993,926	—	£2	£10	£25
1932	12,168,101	—	£2	£10	£25
1933	11,511,624	—	£2	£10	£25
*1934	6,138,463	—	£2	£12	£35
1935	9,183,462	—	£2	£6	£15
1936	11,910,613	—	£2	£4	£10

George V Second obverse

GEORGE VI (1936–52)

E = England rev. (lion standing on large crown). S = Scotland rev. (lion seated on small crown holding sword and mace)

1937 E	8,359,122	—	£1	£2	£5
1937 E Proof	26,402	—	—	—	£8
1937 S	6,748,875	—	£1	£2	£5
1937 S Proof	26,402	—	—	—	£8
1938 E	4,833,436	—	£1	£7	£12

DATE	MINTAGE	F	VF	EF	UNC
1938 S	4,797,852	—	£1	£7	£12
1939 E	11,052,677	—	£1	£2	£5
1939 S	10,263,892	—	£1	£2	£5
1940 E	11,099,126	—	—	£2	£5
1940 S	9,913,089	—	—	£2	£5
1941 E	11,391,883	—	—	£2	£5
1941 S	8,086,030	—	—	£2	£5
1942 E	17,453,643	—	—	£2	£4
1942 S	13,676,759	—	—	£2	£4
1943 E	11,404,213	—	—	£2	£4
1943 S	9,824,214	—	—	£2	£4
*1944 E	11,586,751	—	—	£2	£4
*1944 S	10,990,167	—	—	£2	£4
1945 E	15,143,404	—	—	£2	£5
1945 S	15,106,270	—	—	£2	£5
1946 E	16,663,797	—	—	£2	£5
1946 S	16,381,501	—	—	£2	£5
1947 E	12,120,611	—	—	—	£2
1947 S	12,283,223	—	—	—	£2
1948 E	45,576,923	—	—	—	£2
1948 S	45,351,937	—	—	—	£2
1949 E	19,328,405	—	—	—	£4
1949 S	21,243,074	—	—	—	£4
1950 E	19,243,872	—	—	—	£4
1950 E Proof	17,513	—	—	—	£8
1950 S	14,299,601	—	—	—	£4
1950 S Proof	17,513	—	—	—	£8
1951 E	9,956,930	—	—	—	£4
1951 E Proof	20,000	—	—	—	£8
1951 S	10,961,174	—	—	—	£4
1951 S Proof	20,000	—	—	—	£8

English reverse

Scottish reverse

ELIZABETH II (1952–)

E = England rev. (shield with three lions). S = Scotland rev. (shield with one lion).

DATE	MINTAGE	F	VF	EF	UNC
1953 E	41,942,894	—	—	—	£1
1953 E Proof	40,000	—	—	—	£3
1953 S	20,663,528	—	—	—	£1
1953 S Proof	40,000	—	—	—	£3
*1954 E	30,262,032	—	—	—	£2
*1954 S	26,771,735	—	—	—	£2
1955 E	45,259,908	—	—	—	£2
1955 S	27,950,906	—	—	—	£2
1956 E	44,907,008	—	—	—	£7
1956 S	42,853,639	—	—	—	£7
1957 E	42,774,217	—	—	—	£1
1957 S	17,959,988	—	—	—	£9
1958 E	14,392,305	—	—	—	£9
1958 S	40,822,557	—	—	—	£1
1959 E	19,442,778	—	—	—	£1
1959 S	1,012,988	£1	£2	£4	£15
1960 E	27,027,914	—	—	—	£1
1960 S	14,376,932	—	—	—	£1
1961 E	39,816,907	—	—	—	£1
1961 S	2,762,558	—	—	—	£3
1962 E	36,704,379	—	—	—	£1
1962 S	17,475,310	—	—	—	£1
1963 E	49,433,607	—	—	—	£1
1963 S	32,300,000	—	—	—	£1
1964 E	8,590,900	—	—	—	£1
1964 S	5,239,100	—	—	—	£1
1965 E	9,216,000	—	—	—	£1
1965 S	2,774,000	—	—	—	£1
1966 E	15,002,000	—	—	—	—
1966 S	15,604,000	—	—	—	—

English reverse

Scottish reverse

SIXPENCES

DATE	F	VF	EF	UNC

OLIVER CROMWELL

1658 Patterns by Thos. Simon & Tanner
All are very Rare 4 Varieties .... Extremely Rare

CHARLES II (1660–85)

DATE	F	VF	EF	UNC
1674	£40	£90	£250	—
1675	£40	£90	£250	—
1676	£40	£90	£250	—
*1677	£40	£90	£250	—
1678/7	£40	£90	£250	—
1679	£40	£90	£250	—
1680	£50	£110	£340	—
1681	£35	£90	£250	—
1682/1	£40	£90	£250	—
1682	£40	£90	£250	—
1683	£40	£90	£250	—
1684	£50	£100	£260	—

JAMES II (1685–88)

DATE	F	VF	EF	UNC
1686 Early shields	£60	£140	£425	—
1687/6 —	£60	£140	£425	—
1687 Late shields	£60	£130	£400	—
1688 —	£60	£140	£425	—

WILLIAM & MARY (1688–94)

DATE	F	VF	EF	UNC
*1693	£70	£150	£400	—
1694	£70	£165	£450	—

WILLIAM III (1694–1702)

Many of William's sixpences carry privy marks or initials below the bust as follows: B: Bristol. C: Chester. E: Exeter. N: Norwich. Y or y: York.

DATE	F	VF	EF	UNC
1695 First bust, early harp in 4th shield on rev.	£12	£50	£130	—
1696 — —	£12	£35	£90	—
1696 — — B	£15	£40	£140	—
1696 — — C	£15	£40	£150	—
1696 — — E	£15	£45	£160	—
1696 — — N	£15	£40	£150	—
1696 — — y	£15	£40	£150	—
1696 — — Y	£20	£45	£170	—
1696 — Later harp	£30	£100	£300	—
1696 — — B	£25	£80	£260	—
1696 — — C	£35	£125	—	—
1696 — — N	£30	£110	—	—
1696 Second bust	£70	£220	—	—
1697 First bust, later harp	£15	£30	£100	—
1697 — — B	£15	£40	£150	—
1697 — — C	£15	£55	£170	—
1697 — — E	£15	£50	£150	—
1697 — — N	£15	£50	£150	—
1697 — — Y	£15	£50	£150	—
1697 Second bust	£60	£110	£550	—
1697 Third bust	£12	£35	£100	—
1697 — B	£18	£55	£160	—
1697 — C	£20	£75	£250	—
1697 — E	£20	£70	£220	—
1697 — Y	£20	£70	£225	—
1698 —	£22	£70	£200	—

179

DATE	MINTAGE	F	VF	EF	UNC
1698 — Plumes in angles on rev.		£22	£85	£240	—
1699 —		£35	£120	£360	—
1699 — Plumes in angles on rev.		£35	£110	£260	—
1699 — Roses in angles on rev.		£35	£100	£260	—
1700 —		£20	£55	£165	—
1700 — Plume below bust		£70	£240	—	—
1701 —		£22	£70	£200	—

ANNE (1702–14)

DATE	MINTAGE	F	VF	EF	UNC
1703 VIGO below bust (pre-Union with Scotland)		£20	£45	£140	—
1705 Plain		£35	£100	£250	—
*1705 Plumes in angles on rev.		£20	£55	£170	—
1705 Roses & Plumes in angles on rev.		£20	£50 .	£10	—
1707 Roses & Plumes in angles on rev.		£18	£50	£150	—
1707 (Post-Union), Plain		£15	£30	£125	—
1707 E (Edinburgh) below bust		£15	£35	£130	—
1707 Plumes in angles on rev.		£15	£40	£140	—
1708 Plain		£15	£35	£125	—
1708 E below bust		£15	£35	£140	—
1708 E* below bust		£20	£50	£170	—
1708 "Edinburgh" bust E* below		£20	£65	£180	—
1708 Plumes in angles on rev.		£20	£40	£150	—
1710 Roses & Plumes in angles on rev.		£20	£50	£180	—
1711 Plain		£15	£30	£100	—

GEORGE I (1714–27)

DATE	MINTAGE	F	VF	EF	UNC
*1717 Roses & Plumes in angles on rev.		£40	£90	£240	—
1720 —		£30	£80	£240	—
1723 SSC in angles on rev.		£10	£30	£100	—
1726 Small Roses & Plumes in angles on rev. .		£65	£160	£425	—

GEORGE II (1727–60)

DATE	MINTAGE	F	VF	EF	UNC
1728 Young head, Plain		£20	£85	£325	—
1728 — Proof		—	—	£1250	—
1728 — Plumes in angles on rev.		£25	£80	£250	—
1728 — Roses & Plumes in angles on rev.		£20	£70	£160	—
1731 — —		£20	£50	£150	—
*1732 — —		£20	£50	£150	—
1734 — —		£20	£60	£160	—
1735 — —		£20	£50	£150	—
1736 — —		£20	£50	£150	—
1739 — Roses in angles on rev.		£15	£40	£110	—
1741 —		£12	£40	£110	—
1743 Old head, Roses in angles on rev.		£12	£40	£100	—
1745 — —		£10	£28	£100	—
1745 — Plain, LIMA below bust		£12	£20	£75	—
1746 — —		£10	£20	£75	—
1746 — — Proof		—	—	£350	—
1750 — —		£12	£25	£90	—
1751 — —		£15	£35	£110	—
1757 — —		£10	£18	£50	—
1758 — —		£10	£18	£50	—

GEORGE III (1760–1820)

DATE	MINTAGE	F	VF	EF	UNC
1787 rev. no semée of hearts on 4th shield		£6	£14	£35	—
1787 rev. with semée of hearts		£6	£14	£32	—

NEW COINAGE

DATE	MINTAGE	F	VF	EF	UNC
1816	—	£3	£9	£30	£55
1817	10,921,680	£3	£9	£30	£55
1818	4,284,720	£5	£12	£40	£70
1819	4,712,400	£3	£9	£30	£55
1820	1,488,960	£3	£9	£30	£60

DATE	MINTAGE	F	VF	EF	UNC

GEORGE IV (1820–30)

DATE	MINTAGE	F	VF	EF	UNC
*1821 First bust, first reverse	863,280	£8	£22	£60	£125
1821 — — Proof	incl. above	—	—	—	£350
1824 — Second (garter) reverse	633,600	£8	£22	£70	£125
1825 —	483,120	£8	£22	£70	£125
1826 —	689,040	£15	£45	£110	£220
1826 Second bust, third (lion on crown) reverse	incl. above	£5	£15	£45	£90
1826 — — Proof	incl. above	—	—	—	£125
1827 — —	166,320	£8	£22	£80	£150
1828 — —	15,840	£8	£22	£80	£130
1829 — —	403,290	£8	£22	£80	£125

WILLIAM IV (1830–37)

DATE	MINTAGE	F	VF	EF	UNC
1831	1,340,195	£7	£20	£60	£100
1831 Proof	incl. above	—	—	£90	£175
*1834	5,892,480	£7	£20	£60	£90
1835	1,552,320	£7	£20	£60	£100
1836	1,987,920	£9	£30	£100	£160
1837	506,880	£9	£25	£90	£140

VICTORIA (1837–1901)

YOUNG HEAD ISSUES
First head

DATE	MINTAGE	F	VF	EF	UNC
1838	1,607,760	£5	£18	£40	£75
1839	3,310,560	£5	£18	£40	£80
1839 Proof	incl. above	—	—	—	£150
1840	2,098,800	£5	£18	£40	£100
1841	1,386,000	£5	£20	£45	£120
1842	601,920	£5	£18	£65	£110
1843	3,160,080	£5	£20	£45	£100
1844	3,975,840	£5	£18	£45	£90
1844 Large 44 in date	incl. above	£7	£25	£75	£130
1845	3,714,480	£5	£18	£45	£100
1846	4,226,880	£5	£18	£45	£100
1848	586,080	£15	£45	£120	£250
1850	498,960	£5	£20	£45	£100
1851	2,288,107	£5	£20	£45	£100
1852	904,586	£5	£18	£40	£1000
1853	3,837,930	£5	£18	£40	£100
1853 Proof	incl above	—	—	—	£300
1854	840,116	£35	£100	£225	£340
1855	1,129,684	£5	£18	£45	£95
1856	2,779,920	£5	£18	£45	£95
1857	2,233,440	£5	£18	£45	£95
1858	1,932,480	£5	£18	£45	£95
1859	4,688,640	£5	£18	£45	£95
1860	1,100,880	£5	£18	£45	£95
1862	990,000	£20	£50	£130	£300
1863	491,040	£20	£50	£130	£300

Die no. added above date from 1864 to 1879

DATE	MINTAGE	F	VF	EF	UNC
1864	4,253,040	£5	£18	£40	£90
1865	1,631,520	£5	£20	£45	£90
1866	4,140,080	£5	£18	£40	£80
1866 no Die no.	incl. above	£15	£60	£150	£220

Second head

DATE	MINTAGE	F	VF	EF	UNC
1867	1,362,240	£5	£18	£45	£90
1868	1,069,200	£5	£18	£45	£90
1869	388,080	£5	£18	£45	£90
1870	479,613	£5	£18	£45	£85
1871	3,662,684	£5	£16	£45	£75
1871 no Die no.	incl. above	£5	£16	£45	£80
1872	3,382,048	£5	£16	£45	£80
1873	4,594,733	£5	£16	£45	£80
1874	4,225,726	£5	£16	£45	£80
1875	3,256,545	£5	£16	£45	£80

DATE	MINTAGE	F	VF	EF	UNC
1876	841,435	£5	£16	£45	£85
1877	4,066,486	£5	£16	£40	£85
1877 no Die no	*incl. above*	£5	£16	£40	£75
1878	2,624,525	£5	£16	£40	£75
1878 Dritanniar Error	*incl. above*	£50	£140	—	—
1879	3,326,313	£5	£16	£45	£75
1879 no Die no	*incl. above*	£4	£16	£45	£75
1880 no Die no	3,892,501	£4	£16	£45	£75
Third head					
1880	*incl above*	£4	£18	£35	£50
1881	6,239,447	£4	£18	£35	£50
1882	759,809	£4	£18	£60	£110
1883	4,986,558	£4	£16	£35	£55
1884	3,422,565	£4	£16	£35	£55
1885	4,652,771	£4	£16	£35	£55
1886	2,728,249	£4	£16	£35	£55
1887	3,675,607	£4	£15	£32	£60
JUBILEE HEAD ISSUES					
*1887 Shield reverse	*incl. above*	£3	£5	£9	£16
1887 — Proof	*incl. above*	—	—	—	£50
1887 Six Pence in wreath reverse	*incl. above*	£2	£4	£9	£16
1888 —	4,197,698	£3	£7	£16	£30
*1889 —	8,738,928	£3	£7	£20	£40
1890 —	9,386,955	£3	£7	£22	£40
1891 —	7,022,734	£3	£7	£22	£40
1892 —	6,245,746	£3	£7	£22	£40
1893 —	7,350,619	£150	£300	£800	£1500
OLD HEAD ISSUES					
1893	*incl. above*	£3	£7	£16	£32
1893 Proof	1,312	—	—	—	£60
1894	3,467,704	£5	£12	£35	£60
1895	7,024,631	£4	£10	£30	£50
1896	6,651,699	£4	£8	£25	£40
1897	5,031,498	£4	£8	£25	£40
1898	5,914,100	£4	£8	£25	£40
1899	7,996,80	£4	£8	£25	£40
1900	8,984,354	£4	£8	£25	£40
1901	5,108,757	£3	£6	£20	£35

EDWARD VII (1901–10)

1902	6,367,378	£1	£4	£18	£30
1902 "Matt Proof"	15,123	—	—	—	£20
1903	5,410,096	£3	£10	£35	£75
1904	4,487,098	£5	£20	£50	£100
1905	4,235,556	£4	£15	£40	£80
1906	7,641,146	£3	£8	£30	£60
1907	8,733,673	£3	£8	£30	£60
*1908	6,739,491	£4	£14	£35	£70
1909	6,584,017	£3	£10	£30	£60
1910	12,490,724	£1	£5	£15	£30

GEORGE V (1910–36)

First issue					
1911	9,155,310	£1	£2	£7	£20
1911 Proof	6,007	—	—	—	£30
1912	10,984,129	£1	£2	£15	£28
1913	7,499,833	£1	£5	£18	£35
1914	22,714,602	£1	£2	£7	£20
*1915	15,694,597	£1	£2	£10	£25
1916	22,207,178	£1	£2	£8	£18
1917	7,725,475	£1	£5	£18	£45
1918	27,553,743	£1	£2	£8	£20
1919	13,375,447	£1	£3	£10	£22
1920	14,136,287	£1	£3	£10	£22
Second issue—debased silver					
1920	*incl. above*	£1	£3	£8	£25
1921	30,339,741	£1	£3	£8	£25
1922	16,878,890	£1	£2	£10	£25

Victoria Jubilee Head

Shield reverse

New reverse

DATE	MINTAGE	F	VF	EF	UNC
1923	6,382,793	£1.50	£5	£22	£45
1924	17,444,218	£1	£5	£10	£20
1925	12,720,558	£1	£2	£10	£20
1925 Broad rim	incl. above	£1	£2	£8	£20
1926 —	21,809,621	£1	£2	£8	£20
Third issue—*Modified bust*					
1926	incl. above	£1	£2	£8	£24
1927	8,924,873	—	£1	£7	£22
Fourth issue—*New design (oakleaves)*					
1927 Proof only	15,000	—	—	—	£20
1928	23,123,384	—	£1	£5	£15
1929	28,319,326	—	£1	£5	£15
1930	16,990,289	—	£1	£5	£15
1931	16,873,268	—	£1	£5	£15
1932	9,406,117	—	£1	£5	£15
1933	22,185,083	—	£1	£5	£15
1934	9,304,009	£1	£2	£7	£18
1935	13,995,621	—	£1	£4	£8
*1936	24,380,171	—	£1	£4	£7

George V second reverse

GEORGE VI (1936–52)

First type					
1937	22,302,524	—	—	£1	£4
1937 Proof	26,402	—	—	—	£5
1938	13,402,701	—	£1	£3	£11
1939	28,670,304	—	—	£1	£5
1940	20,875,196	—	—	£1	£5
1941	23,086,616	—	—	£1	£5
1942	44,942,785	—	—	£1	£4
1943	46,927,111	—	—	£1	£4
1944	36,952,600	—	—	£1	£4
1945	39,939,259	—	—	£1	£3
1946	43,466,407	—	—	£1	£3
1947	29,993,263	—	—	£1	£3
1948	88,323,540	—	—	£1	£3
Second type—*new cypher on rev.*					
1949	41,335,515	—	—	£1	£3
1950	32,741,955	—	—	£1	£3
1950 Proof	17,513	—	—	—	£5
1951	40,399,491	—	—	£1	£3
1951 Proof	20,000	—	—	—	£5
1952	1,013,477	£2	£8	£15	£30

George VI first reverse

ELIZABETH II (1952–   )

1953	70,323,876	—	—	—	£2
1953 Proof	40,000	—	—	—	£4
1954	105,241,150	—	—	—	£3
1955	109,929,554	—	—	—	£1
1956	109,841,555	—	—	—	£1
1957	105,654,290	—	—	—	£1
1958	123,518,527	—	—	—	£3
1959	93,089,441	—	—	—	£1
1960	103,283,346	—	—	—	£3
1961	115,052,017	—	—	—	£3
1962	166,483,637	—	—	—	—
1963	120,056,000	—	—	—	—
1964	152,336,000	—	—	—	—
1965	129,644,000	—	—	—	—
1966	175,676,000	—	—	—	—
1967	240,788,000	—	—	—	—

George VI second reverse

GROATS OR FOURPENCES

DATE	MINTAGE	F	VF	EF	UNC

WILLIAM IV (1831–37)

DATE	MINTAGE	F	VF	EF	UNC
*1836	—	£5	£12	£28	£50
1837	962,280	£5	£12	£28	£50

VICTORIA (1838–1901)

DATE	MINTAGE	F	VF	EF	UNC
1837	Extremely Rare Proofs or Patterns only				
1838	2,150,280	£5	£12	£30	£55
1839	1,461,240	£6	£14	£30	£55
1839 Proof	incl. above	—	—	—	£125
1840	1,496,880	£6	£12	£30	£55
1841	344,520	£6	£14	£33	£55
1842	724,680	£6	£14	£33	£55
1843	1,817640	£6	£14	£35	£55
1844	855,360	£6	£14	£35	£55
1845	914,760	£6	£14	£35	£55
1846	1,366,200	£6	£14	£35	£55
1847 7 over 6	225,720	£10	£25	£100	—
1848	712,800	£6	£14	£30	£50
1849	380,160	£6	£14	£30	£50
*1851	594,000	£16	£45	£150	£220
1852	31,300	£25	£80	£240	—
1853	11,880	£30	£90	£300	—
1853 Proof	incl. above	—	—	—	£300
1854	1,096,613	£6	£14	£35	£55
1855	646,041	£6	£14	£35	£55
1888 JH	—	£6	£14	£35	£60

THREEPENCES

JAMES II (1685–88)

DATE	F	VF	EF	UNC
1685	£6	£16	£35	—
1686	£7	£16	£35	—
1687/6	£7	£16	£35	—
1688	£10	£20	£40	—

WILLIAM & MARY (1688–94)

DATE	F	VF	EF	UNC
*1689 First busts	£7	£16	£35	—
1690 —	£7	£16	£35	—
1691 —	£15	£30	£50	—
1691 Second busts	£10	£20	£45	—
1692 —	£10	£20	£45	—
1693 —	£8	£16	£40	—
1694 —	£10	£18	£35	—

WILLIAM III (1694–1702)

DATE	F	VF	EF	UNC
1698	£12	£28	£50	—
1699	£14	£30	£55	—
1700	£12	£28	£50	—
1701	£12	£22	£50	—

ANNE (1702–1714)

DATE	F	VF	EF	UNC
1703 First head	£10	£22	£45	—
1704 Second head	£7	£15	£33	—
1705 —	£7	£15	£33	—
1706 —	£8	£18	£40	—
1707 Third head	£7	£18	£40	—

DATE	MINTAGE	F	VF	EF	UNC
1708 Third head		£7	£18	£40	—
1708 —		£8	£18	£40	—
1709 —		£8	£18	£40	—
1710 —		£8	£18	£40	—
*1713 —		£8	£18	£40	—

GEORGE I (1714–27)

DATE	MINTAGE	F	VF	EF	UNC
1717		£10	£22	£45	—
1721		£10	£22	£45	—
1723		£10	£25	£40	—
1727		£10	£25	£40	

GEORGE II (1727–60)

DATE	MINTAGE	F	VF	EF	UNC
1729		£8	£16	£35	—
1731		£8	£16	£35	—
1732		£8	£16	£35	—
1735		£8	£16	£35	—
1737		£8	£16	£35	—
1739		£8	£16	£35	—
1740		£8	£16	£35	—
*1743		£8	£16	£35	—
1746		£8	£16	£35	—
1760		£8	£16	£35	—

GEORGE III (1760–1820)

DATE	MINTAGE	F	VF	EF	UNC
1762		£5	£11	£22	—
1763		£5	£11	£22	—
1765		£100	£175	£450	—
1766		£5	£11	£25	—
1770		£6	£12	£25	—
1772		£5	£11	£25	—
1780		£5	£11	£25	—
1784		£5	£11	£25	—
1792		£12	£25	£40	—
1795		£5	£11	£25	—
1800		£5	£11	£25	—

WILLIAM IV (1830–37)

(issued for use in the West Indies)

DATE	MINTAGE	F	VF	EF	UNC
1834		£5	£10	£30	£50
1835		£5	£10	£30	£50
1836		£5	£10	£30	£50
1837		£5	£10	£32	£55

VICTORIA (1837–1901)

YOUNG HEAD ISSUES

DATE	MINTAGE	F	VF	EF	UNC
1838	—	£4	£15	£35	£60
1839	—	£4	£15	£40	£70
1940	—	£4	£15	£40	£70
1841	—	£4	£15	£45	£70
1842	—	£4	£15	£45	£75
1843	—	£4	£15	£30	£50
1844	—	£4	£15	£50	£75
*1845	1,314,720	£5	£15	£30	£55
1846	47,520	£5	£20	£60	£100
1849	126,720	£5	£16	£50	£85
1850	950,400	£4	£15	£35	£60
1851	479,065	£4	£15	£35	£60
1853	31,680	£5	£15	£40	£65
1854	1,467,246	£4	£15	£40	£55
1855	383,350	£4	£15	£45	£70
1856	1,013,760	£4	£15	£40	£70
1857	1,758,240	£4	£15	£45	£70
1858	1,441,440	£4	£15	£45	£60
1859	3,579,840	£4	£15	£30	£55

DATE	MINTAGE	F	VF	EF	UNC
1860	3,405,600	£4	£15	£25	£55
1861	3,294,720	£4	£15	£30	£55
1862	1,156,320	£4	£15	£35	£60
1863	950,400	£4	£15	£35	£65
1864	1,330,560	£4	£15	£25	£55
1865	1,742,400	£4	£15	£30	£75
1866	1,900,800	£4	£15	£25	£55
1867	712,800	£4	£15	£35	£65
1868	1,457,280	£4	£15	£25	£60
1868 Rrittanniar error	incl. above	£50	£100	£220	—
1869	—	£15	£40	£90	£140
1870	1,283,218	£4	£15	£40	£55
1871	999,633	£4	£12	£30	£55
1872	1,293,271	£4	£12	£30	£55
1873	4,055,550	£4	£12	£30	£50
1874	4,427,031	£4	£12	£30	£50
1875	3,306,500	£4	£12	£30	£50
1876	1,834,389	£4	£12	£30	£50
1877	2,622,393	£4	£12	£30	£50
1878	2,419,975	£4	£12	£30	£50
1879	3,140,265	£4	£12	£30	£50
1880	1,610,069	£4	£12	£30	£50
1881	3,248,265	£4	£12	£30	£50
1882	472,965	£4	£16	£40	£85
1883	4,369,971	£4	£8	£25	£40
1884	3,322,424	£4	£8	£25	£40
1885	5,183,653	£4	£8	£25	£40
1886	6,152,669	£4	£8	£25	£40
1887	2,780,761	£4	£8	£25	£40

JUBILEE HEAD ISSUES

DATE	MINTAGE	F	VF	EF	UNC
1887	incl. above	£1	£3	£8	£15
1887 Proof	incl. above	—	—	—	£30
1888	518,199	£1	£4	£15	£30
*1889	4,587,010	£1	£4	£15	£30
1890	4,465,834	£1	£4	£15	£30
1891	6,323,027	£1	£4	£15	£30
1892	2,578,226	£1	£4	£15	£30
1893	3,067,243	£6	£20	£80	£125

OLD HEAD ISSUES

DATE	MINTAGE	F	VF	EF	UNC
1893	incl. above	£1	£3	£12	£20
1893 Proof	incl. above	—	—	—	£35
1894	1,608,603	£1	£5	£20	£35
1895	4,788,609	£1	£5	£16	£30
1896	4,598,442	£1	£5	£16	£30
1897	4,541,294	£1	£5	£16	£30
1898	4,567,177	£1	£5	£16	£30
*1899	6,246,281	£1	£5	£16	£30
1900	10,644,480	£1	£3	£16	£30
1901	6,098,400	£1	£3	£12	£25

EDWARD VII (1901–10)

DATE	MINTAGE	F	VF	EF	UNC
1902	8,268,480	£1	£2	£7	£14
1902 "Matt Proof"	incl. above	—	—	—	£15
1903	5,227,200	£1	£3	£18	£30
1904	3,627,360	£1	£5	£30	£60
1905	3,548,160	£1	£3	£22	£50
1906	3,152,160	£1	£3	£18	£40
1907	4,831,200	£1	£3	£18	£30
1908	8,157,600	£1	£2	£18	£30
1909	4,055,040	£1	£3	£18	£30
*1910	4,563,380	£1	£3	£14	£28

GEORGE V (1910–36)

First issue

DATE	MINTAGE	F	VF	EF	UNC
1911	5,841,084	—	—	£2	£8
1911 Proof	incl. above	—	—	—	£20
1912	8,932,825	—	—	£2	£8
1913	7,143,242	—	—	£2	£8
1914	6,733,584	—	—	£2	£8
1915	5,450,617	—	—	£2	£8
1916	18,555,201	—	—	£2	£7

DATE	MINTAGE	F	VF	EF	UNC
1917	21,662,490	—	—	£2	£7
7918	20,630,909	—	—	£2	£7
1919	16,845,687	—	—	£2	£7
1920	16,703,597	—	—	£2	£7

Second issue—*debased silver*

1920	*incl. above*	—	—	£2	£7
1921	8,749,301	—	—	£2	£7
1922	7,979,998	—	—	£2	£7
1925	3,731,859	—	—	£5	£20
1926	4,107,910	—	—	£7	£20

Third issue—*Modified bust*

1926	*incl. above*	—	—	£7	£16

Fourth issue—*new design (oakleaves)*

1927 Proof only	15,022	—	—	—	£35
1928	1,302,106	£1	£5	£18	£35
1930	1,319,412	£1	£3	£7	£15
1931	6,251,936	—	—	£2	£5
1932	5,887,325	—	—	£2	£5
1933	5,578,541	—	—	£2	£5
1934	7,405,954	—	—	£2	£5
1935	7,027,654	—	—	£2	£5
1936	3,328,670	—	—	£2	£5

GEORGE VI (1936–52)

Silver

1937	8,148,156	—	—	£1	£3
1937 Proof	26,402	—	—	—	£5
1938	6,402,473	—	—	£1	£3
1939	1,355,860	—	—	£2	£6
1940	7,914,401	—	—	£1	£3
1941	7,979,411	—	—	£1	£3
1942	4,144,051	£2	£5	£12	£30
1943	1,397,220	£2	£5	£12	£30
1944	2,005,553	£4	£12	£35	£70
1945	Only one known				

Brass

1937	45,707,957	—	—	£1	£3
1937 Proof	26,402	—	—	—	£3
1938	14,532,332	—	—	£1	£8
1939	5,603,021	—	—	£2	£16
1940	12,636,018	—	—	£1	£6
1941	60,239,489	—	—	—	£4
1942	103,214,400	—	—	£1	£5
1943	101,702,400	—	—	£1	£5
1944	69,760,000	—	—	£1	£6
1945	33,942,466	—	—	£1	£4
1946	620,734	£1.50	£10	£55	£150
1948	4,230,400	—	—	—	£6
1949	464,000	£2.50	£7	£50	£150
1950	1,600,000	—	£1	£7	£20
1950 Proof	17,513	—	—	—	£5
1951	1,184,000	—	£1	£7	£25
1951 Proof	20,000	—	—	—	£5
1952	25,494,400	—	—	—	£4

ELIZABETH II (1952–   )

1953	30,618,000	—	—	—	£1
1953 Proof	40,000	—	—	—	£5
1954	41,720,000	—	—	—	£4
1955	41,075,200	—	—	—	£4
1956	36,801,600	—	—	—	£4
1957	24,294,500	—	—	—	£3
1958	20,504,000	—	—	—	£6
1959	28,499,200	—	—	—	£3
1960	83,078,400	—	—	—	£2
1961	41,102,400	—	—	—	£1
1962	51,545,600	—	—	—	£1
1963	39,482,866	—	—	—	£1
1964	44,867,200	—	—	—	—
1965	27,160,000	—	—	—	—
1966	53,160,000	—	—	—	—
1967	151,780,800	—	—	—	—

TWO PENCE

DATE	F	VF	EF	UNC

CHARLES II (1660–85)

	F	VF	EF	UNC
1668	£20	£35	£85	—
1670	£15	£30	£55	—
1671	£15	£30	£55	—
1672	£15	£30	£55	—
1673	£15	£30	£55	—
1674	£15	£30	£55	—
1675	£15	£30	£55	—
1676	£15	£30	£55	—
1677	£15	£30	£55	—
1678	£15	£30	£55	—
1679	£15	£30	£55	—
1680	£15	£30	£55	—
1681	£15	£30	£55	—
1682	£15	£30	£55	—
1683	£15	£30	£55	—
1684	£15	£30	£55	—

JAMES II (1685–88)

	F	VF	EF	UNC
1686	£15	£30	£55	—
1687	£15	£30	£55	—
1687 ERA error on rev.	£22	£50	£100	—
1688	£15	£30	£55	—

WILLIAM & MARY (1688–94)

	F	VF	EF	UNC
1689	£15	£30	£55	—
1691	£15	£30	£55	—
1692	£15	£30	£55	—
1693	£15	£30	£55	—
1694	£20	£35	£75	—
1694 MARLA error on obv.	£22	£38	£85	—
1694 HI error on rev.	£22	£38	£85	—

WILLIAM III (1694–1702)

	F	VF	EF	UNC
1698	£20	£35	£65	—
1699	£20	£30	£60	—
1700	£20	£30	£60	—
1701	£20	£30	£60	—

ANNE (1702–14)

	F	VF	EF	UNC
1703 (pre-Union with Scotland)	£16	£30	£65	—
1704	£15	£25	£55	—
1705	£15	£25	£55	—
1706	£15	£25	£55	—
1707 (post-Union)	£15	£25	£55	—
1708	£16	£28	£60	—
1709	£16	£28	£60	—
1711	£15	£25	£55	—
1713	£15	£25	£55	—

GEORGE I (1714–27)

	F	VF	EF	UNC
1717	£15	£25	£50	—
1721	£15	£25	£50	—
1723	£16	£35	£65	—
1726	£15	£25	£50	—
1727	£15	£30	£55	

DATE	F	VF	EF	UNC

GEORGE II (1727–60)

	F	VF	EF	UNC
1729	£12	£28	£45	—
1731	£15	£28	£45	—
1732	£15	£28	£45	—
1735	£15	£28	£45	—
1737	£15	£28	£45	—
1739	£15	£28	£45	—
1740	£15	£28	£45	—
1743	£15	£28	£45	—
1746	£15	£28	£45	—
1756	£15	£28	£45	—
1759	£15	£28	£45	—
1760	£15	£28	£45	—

GEORGE III (1760–1820)

	F	VF	EF	UNC
1763 Young Laureated bust	£15	£25	£45	—
1765 —	£80	£250	£600	—
1766 —	£12	£22	£35	—
1772 —	£12	£22	£35	—
1776 —	£12	£22	£35	—
1780 —	£12	£22	£35	—
1784 —	£12	£22	£35	—
1786 —	£12	£22	£35	—
1792 Small draped bust	£15	£35	£55	—
1795 —	£12	£15	£25	—

It is generally accepted that later issues were only produced for inclusion with the Maundy sets, q.v., except for those listed below

	F	VF	EF	UNC
1797 "Cartwheel"	£15	£35	£150	£500
1797 Copper Proof	—	—	—	£500

Proofs also exist in various other metals

VICTORIA (1837–1901)

For use in the Colonies

	F	VF	EF	UNC
1838	£4	£10	£18	£30
1848	£4	£12	£20	£35

THREE-HALFPENCE

WILLIAM IV (1830–37)

For use in the Colonies

	F	VF	EF	UNC
1834	£5	£12	£20	£50
1835 over 4	£5	£12	£20	£50
1836	£7	£15	£25	£60
1837	£12	£35	£90	£155

VICTORIA (1837–1901)

For use in the Colonies

	F	VF	EF	UNC
1838	£5	£12	£20	£45
1839	£5	£12	£20	£45
1840	£6	£15	£30	£65
1841	£5	£12	£20	£45
1842	£5	£15	£25	£55
1843	£5	£12	£18	£40
1860	£7	£17	£50	£85
1862	£7	£16	£45	£75

PENNIES

DATE	MINTAGE	F	VF	EF	UNC

CHARLES II (1660–85)

Silver up to 1781

1670		£8	£18	£40	—
1671		£8	£18	£40	—
1672/1		£8	£18	£40	—
1673		£8	£18	£40	—
1674		£8	£18	£40	—
1675		£8	£18	£40	—
1676		£10	£20	£45	—
1677		£8	£18	£40	—
1678		£8	£18	£40	—
1679		£15	£30	£55	—
1680		£8	£18	£40	—
1681		£10	£20	£48	—
1682		£10	£20	£45	—
1683		£8	£18	£40	—
1684		£10	£20	£45	—

Charles II

JAMES II (1685–88)

1685		£7	£14	£35	—

James II

WILLIAM & MARY (1688–94)

1690		£8	£15	£35	—

George II

GEORGE I (1714–27)

1716		£7	£18	£40	—
1718		£7	£18	£40	—
1720		£7	£18	£40	—
1725		£8	£20	£45	—
1726		£8	£20	£45	—

GEORGE II (1727–60)

1750		£7	£15	£35	—
1752		£7	£15	£35	—
1753		£7	£15	£35	—
1754		£7	£15	£35	—
1755		£7	£15	£35	—
1756		£7	£15	£35	—
1757		£7	£15	£35	—
1758		£7	£15	£35	—
1759		£7	£15	£35	—

GEORGE III (1760–1820)

1770		£6	£12	£30	
1776		£6	£12	£30	—
1779		£6	£12	£30	—
1781		£6	£12	£30	—

Copper

*1797 "Cartwheel" Penny	8,601,600	£10	£25	£110	£300
1806 Third type	unknown	£3	£10	£50	£110
1807 —	unknown	£3	£10	£55	£120
1808 —				Only one known	

"Cartwheel" penny

DATE	MINTAGE	F	VF	EF	UNC

GEORGE IV (1820–30)

DATE	MINTAGE	F	VF	EF	UNC
1825	1,075,200	£8	£25	£75	£220
*1826 (varieties)	5,913,600	£8	£25	£75	£220
1826 Proof	—	—	—	£90	£150
1827	1,451,520	£45	£125	£650	£1250

WILLIAM IV (1830–37)

DATE	MINTAGE	F	VF	EF	UNC
1831(varieties)	806,400	£12	£30	£100	£225
1831 Proof	—	—	—	£100	£180
1834	322,560	£12	£30	£100	£240
1837	174,720	£12	£30	£100	£250

VICTORIA (1837–1901)

YOUNG HEAD ISSUES

Copper

DATE	MINTAGE	F	VF	EF	UNC
1839 Proof	unrecorded	—	—	—	£175
*1841	913,920	£5	£12	£40	£90
1843	483,840	£20	£70	£200	£375
1844	215,040	£5	£12	£40	£100
1845	322,560	£6	£15	£70	£120
1846	483,840	£6	£15	£70	£120
1847	430,080	£5	£12	£55	£90
1848	161,280	£5	£12	£55	£90
1849	268,800	£30	£125	£300	£500
1851	268,800	£7	£18	£70	£135
1853	1,021,440	£4	£10	£35	£65
1853 Proof	—	—	—	—	£300
1854	6,720,000	£4	£10	£35	£65
1855	5,273,856	£4	£10	£35	£65
1856	1,212,288	£10	£35	£90	£170
1857	752,640	£4	£12	£35	£80
1858	1,599,040	£4	£10	£35	£80
1859	1,075,200	£5	£16	£50	£100
1860/59	32,256	£275	£450	£1000	—

Bronze

DATE	MINTAGE	F	VF	EF	UNC
1860 Beaded border	5,053,440	£4	£8	£30	£60
1860 Toothed border	incl. above	£4	£10	£40	£80
1861	36,449,280	£3	£8	£30	£60
1862	50,534,400	£3	£7	£28	£60
1863	28,062,720	£3	£7	£24	£55
1864 Plain 4	3,440,640	£8	£35	£200	£300
1864 Crosslet 4	incl. above	£8	£35	£200	£3000
1865	8,601,600	£4	£12	£35	£65
1866	9,999,360	£4	£12	£35	£65
1867	5,483,520	£4	£12	£35	£65
*1868	1,182,720	£7	£30	£90	£160
1869	2,580,480	£35	£110	£350	£625
1870	5,695,022	£5	£18	£75	£140
1871	1,290,318	£20	£90	£175	£450
1872	8,494,572	£4	£12	£35	£65
1873	8,494,200	£4	£12	£35	£65
1874	5,621,865	£4	£12	£35	£65
1874 H	6,666,240	£4	£12	£35	£65
1875	10,691,040	£4	£12	£35	£65
1875 H	752,640	£25	£80	£225	£425
1876 H	11,074,560	£4	£10	£40	£70
1877	9,624,747	£4	£12	£40	£70
1878	2,764,470	£4	£12	£40	£70
1879	7,666,476	£3	£10	£35	£65
1880	3,000,831	£3	£10	£30	£60

DATE	MINTAGE	F	VF	EF	UNC
1881	2,302,362	£4	£10	£35	£65
1881 H	3,763,200	£4	£10	£30	£60
1882 H	7,526,400	£4	£10	£25	£45
1882 No H			Extremely Rare		
1883	6,237,438	£4	£12	£35	£65
1884	11,702,802	£4	£10	£35	£70
1885	7,145,862	£3	£10	£35	£60
1886	6,087,759	£3	£10	£35	£60
1887	5,315,085	£3	£10	£35	£60
1888	5,125,020	£3	£10	£35	£60
1889	12,559,737	£3	£10	£35	£60
1890	15,330,840	£3	£10	£35	£60
1891	17,885,961	£3	£10	£35	£60
1892	10,501,671	£3	£10	£35	£60
1893	8,161,737	£3	£10	£35	£60
1894	3,883,452	£5	£16	£45	£90

OLD HEAD ISSUES

DATE	MINTAGE	F	VF	EF	UNC
1895 Trident 2mm from (PENNY)	5,395,830	£3	£15	£65	£180
1895 Trident 1mm from P	incl. above	—	£2	£12	£35
1896	24,147,156	—	£2	£12	£30
*1897	20,756,620	—	£2	£12	£30
1898	14,296,836	—	£2	£12	£30
1899	26,441,069	—	£2	£12	£30
1900	31,778,109	—	£2	£10	£20
1901	22,205,568	—	£2	£7	£12

EDWARD VII (1901–10)

DATE	MINTAGE	F	VF	EF	UNC
1902	26,976,768	—	£1	£8	£20
1902 "Low tide"	incl. above	—	£5	£20	£50
1903	21,415,296	—	£3	£12	£35
1904	12,913,152	—	£3	£12	£35
1905	17,783,808	—	£3	£12	£35
1906	37,989,504	—	£3	£12	£35
1907	47,322,240	—	£3	£12	£35
*1908	31,506,048	—	£3	£12	£35
1909	19,617,024	—	£3	£15	£40
1910	29,549,184	—	£3	£10	£30

GEORGE V (1910–36)

DATE	MINTAGE	F	VF	EF	UNC
1911	23,079,168	—	£3	£12	£32
1912	48,306,048	—	£3	£12	£32
*1912 H	16,800,000	—	£3	£25	£70
1913	65,497,812	—	£3	£12	£40
1914	50,820,997	—	£3	£12	£40
1915	47,310,807	—	£3	£12	£40
1916	86,411,165	—	£3	£12	£40
1917	107,905,436	—	£3	£12	£40
1918	84,227,372	—	£3	£12	£40
1918 H	3,660,800	£1	£8	£60	£240
1918 KN	incl. above	£5	£45	£200	£650
1919	113,761,090	—	£2	£12	£40
1919 H	5,209,600	£1	£10	£70	£240
1919 KN	incl. above	£6	£50	£220	£675
1920	124,693,485	—	£2	£12	£25
1921	129,717,693	—	£2	£12	£25
1922	16,346,711	—	£2	£12	£30
1926	4,498,519	—	£6	£20	£70
1926 Modified effigy	incl above	£7	£25	£300	£500
1927	60,989,561	—	£2	£8	£22
1928	50,178,00	—	£2	£8	£22
1929	49,132,800	—	£2	£8	£22
1930	29,097,600	—	£2	£10	£35

DATE	MINTAGE	F	VF	EF	UNC
1931	19,843,200	—	£2	£8	£25
1932	8,277,600	—	£2	£9	£28
1933			Only 7 examples known		
1934	13,965,600	—	£2	£8	£25
1935	56,070,000	—	—	£2	£8
1936	154,296,000	—	—	£2	£7

GEORGE VI (1936–52)

1937	88,896,000	—	—	—	£3
1937 Proof	26,402	—	—	—	£5
1938	121,560,00	—	—	—	£3
1939	55,560,000	—	—	—	£4
1940	42,284,400	—	—	—	£6
1944	42,600,000	—	—	—	£6
1945	79,531,200	—	—	—	£5
1946	66,855,600	—	—	—	£3
1947	52,220,400	—	—	—	£3
1948	63,961,200	—	—	—	£3
1949	14,324,400	—	—	—	£3
1950	240,000	£2.50	£6	£12	£18
1950 Proof	17,513	—	—	—	£14
1951	120,000	£5	£8	£16	£25
1951 Proof	20,000	—	—	—	£16

ELIZABETH II (1952–   )

*1953	1,308,400	—	—	£1	£4
1953 Proof	40,000	—	—	—	£6
1954			Only one known		
1961	48,313,400	—	—	—	£1
1962	143,308,600	—	—	—	50p
1963	125,235,600	—	—	—	50p
1964	153,294,000	—	—	—	50p
1965	121,310,400	—	—	—	50p
1966	165,739,200	—	—	—	50p
1967	654,564,000	—	—	—	—

Later issues are included in the Decimal section.

HALFPENNIES

CHARLES II (1660–85)

		F	VF	EF	
1672		£35	£90	£450	—
1673		£35	£90	£450	—
1675		£35	£90	£450	—

JAMES II (1685–88)

1685 (tin)		£90	£200	£1000	—
1686 (tin)		£100	£225	£1000	—
1687 (tin)		£90	£200	£1000	—

WILLIAM & MARY (1688–94)

1689 (tin) Small draped busts		£300	—	—	—
1690 (tin) Large cuirassed busts edge dated		£100	£250	£1000	—
1691 (tin) date on edge and in exergue		£100	£250	£1000	—
1692 (tin) —		£100	£250	£1000	—
*1694 (copper)		£22	£80	£600	—

DATE	F	VF	EF	UNC

WILLIAM III (1694–1702)

	F	VF	EF	UNC
1695 First issue (date in exergue)	£22	£75	£425	—
1696 —	£22	£80	£450	—
1697 —	£22	£75	£425	—
1698 —	£22	£70	£500	—
1698 Second issue (date in legend)	£25	£100	—	—
1699 —	£22	£75	£425	—
1699 Third issue (date in exergue) (Britannia r. hand on knee)	£20	£75	£425	—
1700 —	£20	£70	£425	—
1701 —	£20	£70	£425	—

GEORGE I (1714–27)

	F	VF	EF	UNC
*1717 "Dump" issue	£35	£100	£375	—
1718 —	£20	£50	£275	—
1719 Second issue	£18	£50	£250	—
1720 —	£18	£50	£250	—
1721 —	£18	£50	£250	—
1722 —	£18	£50	£250	—
1723 —	£18	£50	£250	—
1724 —	£18	£0	£250	—

GEORGE II (1727–60)

	F	VF	EF	UNC
1729 Young head	£18	£50	£146	—
1730 —	£15	£45	£150	—
1731 —	£15	£45	£150	—
1732 —	£15	£45	£150	—
1733 —	£15	£45	£150	—
1734 —	£15	£45	£150	—
1735 —	£15	£35	£140	—
1736 —	£15	£35	£135	—
1737 —	£15	£35	£135	—
1738 —	£15	£35	£135	—
1739 —	£15	£35	£135	—
1740 Old head	£10	£32	£130	—
1742 —	£10	£32	£130	—
1743 —	£10	£32	£130	—
1744 —	£10	£32	£130	—
1745 —	£10	£32	£130	—
1746 —	£10	£32	£130	—
1747 —	£10	£32	£130	—
1748 —	£10	£32	£130	—
1749 —	£10	£32	£130	—
1750 —	£10	£32	£130	—
1751 —	£10	£32	£130	—
1752 —	£10	£32	£130	—
1753 —	£10	£3	£130	—
1754 —	£8	£28	£130	—

GEORGE III (1760–1820)

First type—Royal Mint

	F	VF	EF	UNC
1770	£8	£24	£110	—
1771	£8	£24	£110	—
1772	£8	£24	£110	—
1773	£8	£24	£110	—
1774	£8	£24	£110	—
*1775	£10	£28	£120	—

Second type—Soho Mint

	F	VF	EF	UNC
*1799	£2	£6	£30	£65

DATE	MINTAGE	F	VF	EF	UNC

Third type

1806		£2	£6	£30	£65
1807		£2	£6	£30	£66

GEORGE IV (1820–30)

1825	215,040	£8	£25	£70	£125
1826 (varieties)	9,031,630	£7	£20	£45	£90
1826 Proof	—	—	—	£80	£110
1827	5,376,000	£8	£25	£65	£110

WILLIAM IV (1830–37)

1831	806,400	£7	£22	£65	£120
1831 Proof	—	—	—	—	£125
1834	537,600	£7	£22	£65	£120
1837	349,440	£7	£22	£66	£120

VICTORIA (1837–1901)

YOUNG HEAD ISSUES
Copper

1838	456,960	£4	£12	£40	£65
1839 Proof	268,800	—	—	—	£120
1841	1,0745,200	£4	£12	£40	£65
1843	967,680	£8	£25	£60	£120
1844	1,075,200	£4	£15	£40	£70
1845	1,075,200	£20	£65	£200	£375
1846	860,160	£5	£12	£35	£60
1847	725,640	£5	£12	£32	£60
1848	322,560	£5	£12	£32	£65
1851	215,040	£5	£10	£32	£50
1852	637,056	£5	£10	£32	£55

1853	1,559,040	£4	£8	£20	£45
1853 over 2	*incl. above*	£4	£8	£20	£45
1853 Proof	—	—	—	—	£200
1854	12,354,048	£3	£8	£25	£45
1855	1,455,837	£3	£8	£25	£45
1856	1,942,080	£5	£12	£35	£70
1857	1,82,720	£5	£10	£25	£50
1858	2,472,960	£3	£10	£25	£50
1859	1,290,240	£5	£12	£35	£70
1860	*unrecorded*			Extremely	rare

Victoria copper halfpenny

Bronze

1860	6,630,400	£3	£9	£25	£50
1861	54,118,400	£3	£9	£25	£50
1862	61,107,200	£3	£9	£25	£50
1863	15,948,800	£3	£9	£25	£50
1864	537,600	£3	£9	£30	£55
1865	8,064,000	£4	£15	£50	£75
1866	2,508,800	£4	£9	£30	£5
1867	2,508,800	£5	£15	£40	£70
1868	3,046,400	£4	£10	£40	£70
1869	3,225,600	£7	£30	£60	£125

1870	4,350,739	£5	£15	£50	£90
1871	1,075,280	£25	£70	£135	£270
1872	4,659,410	£4	£10	£35	£50
1873	3,404,880	£4	£10	£35	£55
1874	1,347,655	£5	£20	£60	£100
1874 H	5,017,600	£3	£10	£30	£50
1875	5,430,815	£3	£8	£30	£50
1875 H	1,254,400	£4	£10	£35	£65

Victoria bronze halfpenny

DATE	MINTAGE	F	VF	EF	UNC
1876 H	5,809,600	£4	£10	£35	£65
1877	5,209,505	£3	£10	£25	£50
1878	1,425,535	£5	£18	£50	£80
1879	3,582,545	£3	£10	£25	£50
1880	2,423,465	£4	£12	£40	£65
1881	2,007,515	£4	£12	£35	£60
1881 H	1,792,000	£3	£10	£28	£45
1882 H	4,480,000	£3	£10	£22	£45
1883	3,000,725	£3	£10	£22	£45
1884	6,989,580	£3	£10	£22	£45
1885	8,600,574	£3	£10	£22	£45
1886	8,586,155	£3	£10	£22	£45
1887	10,701,305	£3	£10	£22	£45
1888	6,814,670	£3	£10	£22	£45
1889	7,748,234	£3	£10	£22	£45
1890	11,254,235	£3	£10	£22	£45
1891	13,192,260	£3	£10	£22	£45
1892	2,478,335	£3	£10	£22	£45
1893	7,229,344	£3	£10	£22	£45
1894	1,767,635	£5	£12	£30	£65

OLD HEAD ISSUES

1895	3,032,154	£1	£4	£15	£35
1896	9,142,500	£1	£4	£10	£30
1897	8,690,315	£1	£4	£10	£30
1898	8,595,180	£1	£4	£10	£30
1899	12,108,001	£1	£4	£10	£30
1900	13,805,190	£1	£4	£10	£25
1901	11,127,360	£1	£2	£6	£12

EDWARD VII (1901–10)

1902	13,672,960	£2	£4	£8	£18
1902 "Low tide"	incl. above	£4	£12	£40	£70
*1903	11,450,880	£2	£4	£15	£35
1904	8,131,200	£2	£4	£15	£35
1905	10,124,800	£2	£4	£15	£35
1906	16,849,280	£2	£4	£15	£35
1907	16,849,280	£2	£4	£15	£35
1908	16,620,800	£2	£4	£15	£35
1909	8,279,040	£2	£4	£15	£35
1910	10,769,920	£2	£4	£15	£35

GEORGE V (1910–36)

1911	12,570,880	—	£2	£10	£30
1912	21,185,920	—	£2	£10	£30
1913	17,476,480	—	£2	£12	£32
1914	20,289,111	—	£2	£10	£30
1915	21,563,040	£1	£3	£10	£30
1916	39,386,143	—	£2	£10	£30
1917	38,245,436	—	£2	£10	£30
1918	22,321,072	—	£2	£10	£30
1919	28,104,001	—	£2	£10	£30
1920	35,146,793	—	£2	£10	£30
1921	28,027,293	—	£2	£10	£30
*1922	10,734,964	—	£2	£10	£32
1923	12,266,282	—	£2	£10	£30
1924	13,971,038	—	£2	£10	£30
1925	12,216,123	—	£2	£10	£30
1925 Modified effigy	incl. above	£2	£4	£18	£40
1926	6,172,306	—	£2	£10	£30
1927	15,589,622	—	£2	£8	£30

DATE	MINTAGE	F	VF	EF	UNC
1928	20,935,200	—	£2	£7	£18
1929	25,680,000	—	£2	£8	£25
1930	12,532,800	—	£2	£8	£25
1931	16,137,600	—	£2	£8	£25
1932	14,448,000	—	£2	£8	£25
1933	10,560,000	—	£2	£8	£25
1934	7,704,000	—	£2	£10	£20
1935	12,180,000	—	£1	£6	£15
1936	23,008,800	—	£1	£5	£8

GEORGE VI (1936–52)

1937	24,504,000	—	—	£1	£2
1937 Proof	26,402	—	—	£1	£5
1938	40,320,000	—	—	£1	£4
1939	28,924,800	—	—	£1	£4
1940	32,162,400	—	—	£1	£5
1941	45,120,000	—	—	£1	£5
1942	71,908,800	—	—	£1	£3
1943	76,200,000	—	—	£1	£3
1944	81,840,000	—	—	£1	£3
1945	57,000,000	—	—	£1	£3
1946	22,725,600	—	—	£1	£5
1947	21,266,400	—	—	£1	£3
1948	26,947,200	—	—	£1	£2
*1949	24,744,000	—	—	£1	£2
1950	24,153,600	—	—	£1	£4
1950 Proof	17,513	—	—	£1	£5
1951	14,868,000	—	—	£1	£5
1951 Proof	20,000	—	—	£1	£5
1952	33,78,400	—	—	£1	£2

ELIZABETH II (1952–   )

1953	8,926,366	—	—	—	£1
1953 Proof	40,000	—	—	—	£3
*1954	19,375,000	—	—	—	£3
1955	18,799,200	—	—	—	£3
1956	21,799,200	—	—	—	£3
1957	43,684,800	—	—	—	£1
1958	62,318,400	—	—	—	£1
1959	79,176,000	—	—	—	£1
1960	41,340,000	—	—	—	£1
1962	41,779,200	—	—	—	£1
1963	45,036,000	—	—	—	20p
1964	78,583,200	—	—	—	20p
1965	98,083,200	—	—	—	20p
1966	95,289,600	—	—	—	20p
1967	146,491,200	—	—	—	10p

Later issues are included in the Decimal section.

FARTHINGS

OLIVER CROMWELL

(copper) Draped bust, shield rev. (variations)
Undated .... Extremely rare

CHARLES II (1660–85)

1672 (copper)	£18	£40	£200	—

DATE	MINTAGE	F	VF	EF	UNC
*1673 (copper)		£18	£40	£200	—
1674 (copper)		£18	£45	£200	—
1675 (copper)		£18	£45	£200	—
1679 (copper)		£20	£50	£250	—
1684 (tin) with date on edge		£150	£375	—	—
1685 (tin) —		£300	—	—	—

JAMES II (1685–88)

1684 (tin) Cuirassed bust		£60	£200	£800	—
1685 (tin) —		£70	£200	£750	—
1686 (tin) —		£75	£200	£800	—
1687 (tin) —			Extremely rare		
1687 (tin) Draped bust		£150	£350	—	—

WILLIAM & MARY (1688–94)

1689 (tin) Small draped busts		£300	—	—	—
1689 (tin) — with edge date 1690			Extremely rare		
1690 (tin) Large cuirassed busts		£100	£225	£850	—
1690 (tin) — with edge date 1689		£200	—	—	—
1691 (tin) —		£125	£325	—	—
1692 (tin) —		£100	£225	£900	—
1694 (copper) —		£22	£60	£500	—

WILLIAM III (1694–1702)

1695 First issue (date in exergue)		£22	£75	£400	—
1696 —		£22	£75	£400	—
1697 —		£22	£77	£400	—
1698 —		£60	£150	—	—
1698 Second issue (date in legend) ..		£25	£80	£450	—
1699 First issue		£22	£80	£450	—
1699 Second issue		£22	£85	£450	—
1700 First issue		£22	£75	£400	—

ANNE (1702–14)

*1714		£90	£240	£400	—

GEORGE I (1714–27)

1717 First small "Dump" issue		£30	£100	£400	—
1719 Second issue		£18	£50	£200	—
1720 —		£18	£50	£200	—
1721 —		£18	£50	£200	—
1722 —		£18	£50	£200	—
1723 —		£18	£50	£200	—
1724 —		£18	£50	£200	—

GEORGE II (1727–60)

1730 Young head		£12	£40	£150	—
1731 —		£12	£40	£150	—
1732 —		£12	£40	£150	—
1733 —		£12	£40	£140	—
1734 —		£10	£30	£140	—
1735 —		£10	£30	£140	—
1736 —		£10	£30	£150	—
1737 —		£9	£30	£140	—
1739 —		£9	£30	£140	—
1741 Old Head		£8	£25	£120	—
1744 —		£8	£25	£120	—

DATE	MINTAGE	F	VF	EF	UNC
1746 —		£8	£25	£120	—
1749 —		£8	£25	£120	—
1750 —		£7	£22	£125	—
1754 —		£7	£18	£120	—

GEORGE III (1760–1820)

1771 First (London) issue		£12	£35	£130	—
1773 —		£10	£25	£90	—
1774 —		£8	£25	£100	—
1775 —		£8	£25	£110	—
1797 Second (Soho Mint) issue				Patterns only	
*1799 Third (Soho Mint) issue		£2	£7	£30	£60
*1806 Fourth (Soho Mint) issue		£2	£7	£30	£60
1807 —		£2	£7	£30	£60

George III third Soho Mint issue

GEORGE IV (1820–30)

1821 First bust (laureate, draped), first reverse (date in exergue) .	2,688,000	£2	£8	£30	£55
*1822 —	5,924,350	£2	£8	£30	£55
1823 —	2,365,440	£2	£8	£30	£65
1825 —	4,300.800	£2	£8	£30	£65
1826 —	6,666,240	£2	£8	£30	£55
1826 Second bust (couped, date below), second reverse (ornament in exergue)	*incl. above*	£2	£8	£30	£75
1826 — Proof	—	—	—	£70	£120
1827 —	2,365,440	£2	£9	£30	£70
1828 —	2,365,440	£2	£9	£30	£70
1829 —	1,505,280	£2	£10	£35	£85
1830 —	2,365,440	£2	£8	£30	£70

George III Fourth Soho Mint issue

WILLIAM IV (1830–37)

1831	2,688,000	£5	£12	£30	£75
1831 Proof	—	—	—	—	£100
1834	1,935,360	£5	£12	£30	£75
1835	1.720,320	£5	£12	£30	£75
1836	1,290.240	£5	£12	£30	£75
1837	3.010,560	£5	£12	£30	£75

VICTORIA (1837–1901)

YOUNG HEAD ISSUES

1838	591,360	£4	£12	£35	£60
1839	4,300,800	£4	£12	£35	£60
1839 Proof	—	—	—	—	£140
1840	3,010,560	£4	£12	£35	£50
1841	1,720,320	£4	£12	£35	£50
1842	1,290,240	£6	£16	£45	£85
1843	4,085,760	£4	£10	£35	£55
1844	430,080	£30	£75	£175	£450
1845	3,225,600	£4	£10	£35	£60
1846	2,580,480	£5	£15	£40	£75
*1847	3,879,720	£4	£10	£35	£55
1848	1,290,240	£4	£10	£35	£55
1849	645,120	£10	£30	£60	£125
1850	430,080	£4	£10	£35	£50
1851	1,935,360	£5	£15	£45	£75
1852	822,528	£5	£15	£40	£65
1853	1,028,628	£3	£7	£28	£40
1853 Proof	—	—	—	—	£250

DATE	MINTAGE	F	VF	EF	UNC
1854	6,504,960	£3	£8	£30	£45
1855	3,440,640	£3	£8	£30	£45
1856	1,771,392	£5	£10	£40	£75
1857	1,075,200	£3	£8	£30	£45
1858	1,720,320	£3	£7	£30	£45
1859	1,290,240	£6	£20	£50	£110
1860	*unrecorded*		Extremely	rare	

YOUNG OR "BUN" HEAD (BRONZE) ISSUES

DATE	MINTAGE	F	VF	EF	UNC
1860 Toothed border	2,867,200	£1	£5	£20	£40
1860 Beaded border	*incl. above*	£2	£5	£20	£40
1861	8,601,600	£1	£5	£20	£40
1862	14,336,000	£1	£5	£20	£35
1863	1,433,600	£16	£40	£120	£190
1864	2,508,800	£1	£5	£20	£40
1865	4,659,200	£1	£5	£20	£40
1866	3,584,000	£1	£5	£20	£40
1867	5,017,600	£1	£5	£20	£40
1868	4,851,210	£1	£5	£20	£40
1869	3,225,600	£1	£6	£22	£40
1872	2,150,400	£1	£5	£20	£35
1873	3,225,620	£1	£5	£20	£35
1874 H	3,584,000	£1	£5	£20	£35
1874 H both Gs over G	*incl. above*	£70	£150	£300	—
1875	712,760	£2	£7	£30	£60
1875 H	6,092,800	£1	£5	£20	£50
1876 H	1,175,200	£2	£9	£28	£60
*1878	4,008,540	£1	£4	£15	£35
1879	3,977,180	£1	£4	£15	£35
1880	1,842,710	£1	£4	£15	£35
1881	3,494,670	£1	£4	£15	£35
1881 H	1,792,000	£1	£4	£15	£30
1882 H	1,792,000	£1	£5	£15	£30
1883	1,128,680	£2	£10	£35	£55
1884	5,782,000	£1	£4	£15	£25
1885	5,442,308	£1	£4	£15	£25
1886	7.707,790	£1	£4	£15	£25
1887	1,340,800	£1	£4	£15	£25
1888	1,887,250	£1	£4	£15	£25
1890	2,133,070	£1	£4	£15	£25
1891	4,959,690	£1	£4	£15	£25
1892	887,240	£1	£6	£25	£50
1893	3,904,320	£1	£4	£15	£25
1894	2,396,770	£1	£4	£15	£25
1895	2,852,852	£10	£20	£55	£110

OLD HEAD ISSUES

DATE	MINTAGE	F	VF	EF	UNC
1895 Bright finish	*incl. above*	£1	£2	£10	£18
1896 —	3,668,610	£1	£2	£10	£18
1897 —	4,579,800	£1	£2	£10	£18
1897 Dark finish	*incl. above*	£1	£2	£10	£18
1898 —	4,010,080	£1	£2	£10	£18
1899 —	3,864,616	£1	£2	£10	£18
1900 —	5,969,317	£1	£2	£10	£18
*1901 —	8,016,460	£1	£2	£5	£11

EDWARD VII (1901–10)

DATE	MINTAGE	F	VF	EF	UNC
1902	5,125,120	50p	£1	£7	£12
1903	5,331,200	50p	£1	£7	£14
1904	3,628,800	50p	£1	£8	£18
1905	4,076,800	50p	£1	£7	£19
1906	5,340,160	50p	£1	£7	£14

DATE	MINTAGE	F	VF	EF	UNC
*1907	4,399,360	50p	£1	£7	£14
1908	4,264,960	50p	£1	£7	£14
1909	8,852,480	50p	£1	£7	£14
1910	2,298,400	£1	£5	£12	£40

GEORGE V (1910–36)

1911	5,196,800	25p	50p	£4	£10
1912	7,669,760	25p	50p	£4	£10
1913	4,184,320	25p	50p	£4	£10
1914	6,126,988	25p	50p	£4	£10
1915	7,129,255	25p	50p	£4	£10
1916	10,993,325	25p	50p	£4	£10
*1917	21,434,844	25p	50p	£4	£10
1918	19,362,818	25p	50p	£4	£10
1919	15,089,425	25p	50p	£4	£10
1920	11,480,536	25p	50p	£4	£8
1921	9,469,097	25p	50p	£4	£8
1922	9,956,983	25p	50p	£4	£8
1923	8,034,457	25p	50p	£4	£8
1924	8,733,414	25p	50p	£4	£8
1925	12,634,697	25p	50p	£4	£8
1926 Modified effigy	9,792,397	25p	50p	£4	£8
1927	7,868,355	25p	50p	£4	£8
1928	11,625,600	25p	50p	£4	£8
1929	8,419,200	25p	50p	£3	£8
1930	4,195,200	25p	50p	£3	£8
1931	6,595,200	25p	50p	£3	£8
1932	9,292,800	25p	50p	£3	£8
1933	4,560,000	25p	50p	£3	£8
1934	3,052,800	25p	50p	£3	£8
1935	2.227,200	50p	£1	£6	£16
1936	9,734,400	25p	50p	£2	£5

GEORGE VI (1936–52)

1937	8,131,200	—	—	50p	£1
1937 Proof	26,402	—	—	50p	£3
1938	7,449,600	—	—	50p	£4
1939	31,440,000	—	—	50p	£1
1940	18,360,000	—	—	50p	£1
1941	27,312,000	—	—	50p	£1
1942	28,857,600	—	—	50p	£1
1943	33,345,600	—	—	50p	£1
1944	25,137,600	—	—	50p	£1
1945	23,736,000	—	—	50p	£1
1946	24,364,800	—	—	50p	£1
1947	14,745,600	—	—	50p	£1
1948	16,622,400	—	—	50p	£1
*1949	8,424,000	—	—	50p	£1
1950	10,324,800	—	—	50p	£1
1950 Proof	17,513	—	—	50p	£3
1951	14,016,000	—	—	50p	£1
1951 Proof	20,000	—	—	50p	£3
1952	5,251,200	—	—	50p	£1

ELIZABETH II (1952–   )

1953	6,131,037	—	—	—	£1
1953 Proof	40,000	—	—	—	£2
*1954	6,566,400	—	—	—	£1
1955	5,779,200	—	—	—	£1
1956	1,996,800	—	—	50p	£2

HALF FARTHING

DATE	MINTAGE	F	VF	EF	UNC

GEORGE IV (1820–30)

1828 (two different obverses) (issued for Ceylon)	7,680,000	£7	£15	£35	£55
1830 (large or small date) (issued for Ceylon)	8,766,320	£7	£15	£35	£60

WILLIAM IV (1830–37)

1837 (issued for Ceylon)	1,935,360	£15	£45	£100	£160

VICTORIA (1837–1901)

1839	2,042,880	£5	£10	£25	£55
1842	unrecorded	£3	£7	£20	£45
1843	3,440,640	£2	£6	£16	£40
1844	6,451,200	£2	£5	£15	£40
1847	3,010,560	£5	£10	£30	£55
1851	unrecorded	£4	£10	£30	£55
1852	989,184	£4	£10	£35	£60
1853	955,224	£4	£12	£40	£70
1853 Proof	incl. above	—	—	—	£150
1854	677,376	£7	£20	£60	£100
1856	913,920	£7	£20	£60	£100

THIRD FARTHINGS

GEORGE IV (1820–30)

1827 (issued for Malta)	unrecorded	£5	£10	£25	£50

WILLIAM IV (1830–37)

1835 (issued for Malta)	unrecorded	£6	£15	£35	£60

VICTORIA (1837–1901)

1844 (issued for Malta)	1,301,040	£8	£20	£60	£110
1866	576,000	£5	£12	£28	£55
1868	144,000	£5	£12	£28	£55
1876	162,000	£5	£12	£28	£55
1878	288,000	£5	£12	£28	£55
1881	144,000	£5	£12	£28	£50
1884	144,000	£5	£12	£28	£50
1885	288,000	£5	£12	£28	£50

EDWARD VII (1902–10)

1902 (issued for Malta)	288,000	£3	£7	£20	£30

GEORGE V (1911–36)

1913 (issued for Malta)	288,000	£3	£7	£20	£30

QUARTER FARTHINGS

VICTORIA (1837–1901)

1839 (issued for Ceylon)	3,840,000	£10	£25	£50	£100
1851 (issued for Ceylon)	2,215,680	£10	£25	£50	£100
1852 (issued for Ceylon)	incl. above	£10	£25	£50	£100
1853 (issued for Ceylon)	incl. above	£10	£25	£50	£100
1853 Proof	incl. above	—	—	—	£240

EMERGENCY ISSUES

DATE	F	VF	EF	UNC

GEORGE III (1760–1820)

To alleviate the shortage of circulating coinage during the Napoleonic Wars the Bank of England firstly authorised the countermarking of other countries' coins, enabling them to pass as English currency. The coins, countermarked with punches depicting the head of George III, were mostly Spanish American 8 reales of Charles III. Although this had limited success it was later decided to completely overstrike the coins with a new English design on both sides— specimens that still show traces of the original host coin's date are avidly sought after by collectors. This overstriking continued for a number of years although all the known coins are dated 1804. Finally, in 1811 the Bank of England issued silver tokens which continued up to 1816 when a completely new regal coinage was introduced.

DOLLAR
Oval countermark of George III

	F	VF	EF	UNC
On "Pillar" type 8 reales	£150	£600	£1000	—
On "Portrait" type	£100	£275	£550	—

Octagonal countermark of George III

	F	VF	EF	UNC
*On "Portrait" type	£175	£500	£850	—

HALF DOLLAR
Oval countermark of George III

	F	VF	EF
On "Portrait" type 4 reales .	£175	£350	£650

FIVE SHILLINGS OR ONE DOLLAR
These coins were overstruck on Spanish-American coins

	F	VF	EF	UNC
*1804	£85	£175	£375	—

— With details of original coin still visible add from 10%.

BANK OF ENGLAND TOKENS
THREE SHILLINGS

	F	VF	EF	UNC
1811 Draped bust	£25	£35	£75	—
1812 —	£25	£40	£100	—
1812 Laureate bust	£25	£35	£75	—
1813 —	£25	£35	£75	—
1814 —	£25	£35	£75	—
1815 —	£25	£35	£75	—
1816 —	£100	£200	£650	—

ONE SHILLING AND SIXPENCE

	F	VF	EF	UNC
1811 Draped bust	£15	£30	£55	£120
1812 —	£15	£30	£55	£120
*1812 Laureate bust	£15	£30	£55	£120
1812 Proof in platinum				Unique
1813 —	£15	£30	£55	£120
1813 Proof in platinum				Unique
1814 —	£15	£30	£55	£120
1815 —	£15	£30	£55	£120
1816 —	£15	£30	£55	£120

NINEPENCE

	F	VF	EF	UNC
1812 Pattern only	—	—	—	£1500

MAUNDY SETS

DATE	F	VF	EF	UNC

Sets in contemporary dated boxes are usually worth a higher premium.

CHARLES II (1660–85)

DATE	F	VF	EF	UNC
Undated	£65	£120	£350	—
1670	£55	£85	£220	—
1671	£45	£80	£220	—
1672	£55	£80	£225	—
1673	£55	£80	£220	—
1674	£50	£80	£220	—
1675	£50	£80	£220	—
1676	£50	£80	£220	—
1677	£50	£80	£220	—
1678	£55	£90	£275	—
1679	£50	£80	£225	—
1680	£45	£80	£220	—
1681	£55	£90	£275	—
1682	£50	£85	£250	—
1683	£50	£80	£220	—

JAMES II (1685–88)

DATE	F	VF	EF	UNC
1686	£50	£110	£250	—
1687	£50	£110	£250	—
1688	£50	£110	£250	—

WILLIAM & MARY (1688–94)

DATE	F	VF	EF	UNC
1689	£155	£400	£650	—
1691	£60	£140	£275	—
1692	£60	£140	£275	—
1693	£65	£160	£300	—
1694	£60	£140	£285	—

WILLIAM III (1694–1702)

DATE	F	VF	EF	UNC
1698	£65	£125	£275	—
1699	£80	£135	£325	—
1700	£80	£135	£325	—
1701	£65	£130	£265	—

ANNE (1702–114)

DATE	F	VF	EF	UNC
1703	£60	£120	£260	—
1705	£60	£120	£260	—
1706	£60	£120	£260	—
1708	£60	£120	£260	—
1709	£60	£120	£260	—
1710	£95	£155	£325	—
1713	£55	£120	£260	—

GEORGE I (1714–27)

DATE	F	VF	EF	UNC
1723	£60	£135	£285	—
1727	£60	£135	£285	—

GEORGE II (1727–60)

DATE	F	VF	EF	UNC
1729	£50	£100	£220	—
1731	£50	£100	£220	—
1732	£50	£100	£185	—
1735	£50	£100	£185	—
1737	£50	£100	£185	—
1739	£50	£100	£185	—
1740	£50	£100	£185	—

DATE	MINTAGE	F	VF	EF	UNC
1743		£50	£90	£185	—
1746		£50	£90	£185	—
1760		£50	£90	£185	—

GEORGE III (1760–1820)

DATE	MINTAGE	F	VF	EF	UNC
1763		£40	£60	£135	—
1766		£40	£60	£135	—
1772		£40	£60	£135	—
1780		£40	£60	£135	—
1784		£40	£60	£135	—
1786		£40	£60	£135	—
1792 Wire		£90	£150	£300	—
1795		£40	£60	£110	—
1800		£40	£50	£110	—
New Coinage					
1817		£40	£60	£100	£155
1818		£40	£60	£100	£155
1820		£40	£60	£100	£155

GEORGE IV (1820–30)

DATE	MINTAGE	F	VF	EF	UNC
1822		—	£50	£100	£160
1823		—	£50	£100	£160
1824		—	£50	£100	£160
1825		—	—	£100	£160
1826		—	£50	£100	£160
1827		—	—	£100	£160
1828		—	£50	£100	£160
1829		—	£50	£100	£160
1830		—	£50	£100	£160

WILLIAM IV (1830–37)

DATE	MINTAGE	F	VF	EF	UNC
1831		—	£50	£90	£165
1831 Proof		—	£50	—	£275
1832		—	£50	£90	£165
1833		—	£50	£90	£165
1834		—	£50	£90	£165
1835		—	£50	£90	£165
1836		—	£50	£90	£165

VICTORIA (1837–1901)

YOUNG HEAD ISSUES

DATE	MINTAGE	F	VF	EF	UNC
1838	4,158	—	—	£60	£70
1839	4,125	—	—	£60	£70
1839 Proof	unrecorded	—	—	£60	£220
1840	4,125	—	—	£60	£70
1841	2,574	—	—	£55	£75
1842	4,125	—	—	£60	£70
1843	4,158	—	—	£60	£75
1844	4,158	—	—	£60	£70
1845	4,158	—	—	£60	£70
1846	4,158	—	—	£60	£70
1847	4,158	—	—	£60	£70
1848	4,158	—	—	£60	£70
1849	4,158	—	—	£60	£75
1850	4,158	—	—	£60	£70
1851	4,158	—	—	£60	£70
1852	4,158	—	—	£60	£75

DATE	MINTAGE	EF	UNC
1853	4,158	£50	£75
1853 Proof	unrecorded	—	£450
1854	4,158	£50	£75
1855	4,158	£60	£85
1856	4,158	£50	£70
1857	4,158	£50	£70
1858	4,158	£50	£70
1859	4,158	£50	£70
1860	4,158	£50	£70
1861	4,158	£50	£70
1862	4,158	£50	£70
1863	4,158	£50	£70
1864	4,158	£50	£70
1865	4,158	£50	£70
1866	4,158	£50	£70
1867	4,158	£50	£70
1868	4,158	£50	£70
1869	4,158	£60	£80
1870	4,458	£50	£65
1871	4,488	£50	£65
1872	4,328	£50	£65
1873	4,162	£50	£65
1874	4,488	£50	£65
1875	4,154	£50	£65
1876	4,488	£50	£65
1877	4,488	£50	£65
1878	4,488	£50	£65
1879	4,488	£50	£65
1880	4,488	£50	£65
1881	4,488	£50	£65
1882	4,146	£50	£65
1883	4,488	£50	£65
1884	4,488	£50	£65
1885	4,488	£50	£65
1886	4,488	£50	£65
1887	4,488	£50	£65

JUBILEE HEAD ISSUES

DATE	MINTAGE	EF	UNC
1888	4,488	£50	£70
1889	4,488	£50	£70
1890	4,488	£50	£70
1891	4,488	£50	£70
1892	4,488	£50	£70

OLD HEAD ISSUES

DATE	MINTAGE	EF	UNC
1893	8,976	£45	£55
1893 Proof	unrecorded	—	£120
1894	8,976	£45	£65
1895	8,976	£45	£65
1897	8,976	£45	£65
1898	8,976	£45	£65
1899	8,976	£45	£65
1900	8,976	£45	£65
1901	8,976	£45	£65

EDWARD VII (1902–110)

DATE	MINTAGE	EF	UNC
1902	8,976	£45	£65
1902 Matt proof	15,123	—	£65
1903	8,976	£45	£55
1904	8,976	£45	£55
1905	8,976	£45	£55
1906	8,800	£45	£55
1907	8.760	£45	£55
1908	8,769	£45	£55
1909	1,983	£55	£80
1910	1,440	£65	£90

GEORGE V (1911–136)

DATE	MINTAGE	EF	UNC
1911	1,786	£45	£55
1911 Proof	6,007	—	£55
1912	1,246	£45	£55

DATE	MINTAGE	EF	UNC
1913	1,228	£45	£55
1914	982	£45	£55
1915	1,293	£45	£55
1916	1,128	£45	£55
1917	1,237	£45	£55
1918	1,375	£45	£55
1919	1,258	£45	£55
1920	1,399	£45	£55
1921	1,386	£45	£55
1922	1,373	£45	£55
1923	1,430	£45	£55
1924	1,515	£45	£55
1925	1,438	£45	£55
1926	1,504	£45	£55
1927	1,647	£45	£55
1928	1,642	£45	£55
1929	1,761	£45	£55
1930	1,724	£45	£55
1931	1,759	£45	£55
1932	1,835	£45	£55
1933	1,872	£45	£55
1934	1,887	£45	£55
1935	1,928	£45	£55
1936	1,323	£60	£70

GEORGE VI (1936–52)

DATE	MINTAGE	EF	UNC
1937	1,325	£45	£55
1937 Proof	20,900	£45	£55
1938	1,275	£45	£55
1939	1,234	£45	£55
1940	1,277	£45	£55
1941	1,253	£45	£55
1942	1,231	£45	£55
1943	1,239	£45	£55
1944	1,259	£45	£55
1945	1,355	£45	£55
1946	1,365	£45	£55
1947	1,375	£45	£55
1948	1,385	£45	£55
1949	1,395	£45	£55
1950	1,405	£45	£55
1951	1,468	£45	£55
1952	1,012	£45	£75

ELIZABETH II (1952–)

DATE	MINTAGE	EF	UNC
1953	1,025	—	£225
1954	1,020	—	£55
1955	1,036	—	£55
1956	1,088	—	£55
1957	1,094	—	£55
1958	1,100	—	£65
1959	1,106	—	£50
1960	1,112	—	£55
1961	1,118	—	£55
1962	1,125	—	£55
1963	1,131	—	£55
1964	1,137	—	£55
1965	1,143	—	£55
1966	1,206	—	£55
1967	986	—	£55
1968	964	—	£55
1969	1,002	—	£55
1970	980	—	£55

Later issues are listed in the Decimal section.

DECIMAL COINAGE

Since the initial introduction of the Decimal system in the UK, the majority of coins have been issued in vast quantities, although in some years certain denominations have either not been struck at all or only limited numbers are available to collectors so, surprisingly, there are a number of potential scarcities worth looking out for—this scarcity is reflected in the prices quoted. In this section it has been decided to only include the mintage figures of coins struck in precious metals where these are available. Where dates are available in uncirculated grade at, or just above, face value no price has been quoted.

Proof issues of circulation coinage (£1–½ pence) of the decimal series were only issued as part of the appropriate year sets, but over the passage of time many of these sets have been broken up and the individual coins are now appearing on the market, hence the decision to include these coins in the appropriate sections.

A new portrait of Her Majesty the Queen, executed by Ian Rank-Broadley, FRBS, FSNAD, was introduced on the British coinage in 1998, making it the fourth portrait of Her Majesty to appear on the coins and the third since the introduction of decimal coinage in 1968.

FIVE POUNDS

ST. GEORGE REVERSE—GOLD

	Mintage	UNC
1980 Proof only	10,000	£475
1981 Proof only	5,400	£475
1982 Proof only	2,500	£500
1984 Proof	905	£475
1984 with U in circle	15,104	£450
1985 New portrait Proof	6,130	£475
1985 with U in circle	13,626	£450
1986 with U in circle	7,723	£450
1987 with U in circle	5,694	£475
*1988 with U in circle	3,315	£475
1990 Proof	1,721	£500
1990 with U in circle	1,226	£475
1991 Proof	1,336	£550
1991 with U in circle	976	£500
1992 Proof	1,165	£550
1992 with U in circle	797	£500
1993 Proof	1,078	£550
1993 with U in circle	906	£500
1994 Proof	918	£550
1994 with U in circle	1,000	£550
1995 Proof	1,250	£550
1995 with U in circle	1,000	£550
1996 Proof	1,250	£550
1996 with U in circle	1,000	£550
1997 Proof	1,000	£600
1997 with U in circle	1,000	£600
1998 Proof	1,500	£650
1998 with U in circle	1,000	£600
1999 Proof	1,000	£650
1999 with U in circle	1,000	£600

The obverse of the 1989 gold coins portray HM the Queen enthroned

COMMEMORATIVE

*1989 500th Anniversary of the Sovereign, Gold	2,937	£550
1989 — Proof	5,000	£600
1990 Queen Mother's 90th Birthday. Crown. Cupro-nickel	48,477	£8
1990 — in Presentation folder	incl. above	£9
1990 — Silver Proof	56,800	£32
1990 — Gold Proof	2,500	£525
1993 40th Anniversary of the Coronation. Crown. Cu-Ni	—	£8
1993 — in Presentation folder	—	£9
1993 — Proof	—	£15
1993 — Silver Proof	100,000	£32
1993 — Gold Proof	2,500	£525
*1996 Her Majesty the Queen's 70th Birthday. Crown. Cu-Ni	—	£10
1996 — in Presentation folder	—	£12
1996 — Proof	—	£18
1996 — Silver Proof	70,000	£35
1996 — Gold Proof	2,750	£650
*1997 Golden Wedding Anniversary of Her Majesty the Queen and Prince Philip. Crown. Cu-Ni	—	£6
1997 — in Presentation folder	—	£9
1997 — — with £5 note	5,000	£45
1997 — Proof	—	£20
1997 — Silver Proof	75,000	£35
1997 — Gold Proof	2,750	£650
1998 50th birthday of the Prince of Wales. Crown. Cu-Ni	—	£6
1998 — in Presentation folder	—	£10
1998 — Proof	—	£20
1998 — Silver Proof	—	£40
1998 — Gold Proof	—	£650
1999 Princess of Wales Memorial. Cu-Ni	—	£7
1999 — in Presentation folder	—	£12
1999 — Proof	—	£20
1999 — Silver Proof	350,000	£40
1999 — Gold Proof	7,500	£650

The obverse of the 1997 £5 crown shows the conjoined portraits of HM the Queen and Prince Philip

DATE	Mintage	UNC
1999 Millennium. Cu-Ni	—	£7
1999 — in Presentation folder	—	£12
1999 — Proof	—	£20
1999 — Silver Proof	100,000	£40
1999 — Gold Proof	2,500	£650

TWO POUNDS

ST GEORGE REVERSE—*Gold*

1980 Proof only	10,000	£250
1982 Proof only	2,500	£250
1983 Proof only	12,500	£200
1985 Proof only	5,849	£250
1986 Proof only	15,777	£250
1987 Proof only	14,301	£250
1988 Proof only	12,743	£250
1989 Proof only	14,936	£250
*1990 Proof only	4,374	£250
1991 Proof only	3,108	£250
1992 Proof only	2,608	£275
1993 Proof only	2,155	£275
1996 Proof only	3,167	£275
1998 Proof only	4,500	£300
1999 Proof only	2,250	£300

COMMEMORATIVE

*1986 Commonwealth Games. Nickel-brass	£5
1986 — in Presentation folder	£6
1986 — Proof	£10
1986 — Silver	£15
1986 — Silver Proof	£20
1986 — Gold Proof	£250
*1989 300th Anniversary of Bill of Rights. Nickel-brass	£5
1989 — in Presentation folder	£6
1989 — Proof	£10
1989 — Silver Proof	£22
1989 — Silver Proof Piedfort	£45
*1989 300th Anniversary of Claim of Right. Nickel-brass	£10
1989 — in Presentation folder	£12
1989 — Proof	£15
1989 — Silver Proof	£25
1989 — Silver Proof Piedfort	£48
1989 500th Anniversary of the Sovereign. Gold Proof	£265
1994 Tercentenary of the Bank of England. Nickel-brass	£4
1994 — in Presentation folder	£6
1994 — Proof	£9
1994 — Silver Proof	£28
1994 — Silver Proof Piedfort	£60
1994 — Gold Proof	£400
1994 — — obverse error (no denomination, as standard £2)	£550
1995 50th Anniversary of End of WW2. Nickel-brass	£3
1994 — in Presentation folder	£5
1995 — Proof	£8
1995 — Silver Proof	£35
1995 — Silver Proof Piedfort	£55
1995 — Gold Proof	£450
1995 50th Anniversary of The United Nations. Nickel-brass	£3
1994 — in Presentation folder	£5
1995 — Silver Proof	£30
1995 — Silver Proof Piedfort	£55
1995 — Gold Proof	£450
1996 European Football Championships. Nickel-brass	£3
1996 — in Presentation folder	£4
1996 — Proof	£6
1996 — Silver Proof	£30
1996 — Silver Proof Piedfort	£55
1996 — Gold Proof	£450
1999 Rugby World Cup. Bi-metallic	—
1999 — Silver Proof	£30
1999 — Silver Proof Piedfort with Hologram	£85
1999 — Gold Proof	£350

209

DATE	MINTAGE	UNC
CIRCULATING COINAGE		
*1997 First Bi-metallic currency		£4
1997 — in Presentation folder		£7
1997 — Proof		£10
1997 — Silver Proof		£35
1997 — Gold (two types) Proof		£350
1998 Bi-metallic currency		£3
1998 — in Presentation folder		£6
1998 — Proof		£8
1998 — Silver Proof		£30
1998 — Gold Proof		£350
1999		—

SOVEREIGN

1974	—	£65
1976	—	£65
1978	—	£65
1979	—	£65
1979 Proof	50,000	£95
1980	—	£65
1980 Proof	91,200	£85
1981	—	£65
1981 Proof	32,960	£85
1982	—	£65
1982 Proof	22,500	£85
1983 Proof only	21,250	£90
1984 Proof only	19,975	£90
1985 New portrait Proof only	17,242	£95
1986 Proof only	17,579	£90
1987 Proof only	22,479	£90
1988 Proof only	18,862	£90
1989 500th Anniversary of the Sovereign Proof only ..	23,471	£175
1990 Proof only	8,425	£130
1991 Proof only	7,201	£130
1992 Proof only	6,854	£150
1993 Proof only	6,090	£150
1994 Proof only	7,165	£150
1995 Proof only	9,500	£150
1996 Proof only	10,000	£150
1997 Proof only	9,750	£165
1998 Proof only	13,500	£165
1999 Proof only	12,250	£165

HALF SOVEREIGN

1980 Proof only	86,700	£65
1982	—	—
1982 Proof	21,590	£65
1983 Proof only	19,710	£65
1984 Proof only	19,505	£65
1985 New portrait Proof only	15,800	£50
1986 Proof only	17,075	£50
1987 Proof only	20,687	£50
1988 Proof only	18,266	£55
1989 500th Anniversary of the Sovereign Proof only ..	21,824	£85
1990 Proof only	7,889	£55
1991 Proof only	6,076	£55
1992 Proof only	5,915	£65
1993 Proof only	4,651	£65
1994 Proof only	7,167	£75
1995 Proof only	7,500	£85
1996 Proof only	10,500	£85
1997 Proof only	9,750	£85
1998 Proof only	11,000	£85
199 Proof only	9,750	£85

ONE POUND

DATE	UNC
1983 Royal Arms Nickel-brass	£4
1983 — in Presentation folder	£5
1983 — Proof	£8
1983 — Silver Proof	£25
1983 — Silver Piedfort Proof	£120
1984 Scottish Thistle Nickel-brass	£3
1984 — in Presentation folder	£5
1984 — Proof	£6
1984 — Silver Proof	£28
1984 — Silver Piedfort Proof	£65
1985 Welsh Leek Nickel-brass	£3
1985 — in Presentation folder	£4
1985 — Proof	£6
1985 — Silver Proof	£28
1985 — Silver Piedfort Proof	£60
1986 Northern Ireland Flax Nickel-brass	£3
1986 — in Presentation folder	£4
1986 — Proof	£6
1986 — Silver Proof	£28
1986 — Silver Piedfort Proof	£60
1987 English Oak Nickel-brass	£3
1987 — in Presentation folder	£4
1987 — Proof	£6
1987 — Silver Proof	£25
1987 — Silver Piedfort Proof	£60
1988 Royal Shield Nickel-brass	£3
1988 — in Presentation folder	£4
1988 — Proof	£7
1988 — Silver Proof	£28
1988 — Silver Piedfort Proof	£60
1989 Scottish Thistle Nickel-brass	£3
1989 — Proof	£6
1989 — Silver Proof	£25
1989 — Silver Piedfort Proof	£55
1990 Welsh Leek Nickel-brass	£3
1990 — Proof	£6
1990 — Silver Proof	£25
1991 Northern Ireland Flax Nickel-brass	£3
1991 — Proof	£6
1991 — Silver Proof	£30
1992 English Oak Nickel-brass	£3
1992 — Proof	£6
1992 — Silver Proof	£30
1993 Royal Arms Nickel-brass	£3
1993 — Proof	£6
1993 — Silver Proof	£30
1993 — Silver Piedfort Proof	£70
1994 Scottish Lion Nickel-brass	£2
1994 — in Presentation folder	£4
1994 — Proof	£6
1994 — Silver Proof	£30
1994 — Silver Piedfort Proof	£65
1995 Welsh Heraldic Dragon Nickel-brass	£2
1995 — in Presentation folder (English)	£5
1995 — — (Welsh)	£6
1995 — Proof	£6
1995 — Silver Proof	£30
1995 — Silver Piedfort Proof	£65
1996 Northern Ireland Celtic Nickel-brass	£2
1996 — in Presentation folder	£4
1996 — Proof	£6
1996 — Silver Proof	£30
1996 — Silver Piedfort Proof	£65

1983, 1993, 1998

1984, 1989

1985, 1990

1986, 1991

1987, 1992

1994, 1999

1995

DATE	UNC
1997 English Lions Nickel-brass	£3
1997 — in Presentation folder	£4
1997 — Proof	£6
1997 — Silver Proof	£30
1997 — Silver Piedfort Proof	£65
1998 New portrait. Royal Arms. Nickel-brass	£3
1998 — in Presentation folder	£5
1998 — Proof	£8
1998 — Silver Proof	£30
1998 — Silver Piedfort Proof	£65
1999 Scottish Lion. Nickel-brass	£2
1999 — in Presentation folder	£5
1999 — Proof	£8
1999 — Silver Proof	£35
1999 — Silver Piedfort Proof	£75

1996

1997

FIFTY PENCE

1969	£3
1970	£4
1971 Proof	£6
1972 Proof	£6
1973 Accession to EEC	£3
1973 — Proof	£4
1974 Proof	£5
1975 Proof	£5
1976	£3
1976 Proof	£4
1977	£3
1977 Proof	£4
1978	£3
1978 Proof	£4
1979	£3
1979 Proof	£4
1980	£3
1980 Proof	£4
1981	£2
1981 Proof	£3
1982 Legend changed to FIFTY PENCE	£3
1982 Proof	£3
1983	£3
1983 Proof	£4
1984	£3
1984 Proof	£4
1985 New portrait	£3
1985 Proof	£4
1986	£4
1986 Proof	£4
1987	£4
1987 Proof	£4
1988	£4
1988 Proof	£4
1989	£4
1989 Proof	£4
1990	£4
1990 Proof	£4
1991	£5
1991 Proof	£6
*1992 Presidency of EC Council and completion of Single Market	£5
1992 — in Presentation folder with Britannia	£7
1992 — Proof	£6
1992 — Silver Proof	£28

DATE	UNC
1992 — Silver Proof Piedfort	£50
1992 — Gold Proof	£400
1993	£2
*1994 Anniversary of the Normandy Landings	£3
1994 — in Presentation folder	£4
1994 — Proof	£6
1994 — Silver Proof	£28
1994 — Silver Proof Piedfort	£55
1994 — Gold Proof	£425
1995	£5
1995 Proof	£6
1996	£5
1996 Proof	£6
1996 Silver Proof	£22
1997	£4
1997 Proof	£6
1997 Silver Proof	£25
1997 *new reduced size*	£3
1997 Proof	£5
1997 Silver Proof	£25
1997 Silver Proof Piedfort	£65
1998 New portrait	£2
1998 Proof	£5
1998 Silver Proof	£25
1998 Silver Proof Piedfort	£65
*1998 Presidency and 25th anniversary of entry into the EU	£2
1998 Proof	£5
1998 Silver Proof	£25
1998 Silver Proof Piedfort	£75
1999	—
1999 Proof	£5
1999 Silver Proof	£25
1999 Silver Proof Piedfort	£75

TWENTY-FIVE PENCE (CROWN)

1972 Royal Silver Wedding Cu-Ni	£2
1972 — Proof	£5
1972 — Silver Proof	£20
1977 Silver Jubilee Cu-Ni	£2
1977 — in Presentation folder	£4
1977 — Proof	£5
1977 — Silver Proof	£17
1980 Queen Mother 80th Birthday Cu-Ni	£2
1980 — in Presentation folder	£3
1980 — Silver Proof	£28
1981 Royal Wedding Cu-Ni	£2
1981 — in Presentation folder	£3
1981 — Silver Proof	£25

TWENTY PENCE

DATE		UNC
1982		£1
1982 Proof		£3
1982 Silver Piedfort Proof		£45
1983		£1
1983 Proof		£3
1984		£1
1984 Proof		£3
1985 New portrait		£1
1985 Proof		£3
1986		£2
1986 Proof		£4
1987		£1
1987 Proof		£3
1988		£1
1988 Proof		£3
1989		£1
1989 Proof		£3

DATE	UNC
1990	£1
1990 Proof	£3
1991	£1
1991 Proof	£3
1992	£1
1992 Proof	£3
1993	£1
1993 Proof	£3
1994	£1
1994 Proof	£3
1995	£1
1995 Proof	£3
1996	£1
1996 Proof	£3
1996 Silver Proof	£15
1997	£1
1997 Proof	£3
1998 New portrait	£1
1998 Proof	£3
1999	£1
1999 Proof	—

TEN PENCE

	UNC
1968	£1
1969	£2
1970	£2
1971	£2
1971 Proof	£2
1972 Proof	£3
1973	£2
1973 Proof	£4
1974	£2
1974 Proof	£4
1975	£2
1975 Proof	£4
1976	£2
1976 Proof	£4
1977	£2
1977 Proof	£4
1978 Proof	£5
1979	£2
1979 Proof	£4
1980	£2
1980 Proof	£3
1981	£2
1981 Proof	£3
1982 Legend changed to TEN PENCE	£4
1982 Proof	£5
1983	£3
1983 Proof	£2

	UNC
1984	£2
1984 Proof	£3
1985 New portrait	£4
1985 Proof	£3
1986	£4
1986 Proof	£3
1987	£4
1987 Proof	£5
1988	£4
1988 Proof	£5
1989	£6
1989 Proof	£5
1990	£6
1990 Proof	£5
1991	£6
1991 Proof	£5
1992	£5
1992 Proof	£6
1992 Silver Proof	£15
1992 Size reduced to 24.5mm	£1
1992 Proof	£4
1992 Silver Proof	£15
1992 Silver Proof piedfort	£35
1993	£1
1993 Proof	£2
1994	£1
1994 Proof	£2
1995	£1
1995 Proof	£2
1996	£1
1996 Proof	£2
1996 Silver Proof	£20
1997	£1
1997 Proof	£2
1998 New portrait	—
1998 Proof	£2
1999	—
1999 Proof	—

FIVE PENCE

DATE	UNC	DATE	UNC
		1985 Proof	£2
		1986	£2
		1986 Proof	£2
		1987	£1
		1987 Proof	£3
		1988	£1
		1988 Proof	£2
		1989	50p
1968	50p	1989 Proof	£3
1969	50p	1990	£2
1970	55p	1990 Proof	£4
1971	50p	1990 Silver Proof	£15
1971 Proof	£4	1990 *Size reduced to 18mm*	£1
1972 Proof	£4	1990 Proof	£2
1973 Proof	£4	1990 Silver Proof	£15
1974 Proof	£4	1990 Silver Proof Piedfort	£30
1975	50p	1991	50p
1975 Proof	£2	1991 Proof	£3
1976 Proof	£4	1992	50p
1977	50p	1992 Proof	£3
1977 Proof	£3	1993	50p
1978	50p	1993 Proof	£4
1978 Proof	£2	1994	50p
1979	50p	1994 Proof	£2
1979 Proof	£2	1995	50p
1980	50p	1995 Proof	£2
1980 Proof	£2	1996	—
1981 Proof	£3	1996 Proof	£2
1982 Legend changed to FIVE PENCE	£3	1996 Silver proof	£15
1982 Proof	£3	1997	—
1983	£4	1997 Proof	£2
1983 Proof	£3	1998	—
1984	£3	1998 Proof	£2
1984 Proof	£2	1999	—
1985 New portrait	£2	1999 Proof	—

TWO PENCE

	UNC		UNC
		1976	50p
		1976 Proof	£1
		1977	50p
		1977 Proof	£1
		1978	50p
		1978 Proof	£1
		1979	50p
		1979 Proof	£1
		1980	50p
		1980 Proof	£1
Bronze		1981	50p
1971	50p	1981 Proof	£1
1971 Proof	£2	1982 Legend changed to TWO PENCE	£2
1972 Proof	£2	1982 Proof	£1
1973 Proof	£2	1983	£1
1974 Proof	£2	1983 Proof	£1
1975	50p	1983 Error reverse as New Pence	Rare
1975 Proof	£1		

DATE	UNC	DATE	UNC
		Copper-plated steel	
1984	£1	1992	—
1984 Proof	£1	1993	—
1985 New portrait	50p	1993 Proof	£1
1985 Proof	£1	1994	—
1986	25p	1994 Proof	£1
1986 Proof	£1	1995	—
1987	25p	1995 Proof	£1
1987 Proof	£1	1996	—
1988	25p	1996 Proof	£1
1988 Proof	£1	1996 Silver Proof	£16
1989	25p	1997	—
1989 Proof	£1	1997 Proof	£1
1990	25p	1998 New portrait	50p
1990 Proof	£1	1998 Proof	£2
1991	25p	1998 *Bronze*	—
1991 Proof	£1	1998 *Bronze* Proof	£1
1992	25p	1999	—
1992 Proof	£1	1999 Proof	—

ONE PENNY

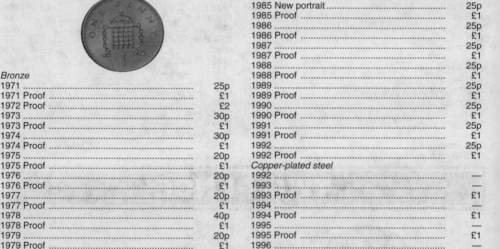

DATE	UNC	DATE	UNC
		1985 New portrait	25p
		1985 Proof	£1
		1986	25p
		1986 Proof	£1
		1987	25p
		1987 Proof	£1
		1988	25p
		1988 Proof	£1
Bronze		1989	25p
1971	25p	1989 Proof	£1
1971 Proof	£1	1990	25p
1972 Proof	£2	1990 Proof	£1
1973	30p	1991	25p
1973 Proof	£1	1991 Proof	£1
1974	30p	1992	25p
1974 Proof	£1	1992 Proof	£1
1975	20p	*Copper-plated steel*	
1975 Proof	£1	1992	—
1976	20p	1993	—
1976 Proof	£1	1993 Proof	£1
1977	20p	1994	—
1977 Proof	£1	1994 Proof	£1
1978	40p	1995	—
1978 Proof	£1	1995 Proof	£1
1979	20p	1996	—
1979 Proof	£1	1996 Proof	£1
1980	15p	1996 Silver Proof	£15
1980 Proof	£1	1997	—
1981	15p	1997 Proof	£1
1981 Proof	£1	1998 New portrait	50p
1982 Legend changed to ONE PENNY	25p	1998 Proof	£2
1982 Proof	£2	1998 *Bronze*	—
1983	25p	1998 *Bronze* Proof	£1
1983 Proof	£1	1999	—
1984	£1	1999 Proof	—
1984 Proof	£1		

It would appear that 1998 year sets include bronze 2p and 1p coins whereas those put into general circulation are copper-plated steel. However, early in 1998 a number of 1998-dated 2ps in bronze were also put into circulation.

HALF PENCE

DATE	UNC

1971	25p
1971 Proof	£1
1972 Proof	£5
1973	50p
1973 Proof	£3
1974	50p
1974 Proof	£2
1975	50p
1975 Proof	£2
1976	50p
1976 Proof	£2

DATE	UNC
1977	50p
1977 Proof	£2
1978	75p
1978 Proof	£2
1979	£1
1979 Proof	£2
1980	50p
1980 Proof	£1
1981	£1
1981 Proof	£1
1982 Legend changed to HALF PENNY	50p
1982 Proof	£1
1983	£1
1983 Proof	£1
1984 (only issued in Unc. year sets)	£3
1984 Proof	£2

MAUNDY SETS

DATE AND PLACE OF ISSUE	MINTAGE	UNC
1971 Tewkesbury Abbey	1,108	£65
1972 York Minster	1,026	£65
1973 Westminster Abbey	1,004	£65
1974 Salisbury Cathedral	1,042	£65
1975 Peterborough Cathedral	1,050	£65
1976 Hereford Cathedral	1,158	£65
1977 Westminster Abbey	1,138	£70
1978 Carlisle Cathedral	1,178	£65
1979 Winchester Cathedral	1,188	£65
1980 Worcester Cathedral	1,198	£65
1981 Westminster Abbey	1,178	£65
1982 St David's Cathedral	1,218	£65
1983 Exeter Cathedral	1,228	£65
1984 Southwell Minster	1,238	£65
1985 Ripon Cathedral	1,248	£65
1986 Chichester Cathedral	1,378	£65
1987 Ely Cathedral	1,390	£75
1988 Lichfield Cathedral	1,402	£75
1989 Birmingham Cathedral	1,353	£75
1990 Newcastle Cathedral	1,523	£75
1991 Westminster Abbey	1,384	£80
1992 Chester Cathedral	1,424	£85
1993 Wells Cathedral	1,440	£85
1994 Truro Cathedral	1,433	£85
1995 Coventry Cathedral	1,466	£90
1996 Norwich Cathedral	1,485	£95
1997 Birmingham Cathedral	1,486	£100
1998 Portsmouth Cathedral	1,488	£100
1999		£100

In keeping with ancient tradition the Royal Maundy sets are made up of four silver coins of 4p, 3p, 2p and 1p. The designs for the reverse of the coins are a crowned numeral in a wreath of oak leaves—basically the same design that has been used for Maundy coins since Charles II.

PROOF AND SPECIMEN SETS

DATE	FDC

GEORGE IV

1826 £5–farthing (11 coins) £17,500

WILLIAM IV

1831 Coronation £2–farthing (14 coins) £15,000

VICTORIA

1839 "Una and the Lion" £5–farthing (15 coins) £28,500
1853 Sovereign–quarter farthing, including "Gothic"crown (16 coins) £25,000
1887 Golden Jubilee £5– 3d (11 coins) £5,500
1887 Golden Jubilee Crown–3d (7 coins) £1,000
1893 £5–3d (10 coins) £6,500
1893 Crown–3d (6 coins) £1,200

EDWARD VII

1902 Coronation £5–Maundy penny matt proofs (13 coins) £1,500
1902 Coronation Sovereign–Maundy penny matt proofs (11 coins) £500

GEORGE V

1911 Coronation £5–Maundy penny (12 coins) £2,500
1911 Sovereign–Maundy penny (10 coins) £750
1911 Coronation Halfcrown–Maundy penny (8 coins) £350
1927 New types Crown–3d (6 coins) £250

GEORGE VI

1937 Coronation £5–half sovereign (4 coins) £1,500
1937 Coronation Crown–farthing including Maundy money (15 coins) £120
1950 Mid-century Halfcrown–farthing (9 coins) £50
1951 Festival of Britain, Crown–farthing (10 coins) £65

ELIZABETH II

1953 Coronation Crown–farthing (10 coins) £50
1953 Coronation Currency (plastic) set halfcrown–farthing (9 coins) £10
1968 Specimen decimal set 10p, 5p, 1971 2p, 1p, ½p in wallet (5 coins) £2
1970 Last £sd coins (sets issued 1971–73) Halfcrown– halfpenny (8 coins) .. £17
1971 Proof (issued 1973), 50p–½p (6 coins) £12
1972 Proof 50p–½p, Silver Wedding crown (7 coins) £15
1973 Proof 50p–½p (6 coins) £10
1974 Proof 50p–½p (6 coins) £15
1975 Proof 50p–½p (6 coins) £15
1976 Proof 50p–½p (6 coins) £15
1977 Proof 50p–½p, Jubilee crown (7 coins) £14
1978 Proof 50p–½p (6 coins) £12
1979 Proof 50p–½p (6 coins) £15
1980 Proof 50p–½p (6 coins) £12
1980 Proof gold £5–half sovereign (4 coins) £750
1981 Commemorative Proof £5–sovereign, Royal Wedding Silver crown, 50p–½p (9 coins) £650
1981 Proof 50p–½p (6 coins) £15
1982 Proof gold £5–half sovereign (4 coins) £750
1982 Proof 50p–½p (7 coins) £15
1982 Uncirculated 50p–½p (7 coins) £10
1983 Proof gold £2–half sovereign (3 coins) £350
1983 Proof £1–½p (8 coins) £18
1983 Uncirculated £1–½p (8 coins) £15
1984 Proof gold £5–half sovereign (3 coins) £600
1984 Proof £1 (Scottish rev.)–½p (8 coins) £15
1984 Uncirculated £1 (Scottish rev.)–½p (8 coins) £14
1985 Proof Gold new portrait £5–half sovereign (4 coins) £750

DATE	FDC
1985 Proof new portrait £1 (Welsh rev.)–1p in de luxe case (7 coins)	£20
1985 Proof as above, in standard case	£15
1985 Uncirculated £1 (Welsh rev.)–1p (7 coins)	£12
1986 Proof Gold Commonwealth Games £2–half sovereign (3 coins)	£400
1986 Commonwealth Games £2, Northern Ireland £1, 50p–1p in de luxe case (8 coins)	£22
1986 Proof as above in standard case (8 coins)	£20
1986 Uncirculated as above in folder (8 coins)	£13
1987 Proof gold Britannia set 1 oz.–1/10 oz. (4 coins)	£750
1987 Proof gold Britannia ¼ oz., 1/10 oz. (2 coins)	£150
1987 Proof gold £2–half sovereign (3 coins)	£350
1987 Proof £1 (English rev.)–1p in de luxe case (7 coins)	£25
1987 Proof £1 (English rev.)–1p in standard case (7 coins)	£17
1987 Uncirculated as above in folder (7 coins)	£10
1988 Proof gold Britannia set 1 oz.–1/10 oz. (4 coins)	£750
1988 Proof gold Britannia ¼ oz., 1/10 oz. (2 coins)	£150
1988 Proof gold £2–half sovereign (3 coins)	£300
1988 Proof £1 (Royal Arms rev.)–1p in de luxe case (7 coins)	£29
1988 Proof as above in standard case (7 coins)	£24
1988 Uncirculated as above in folder (7 coins)	£10
1989 Proof gold Britannia set 1 oz.–1/10 oz. (4 coins)	£750
1989 Proof gold Britannia ¼ oz., 1/10 oz. (2 coins)	£155
1989 Proof gold 500th anniversary of the sovereign. £5–half sovereign (4 coins)	£950
1989 Proof gold 500th anniversary of the sovereign. £2–half sovereign (3 coins)	£450
1989 Proof Bill of Rights £2, Claim of Right £2 (2 coins)	£40
1989 Proof silver piedfort as above (2 coins)	£80
1989 Uncirculated £2 as above in folder (2 coins)	£12
1989 Proof Bill of Rights £2, Claim of Right £2, £1 (Scottish rev.)–1p in de luxe case (9 coins)	£30
1989 Proof as above in standard case (9 coins)	£28
1989 Uncirculated £1 (Scottish rev.)–1p (7 coins)	£16
1990 Proof gold Britannia set 1 oz.–1/10 oz. (4 coins)	£775
1990 Proof gold £5–half sovereign (4 coins)	£850
1990 Proof gold £2–half sovereign (3 coins)	£350
1990 Proof silver 5p, 2 sizes (2 coins)	£25
1990 Proof £1 (Welsh rev.)–1p, two sizes of 5p, in de luxe case (8 coins)	£30
1990 Proof as above in standard case (8 coins)	£25
1990 Uncirculated as above (8 coins)	£16
1991 Proof gold Britannia set 1 oz.–1/10 oz. (4 coins)	£775
1991 Proof gold £5–half sovereign (4 coins)	£1,250
1991 Proof gold £2–half sovereign (3 coins)	£450
1991 Proof £1 (Irish rev.)–1p in de luxe case (7 coins)	£30
1991 Proof as above in standard case (7 coins)	£25
1991 Uncirculated as above (7 coins)	£15
1992 Proof gold Britannia set 1 oz.–1/10 oz. (4 coins)	£775
1992 Proof gold £5–half sovereign (4 coins)	£950
1992 Proof gold £2–half sovereign (3 coins)	£450
1992 Proof £1 (English rev.)–1p (2x10p and 2x50p) in de luxe case (9 coins)	£35
1992 Proof as above in standard case (9 coins)	£30
1992 Uncirculated as above (9 coins)	£15
1993 Proof gold Britannia set 1 oz.–1/10 oz. (4 coins)	£900
1993 Proof gold £5–half sovereign plus silver Pistrucci medal (4 coins + medal)	£1,200
1993 Proof gold £2–half sovereign (3 coins)	£520
1993 Proof £1–1p plus Coronation anniversary £5 in red leather case (8 coins)	£38
1993 Proof as above in standard case (8 coins)	£35
1993 Uncirculated £1–1p plus European Community 50p (8 coins)	£12
1994 Proof gold Britannia set 1 oz.–1/10 oz. (4 coins)	£800
1994 Proof gold £5–half sovereign (4 coins)	£1,200
1993 Proof gold £2–half sovereign (3 coins)	£550
1994 Proof Bank of England Tercentenary £2–1p in red leather case (8 coins)	£34
1994 Proof as above in standard case (8 coins)	£30
1994 Uncirculated £1–1p including Normandy Landings 50p (7 coins)	£15
1995 Proof gold Britannia set 1 oz.–1/10 oz. (4 coins)	£800
1995 Proof gold £5–half sovereign (4 coins)	£1,200

DATE	FDC
1995 Proof gold £2–half sovereign (3 coins)	£520
1995 Proof "Peace" £2–1p in red leather case (8 coins)	£35
1995 Proof as above in standard case (8 coins)	£30
1995 Uncirculated "Peace" £2–1p (8 coins)	£12
1996 Proof gold Britannia set 1oz–¼oz (4 coins)	£900
1996 Proof gold £5–half sovereign (4 coins)	£1,200
1996 Proof gold £2–half sovereign (3 coins)	£520
1996 Proof "Royal 70th Birthday" £5–1p in red leather case (9 coins)	£40
1996 Proof as above in standard case (9 coins)	£35
1996 Uncirculated "Football" £2–1p (8 coins)	£12
1996 silver 25th Anniversary of Decimal currency £1–1p (7 coins)	£120
1997 Proof gold £5–half sovereign (4 coins)	£1,200
1997 Proof gold £2–half sovereign (3 coins)	£500
1997 Proof Royal Golden Wedding £5 in cupro-nickel, Bi-metallic £2, "English" £1, 50p–1p in red leather case (10 coins)	£45
1997 Proof as above in standard case (10 coins)	£35
1997 Uncirculated "Royal Golden Wedding" £5–1p (10 coins)	£14
1997 Proof silver 50p—two sizes (2 coins)	£50
1997 Proof silver Britannia set £2–20p	£95
1998 Proof gold Britannia set (4 coins)	£1,100
1998 Proof gold £5–half sovereign (4 coins)	£1,200
1998 Proof gold £2–half sovereign (3 coins)	£500
1998 Proof silver Britannia set £2–20p	£95
1998 Proof Prince of Wales Birthday £5—1p (10 coins) in leather case	£40
1998 Proof as above in standard case (10 coins)	£35
1998 Uncirculated "Prince's Birthday" £5–1p (10 coins)	£14
1999 Proof gold Britannia set (4 coins)	£1,200
1999 Proof gold £5–half sovereign incl. £2 Rugby World Cup (4 coins)	£1,250
1999 Proof £2 Rugby World Cup–half sovereign (3 coins)	£500
1999 Proof Diana £5–1p (9 coins)	£45
1999 Proof as above in standard case (9 coins)	£35
1999 Uncirculated set £2–1p , no £5 (8 coins)	£12

A 1911 Proof set—a superb example of the minter's art and worthy of pride of place in any collection.

SCOTLAND

The coins illustrated are pennies representative of the reign, unless otherwise stated.

DAVID I (1124–53)

	F	VF
Berwick, Carlisle, Edinburgh and Roxburgh Mints		
Penny	£500	£1250

David I

HENRY (1136–52)

Bamborough, Carlisle and Corbridge Mints for the Earl of Huntingdon and
Northumberland
Penny	£1150	£3000

Henry

MALCOLM IV (1153–65)

Berwick and Roxburgh Mints
Penny (5 different types)	£3500	£9500

William the Lion

WILLIAM THE LION (1165–1214)

Berwick, Edinburgh, Dun (Dunbar?), Perth and
Roxburgh Mints
Penny	£70	£150

ALEXANDER II (1214–49)

Berwick and Roxburgh Mints
Penny	£750	£1500

Alexander II

ALEXANDER III (1249–86)

FIRST COINAGE (1250–80)
Pennies struck at the Mints at

Aberdeen	£75	£225
Ayr	£85	£285
Berwick	£50	£130
"Dun" (Dumfries?)	£120	£350
Edinburgh	£40	£120
Forfar	£120	£375
Forres	£130	£350
Glasgow	£135	£400
Inverness	£130	£380
Kinghorn	£150	£400
Lanark	£100	£350
Montrose	£250	£500
Perth	£50	£150
Renfrew	£175	£500
Roxburgh	£50	£175
St Andrews	£80	£200
Sterling	£125	£350

Alexander III

SECOND COINAGE (1280–86)
Penny	£25	£60
Halfpenny	£75	£185
Farthing	£150	£425

JOHN BALIOL (1292–1306)

FIRST COINAGE *(Rough Surface issue)*
Penny	£100	£250
Halfpenny		*Extremely rare*

SECOND COINAGE *(Smooth Surface issue)*
Penny	£150	£350
Halfpenny	£220	£500

John Baliol

ROBERT BRUCE (1306–29)

Robert Bruce

Berwick Mint	F	VF
*Penny	£250	£600
Halfpenny	£350	£750
Farthing	*Extremely Rare*	

DAVID II (1329–71)

David II

Aberdeen and Edinburgh Mints		
Noble	*Extremely Rare*	
Groat	£65	£200
Halfgroat	£60	£180
Penny	£40	£85
Halfpenny	£150	£350
Farthing	£500	£1500

ROBERT II (1371–90)

Robert II

Dundee, Edinburgh and Perth Mints		
Groat	£55	£185
Halfgroat	£85	£200
Penny	£65	£165
Halfpenny	£120	£400

ROBERT III (1390–1406)

Aberdeen, Dumbarton, Edinburgh, Perth Mints		
*Lion or crown	£425	£900
Demy lion or halfcrown	£350	£800
Groat	£55	£150
Halfgroat	£100	£300
Penny	£150	£325
Halfpenny	£300	£1000

JAMES I (1406–37)

Aberdeen, Edinburgh, Inverness, Linlithgow, Perth, Stirling Mints		
Demy	£350	£600
Half demy	£450	£800
Groat	£120	£265
Penny	£85	£250
Halfpenny	£110	£400

JAMES II (1437–60)

Robert III Lion

Aberdeen, Edinburgh, Linlithgow, Perth, Roxburgh, Stirling Mints		
Demy	£375	£800
Lion	£450	£1400
Half lion	*Extremely rare*	
*Groat	£150	£500
Halfgroat	£385	£850
Penny (billon)	£175	£500

JAMES III (1460–88)

Aberdeen, Berwick and Edinburgh Mints		
Rider	£700	£1700
Half rider	£900	£2000
Quarter rider	£900	£2000
Unicorn	£750	£1700
Groat	£150	£350
Halfgroat	£325	£850
Penny (silver)	£95	£350
Plack (billon)	£55	£155
Half plack	*Extremely rare*	
Penny (billon)	£65	£175
Farthing (copper)	£150	£325

James III Groat, Berwick Mint

	F	VF

JAMES IV (1488–1513)

Edinburgh Mint

	F	VF
Unicorn	£675	£1500
Half unicorn	£550	£1100
Lion or crown	£800	£1750
Half lion	£1500	£3500
Groat	£300	£750
Halfgroat	£300	£650
Penny (silver)	£400	£1000
Plack	£30	£80
Half plack	£75	£180
*Penny (billon)	£45	£100

James IV

JAMES V (1513–42)

Edinburgh Mint

	F	VF
Unicorn	£750	£1800
Half Unicorn	£1450	£4000
Crown	£500	£1250
Ducat or Bonnet piece	£1450	£3100
Two-thirds ducat	£1850	£3200
One-third ducat	£2000	£4000
*Groat	£85	£200
One-third groat	£140	£350
Plack	£30	£100
Bawbee	£25	£85
Half bawbee	£70	£155
Quarter bawbee	*Extremely rare*	

James V Edinburgh Groat

MARY (1542–67)

Edinburgh and Stirling Mints

FIRST PERIOD (1542–58)

	F	VF
Crown	£850	£2350
Twenty shillings	£1750	£3000
Lions (Forty-four shillings)	£800	£1950
Half lions (Twenty-two shillings)	£450	£1500
Ryals (Three pounds)	£1750	£4500
Half ryal	£2750	£6000
Portrait testoon	£1000	£4000
*Non-portrait testoon	£150	£450
Half testoon	£150	£385
Bawbee	£35	£80
Half bawbee	£65	£175
Penny (facing bust)	£175	£500
Penny (no bust)	*Extremely rare*	
Lion	£25	£75
Plack	£25	£75

SECOND PERIOD (Francis and Mary, 1558–60)

	F	VF
Ducat (Sixty shillings)	*Extremely rare*	
Non-portrait testoon	£150	£400
Half testoon	£150	£450
12 penny groat	£85	£200
Lion	£25	£75

Mary First Period Testoon

THIRD PERIOD (Widowhood, 1560–65)

	F	VF
Portrait testoon	£750	£2500
Half testoon	£800	£1850

FOURTH PERIOD (Henry and Mary, 1565–67)

	F	VF
Portrait ryal	*Extremely rare*	
Non-portrait ryal	£180	£500
Two-third ryal	£180	£550

	F	VF
One-third ryal	£420	£1000
Testoon	£200	£800

FIFTH PERIOD (Second widowhood, 1567)

Non-portrait ryal	£185	£550
Two thirds ryal	£200	£525
One-third ryal	£200	£500

JAMES VI
(Before accession to the English throne)
(1567–1603)

FIRST COINAGE (1567–71)

Ryal	£180	£480
Two-third ryal	£175	£450
One-third ryal	£180	£480

SECOND COINAGE (1571–80)

Twenty pounds	*Extremely rare*	
Noble	£75	£350
Half noble	£75	£210
Two merks or Thistle dollar	£900	£1700
Merk	£850	—

THIRD COINAGE (1580–81)

Ducat	*Extremely rare*	
Sixteen shillings	£900	£2500
Eight shillings	£850	£2200
Four shillings	*Extremely rare*	
Two shillings	*Extremely rare*	

James VI Fourth coinage thirty shillings

FOURTH COINAGE (1582–88)

Lion noble	£2000	£6000
Two-third lion noble	£2500	£6500
One-third lion noble	£3000	£7750
Forty shillings	£2500	£7600
*Thirty shillings	£175	£750
Twenty shillings	£125	£400
Ten shillings	£100	£275

FIFTH COINAGE (1588)

Thistle noble	£1200	£3000

SIXTH COINAGE (1591–93)

"Hat" piece	£2500	£6000
"Balance" half merk	£170	£400
"Balance" quarter merk	£250	£575

SEVENTH COINAGE (1594–1601)

Rider	£425	£900
Half rider	£350	£750
Ten shillings	£85	£275
Five shillings	£95	£300
Thirty pence	£75	£250
Twelve pence	£65	£250

EIGHTH COINAGE (1601–04)

Sword and sceptre piece	£265	£500
Half sword and sceptre piece	£215	£375
Thistle-merk	£45	£175
Half thistle-merk	£35	£130
Quarter thistle-merk	£35	£130
Eighth thistle-merk	£40	£160

	F	VF

Billon and copper issues

	F	VF
Plack	£25	£90
Half plack	£85	£400
Hardhead	£25	£80
Saltire plack	£95	£500
Twopence		Very rare
Penny		Very rare

JAMES VI
(After accession to the English throne)
(1603–25)

	F	VF
Unit	£375	£750
Double crown	£450	£1200
British crown	£325	£1000
Halfcrown	£275	£500
Thistle crown	£260	£500
Sixty shillings	£275	£650
*Thirty shillings	£75	£200
Twelve shillings	£65	£175
Six shillings	£115	£550
Two shillings	£50	£250
One shilling	£70	£300
Copper twopence	£25	£60
Copper penny	£30	£75

James VI after accession thirty shillings

CHARLES I (1625–49)

FIRST COINAGE (1625–36)

	F	VF
Unit	£450	£850
Double crown	£1200	£2500
British crown		Extremely rare
Sixty shillings	£250	£750
Thirty shillings	£65	£250
Twelve shillings	£60	£180
Six shillings	£100	£400
Two shillings	£70	£325
One shilling		Extremely rare

SECOND COINAGE (1636)

	F	VF
Half merk	£45	£175
Forty penny piece	£40	£150
Twenty penny piece	£45	£300

THIRD COINAGE (1637–42)

	F	VF
Unit	£425	£950
Half unit	£550	£1750
British crown	£400	£1200
British half crown	£350	£1000
Sixty shillings	£275	£800
*Thirty shillings	£55	£150
Twelve shillings	£50	£165
Six shillings	£50	£145
Half merk	£45	£140
Forty pence	£25	£85
Twenty pence	£20	£60
Three shillings	£45	£125
Two shillings	£45	£130
Twopence (copper)	£20	£75
Penny		Extremely rare
Twopence (CR crowned)	£15	£60
Twopence (Stirling turner)	£15	£55

Charles I Third coinage thirty shillings

225

	F	VF

CHARLES II (1660–85)

FIRST COINAGE
Four merks

1664 Thistle above bust	£250	£600
1664 Thistle below bust	£275	£700
1665	*Extremely rare*	
1670	£180	£550
1673	£180	£550
1674 F below bust	£295	£750
1675	£180	£500

Two merks

1664 Thistle above bust	£185	£500
1664 Thistle below bust	£185	£600
1670	£150	£450
1673	£150	£450
1673 F below bust	£250	£900
1674	£250	£900
1674 F below bust	£200	£800
1675	£150	£450

Merk

1664	£35	£150
1665	£35	£150
1666	£80	£350
1668	£40	£155
1669	£40	£155
1670	£70	£225
1671	£65	£175
1672	£65	£175
1673	£65	£175
1674	£50	£200
1674 F Below bust	£50	£200
*1675 F below bust	£50	£200
1675	£85	£275

Half merk

1664	£55	£185
1665	£55	£185
1666	£70	£195
1667	£55	£180
1668	£55	£180
1669	£75	£200
1670	£100	£350
1671	£60	£150
1672	£60	£150
1673	£50	£155
1675 F below bust	£40	£145
1675	£50	£200

SECOND COINAGE
Dollar

1676	£180	£430
1679	£175	£400
1680	£230	£1000
1681	£150	£450
1682	£140	£300

Half Dollar

1675	£165	£430
1676	£185	£475
1681	£170	£440

Quarter Dollar

1675	£65	£200
1676	£75	£240
1677	£95	£325

Charles II two merks

	F	VF

1679	£70	£325
1680	£65	£265
1681	£75	£350
1682	£95	£250

Eighth Dollar

1676	£50	£150
1677	£50	£150
1678/7		*Rare*
1679	£150	£600
1680	£75	£175
1682	£100	£500

Sixteenth Dollar

1677	£35	£110
1678/7	£75	£175
1679/7		*Rare*
1680	£75	£200
1681	£40	£130

Twopence CR^{II} crowned	£25	£100
Bawbees	£35	£110
Turners	£25	£100

James VII ten shillings

JAMES VII 1685–9

Sixty shillings

| 1688 proof only | — | £1000 |

Forty shillings

| 1687 | £85 | £325 |
| 1688 | £150 | £400 |

Ten shillings

| *1687 | £85 | £275 |
| 1688 | £100 | £300 |

WILLIAM & MARY 1689–94

Sixty shillings

| 1691 | £150 | £550 |
| 1692 | £140 | £500 |

Forty shillings

1689	£90	£285
1690	£85	£280
1691	£70	£200
1692	£85	£285
1693	£100	£400
1694	£100	£400

Twenty shillings

| 1693 | £100 | £375 |
| 1694 | £200 | £500 |

Ten shillings

1689		*Extremely rare*
1690	£95	£275
*1691	£75	£220
1692	£45	£120
1694	£160	£400

Five shillings

| 1691 | £70 | £260 |
| 1694 | £65 | £200 |

Bawbee

| 1691–94 | £45 | £120 |

Bodle

| 1691–94 | £35 | £85 |

William & Mary ten shillings

	F	VF

WILLIAM II 1694–1702

	F	VF
Pistole	£1550	£4000
Half pistole	£1400	£3500
Forty shillings		
1695	£75	£300
1696	£55	£250
1697	£80	£350
1698	£55	£250
1699	£100	£600
1700	£200	£800
Twenty shillings		
1695	£45	£175
1696	£45	£175
1697	£100	—
1698	£85	£320
1699	£85	£320
Ten shillings		
*1695	£75	£250
1696	£80	£280
1697	£80	£300
1698	£80	£300
1699	£100	£350
Five shillings		
1695	£60	£250
1696	£60	£250
1697	£35	£110
1699	£50	£220
1700	£50	£220
1701	£55	£250
1702	£65	£275
Bawbee		
1695–97	£30	£100
Bodle		
1695–97	£35	£150

William II ten shillings

ANNE 1702–14

PRE-UNION 1702–7

	F	VF
Ten shillings		
1705	£65	£180
1706	£110	£360
Five shillings		
1705	£25	£65
*1706	£30	£100

Anne five shillings

POST-UNION 1707–14
See listing in English section.

JAMES VIII 1688–1766 (The Old Pretender)

A number of Guineas and Crowns in various metals were struck in 1828 using original dies prepared by Norbert Roettiers, all bearing the date 1716. These coins are extremely rare and are keenly sought after.

ISLE OF MAN

DATE	F	VF	EF	UNC
PENNY				
*1709 Cast	£15	£55	£150	—
1709 Silver cast Proof	—	—	—	£1200
1709 Brass	£20	£75	£150	—
*1733 "Quocunque"	£12	£28	£125	£200
1733 "Ouocunoue"	£15	£40	£160	£350
1733 Bath metal "Quocunque"	£5	£15	£110	—
1733 Silver Proof	—	—	—	£425
1733 Bronze Proof	—	—	—	£265
1733 Proof	—	—	—	£400
1733 Cap frosted	£6	£22	£125	£185
1733 Brass, cap frosted	£12	£35	£150	£320
1733 Silver Proof cap frosted	—	—	—	£350
1733 Bronze annulets instead of pellets	£25	£50	£200	£450
1758	£8	£25	£110	£225
1758 Proof	—	—	—	£300
1758 Silver Proof	—	—	—	£600
*1786 Engrailed edge	£6	£20	£100	£275
1786 Engrailed edge Proof	—	—	—	£300
1786 Plain edge Proof	—	—	—	£600
1786 Pellet below bust	£10	£40	£150	£300
*1798	£12	£37	£90	£185
1798 Proof	—	—	—	£200
1798 Bronze Proof	—	—	—	£200
1798 Copper-gilt Proof	—	—	—	£1000
1798 Silver Proof	—	—	—	£1500
1813	£8	£25	£85	£175
1813 Proof	—	—	—	£200
1813 Bronze Proof	—	—	—	£160
1813 Copper-gilt Proof	—	—	—	£1500
1839	£6	£20	£65	£125
1839 Proof	—	—	—	£225

229

DATE	F	VF	EF	UNC

HALF PENCE

	F	VF	EF	UNC
*1709 Cast	£22	£40	£125	—
1709 Brass	£30	£120	£300	—
1723 Silver	£500	£1000	£2000	—
1723 Copper	£220	£450	£1100	£1600
1733 Copper	£10	£30	£120	£185
1733 Bronze	£15	£32	£130	£200
1733 Silver Proof plain cap	—	—	—	£300
1733 Silver Proof frosted cap	—	—	—	—
1733 Bronze Proof	—	—	—	£250
1733 Bath metal plain cap	£12	£20	£100	—
1733 Bath metal frosted cap	£12	£28	£120	—
*1758	£14	£30	£130	£185
1758 Proof	—	—	—	£450
1786 Engrailed edge	£6	£18	£55	£160
1786 Proof engrailed edge	—	—	—	£200
1786 Plain edge	£15	£38	£135	£185
1786 Proof plain edge	—	—	—	£400
1786 Bronze Proof	—	—	—	£200
1798	£6	£18	£55	£150
1798 Proof	—	—	—	£200
1798 Bronze Proof	—	—	—	£175
1798 Copper-gilt Proof	—	—	—	£700
1798 Silver Proof	—	—	—	£1000
1813	£6	£15	£50	£120
1813 Proof	—	—	—	£200
1813 Bronze Proof	—	—	—	£175
1813 Copper-gilt Proof	—	—	—	£750
1839	£6	£12	£36	£70
1839 Bronze Proof	—	—	—	£150

FARTHING

	F	VF	EF	UNC
*1839 Copper	£6	£15	£40	£75
1839 Bronze Proof	—	—	—	£200
1839 Copper-gilt Proof	—	—	—	£1500

The last issue of coins made in the Isle of Man had been in 1839 but in 1970 Spink & Son Ltd was commissioned to produce a modern coinage for the Isle of Man Governmant which was struck at the Royal Mint. From 1973 onwards the Pobjoy Mint took over the contract and has been a very prolific producer of definitive and commemorative issues. It is not proposed to give a complete listing of all these coins but the Crown and 25p, which from the collector's point of view are the most interesting in the series, have been selected.

The listings that follow are of the ordinary uncirculated cupro-nickel coins. The Island has also issued most of the coins listed in other metals, including silver, gold and platinum in non proof and proof form and in 1984 some were also issued in silver clad cupro-nickel in proof form.

DATE	UNC
1970 Manx Cat	£2.50
1972 Royal Silver Wedding.....................	£2.50
1974 Centenary of Churchill's birth	£1.50
1975 Manx Cat	£2.50
1976 Bi-Centenary of American Independence	£1.50
1976 Centenary of the Horse Drawn Tram	£1.50
1977 Silver Jubilee......................	£1.50
1977 Silver Jubilee Appeal.....................	£1.50
1978 25th Anniversary of the Coronation	£1.50
1979 300th Anniversary of Manx Coinage	£1.50
1979 Millennium of Tynwald (5 coins)...............	£6.50
1980 Winter Olympics	£1.50
1980 Derby Bicentennial	£1.50
1980 22nd Olympics (3 coins)	£4
1980 80th Birthday of Queen Mother................	£1.50
1981 Duke of Edinburgh Award Scheme (4 coins)	£5.50
1981 Year of Disabled (4 coins)	£5.50
1981 Prince of Wales' Wedding (2 coins)	£2.50
1982 12th World Cup—Spain (4 coins)	£6
1982 Maritime Heritage (4 coins)	£8
1983 Manned Flight (4 coins)	£8
1984 23rd Olympics (4 coins)	£6
1984 Quincentenary of College of Arms (4 coins)	£8
1984 Commonwealth Parliamentary Conference (4 coins)	£8
1985 Queen Mother (6 coins)	£7
1986 13th World Cup—Mexico (6 coins)	£7
1986 Prince Andrew Wedding (2 coins)...............	£4
1987 200th Anniversary of the United States Constitution	£1.25
1987 America's Cup Races (5 coins)	£8
1988 Bicentenary of Steam Navigation (6 coins)	£8
1988 Australia Bicentennial (6 coins)	£8.50
1988 Manx Cat	£2.50
1989 Royal Visit	£2
1989 Bicentenary of the Mutiny on the Bounty (4 coins)	£7
1989 Persian Cat	£3
1989 Bicentenary of Washington's Inauguration (4 coins)	£8
1990 150th Anniversary of the Penny Black	£6.50
1990 World Cup—Italy (4 coins)	£7
1990 25th Anniversary of Churchill's Death (2 coins)	£4
1990 Alley Cat	£3
1990 Queen Mother's 90th Birthday	£3
1991 Norwegian Forest Cat	£3
1991 Centenary of the American Numismatic Association	£2.50
1991 1992 America's Cup......................	£3.50
1991 10th Anniversary of Prince of Wales' Wedding (2 coins) ...	£5.50
1992 Discovery of America (4 coins)	£10
1992 Siamese Cat	£3
1992 1992 America's Cup......................	£2.50
1993 Maine Coon Cat	£2.50

DATE	UNC
1993 Preserve Planet Earth—Dinosaurs (2 coins)	£7
1994 Preserve Planet Earth—Mammoth	£3.50
1994 Year of the Dog	£3.50
1994 World Football Cup (6 coins)	£20
1994 Japanese Bobtail Cat	£3.50
1994 Normandy Landings (8 coins)	£28
1994 Preserve Planet Earth—Endangered Animals (3 coins)	£12
1995 Man in Flight—Series i (8 coins)	£45
1995 Man in Flight—Series ii (8 coins)	£45
1995 Queen Mother's 95th Birthday	£3
1995 Year of the Pig	£3
1995 Turkish Cat	£3
1995 Preserve Planet Earth—Egret and Otter	£7
1995 America's Cup	£3
1995 Aircraft of World War II (19 coins)	£75
1995 Famous World Inventions—Series i (12 coins)	£45
1996 Year of the Rat	£4
1996 70th Birthday of HM the Queen	£4
1996 The Flower Fairies—Series i (4 coins)	£25
1996 Famous World Inventions—Series ii (6 coins)	£25
1996 Olympic Games (6 coins)	£22
1996 Preserve Planet Earth—Killer Whale and Razorbill	£7
1996 Burmese Cat	£4
1996 Robert Burns (4 coins)	£15
1996 King Arthur & the Knights of the Round Table (5 coins)	£22
1996 European Football Championships (8 coins)	£36
1996 Football Championships Winner	£5
1996 Explorers (2 coins)	£10
1997 Year of the Ox	£5
1997 The Flower Fairies—Series ii (4 coins)	£18
1997 Royal Golden Wedding (2 coins)	£9
1997 Explorers—Eriksson and Nansen (2 coins)	£9
1997 Long-haired Smoke Cat	£5
1997 10th Anniversary of the "Cats on Coins" series (silver only)	£28
1997 90th Anniversary of the TT Races (4 coins)	£20
1998 The Millennium (16 coins to be issued in the next 3 years)	—
1998 Year of the Tiger	£5
1998 FIFA World Cup (4 coins)	£18
1998 Birman Cat	£5
1998 The Flower Fairies—Series iii (4 coins)	£20
1998 18th Winter Olympics, Nagano (4 coins)	£22
1998 Explorers—Vasco da Gama and Marco Polo (2 coins)	£10
1998 125th Anniversary of Steam Railway (8 coins)	£45
1998 International Year of the Oceans (4 coins)	£25
1999 50th brithday of HRH the Prince of Wales	£5
1999 Year of the Rabbit	£5
1999 27th Olympics in Sydney (5 coins)	£25
1999 Rugby World Cup (6 coins)	£30
1999 Wedding of HRH Prince Edward and Sophie Rhys-Jones	£5

GUERNSEY

DATE	F	VF	EF	UNC
TEN SHILLINGS				
*1966	—	£1	£1	£1.50
1966 Proof	—	—	—	£3
THREEPENCE				
1956	15p	25p	50p	£1
1956 Proof	—	—	—	£4
1959	15p	25p	50p	£1
1966 Proof	—	—	—	£2
EIGHT DOUBLES				
1834	£2	£4	£25	£85
*1858 5 berries	£2	£4	£26	£85
1858 4 berries	£2	£4	£26	£85
1864 1 stalk	£1	£2	£12	£40
1864 3 stalks	£1	£2	£14	£45
1868	£3	£6	£15	£35
1874	£2	£3	£6	£30
1885H	£2	£3	£5	£20
1889H	£1	£2	£4	£18
1893H small date	£1	£2	£4	£18
1893H large date	£1	£2	£4	£18
1902H	£1	£2	£3	£15
1903H	£1	£2	£4	£15
1910	£1	£2	£5	£18
1911H	£2	£3	£6	£20
1914H	25p	£1	£3	£12
1918H	25p	£1	£3	£10
1920H	25p	£1	£2	£10
1934H	30p	£1	£3	£15
1934H Proof	—	—	—	£80
1938H	30p	£1	£2	£8
1945H	25p	50p	£1	£5
1947H	20p	50p	£1	£5
1949H	20p	50p	£1	£5
1956	15p	25p	75p	£2
1956	15p	25p	75p	£2
1959	15p	25p	75p	£2
1966 Proof	—	—	—	£6
FOUR DOUBLES				
1830	£1	£3	£25	£60
1830 Mule with obv. St Helena ½d	—	£650	—	—
1858	£3	£6	£30	£60
1864 Single stalk	50p	£2	£6	£30
1864 3 stalks	50p	£2	£8	£35
1868	£1	£2	£12	£45
1874	50p	£1	£10	£45
1885H	50p	£1	£5	£18
1889H	50p	£1	£4	£15
1893H	50p	£1	£5	£15
1902H	50p	£1	£3	£12
1903H	50p	£1	£4	£15
1906H	50p	£1.50	£3	£12
1908H	50p	£1	£3	£12
1910H	50p	£1	£3	£12
1911H	50p	£1	£2	£8
1914H	50p	£1	£4	£15
1918H	50p	£1	£4	£15
1920H	50p	£1	£2	£12
1945H	50p	£1	£2	£8
1949H	£1	£2	£6	£16
1956	25p	50p	£1	£3
1966 Proof	—	—	—	£3

DATE	F	VF	EF	UNC

TWO DOUBLES

1858	£2	£5	£28	£95
1868 Single stick	£3	£6	£30	£95
1868 3 stalks	£5	£10	£50	£100
1874	£2	£4	£25	£60
1885H	£1	£2	£4	£15
1889H	£1	£2	£4	£12
1899H	£1	£2.50	£8	£20
1902H	£1	£2	£6	£15
1902H	£1	£2	£8	£18
1906H	£1	£2	£8	£20
1908H	£1	£2	£8	£20
1911H	£1	£2	£10	£22
1914H	£1	£2	£10	£22
1917H	£5	£15	£40	£85
1918H	75p	£2	£4	£12
*1920H	75p	£2	£4	£12
1929H	50p	£1	£2	£5

ONE DOUBLE

*1830	£1	£2	£10	£20
1868	£4	£8	£20	£55
1868/30	£3	£5	£17	£48
1885H	50p	£1	£2	£6
1889H	25p	50p	£1	£5
1893H	25p	50p	£1	£5
1899H	25p	50p	£1	£5
1902	25p	50p	£1	£5
1903H	25p	50p	£1	£5
1911H	25p	£1	£2	£7
1911 (new shield)	25p	50p	£1	£5
1914H	25p	£1	£2	£6
1929H	25p	50p	£1	£5
1933H	25p	50p	£1	£5
1938H	25p	50p	£1	£5

DECIMAL COINAGE

Ordinary circulating coinage from 1986 onwards is usually available in uncirculated condition at a small premium above face value thus it is not listed here. The coins listed are cupro-nickel unless otherwise stated.

TWENTY-FIVE POUNDS—*Gold*

1994 50th Anniversary of Normandy Landings	£175
1995 Queen Mother's 95th Birthday. Proof	£200
1996 HM the Queen's 70th birthday. Proof	£200
1996 European Football Championships. Proof	£200
1997 Royal Golden Wedding. Proof	£200
1998 Royal Air Force. Proof	£200
1999 Wedding of HRH Prince Edward and Sophie Rhys-Jones. Proof ..	£200
1999 Queen Mother. Proof	£200

TEN POUNDS—*Silver*

1997 Royal Golden Wedding. Proof	£150
1999 Millennium	£350

FIVE POUNDS

1995 Queen Mother's 95th birthday	£12
1995 — Silver proof	£38
1996 HM the Queen's 70th birthday	£12
1996 — Silver proof	£38
1996 European Football Championships	£12
1996 — Silver proof	£38
1997 Royal Golden Wedding	£12
1997 — Silver proof	£38
1997 — Small size Gold. BU	£50
1997 Castles of the British Isles—Castle Cornet, Guernsey	£10
1997 — Silver proof	£40
1997 Castles of the British Isles—Caernarfon Castle. Silver proof only .	£40

DATE	UNC
1997 Castles of the British Isles—Leeds Castle. Silver proof only	£40
1998 Royal Air Force. Silver proof	£40
1999 Millennium	£10
1999 — Silver proof	£30
1999 Wedding of HRH Prince Edward and Sophie Rhys-Jones	£12
1999 — Silver proof	£45
1999 Queen Mother	£12
1999 — Silver proof	£45

TWO POUNDS

1985 40th anniversary of Liberation, crown size	£6
1985 — Silver proof	£25
1986 Commonwealth Games, in plastic case	£5
1986 — in special folder	£5
1986 — .500 Silver	£15
1986 — .925 Silver proof	£25
*1987 900th anniv. of death of William the Conqueror, in special folder	£5
1987 — Silver proof	£26
1987 — Gold proof	£900
1988 William II, in presentation folder	£5
1988 — Silver proof	£26
1989 Henry I, in presentation folder	£5
1989 — Silver proof	£28
1989 Royal Visit	£5
1989 — Silver proof	£26
1990 Queen Mother's 90th birthday	£5
1990 — Silver proof	£30
1991 Henry II, in presentation folder	£5
1991 — Silver proof	£30
1993 40th Anniversary of the Coronation	£5
1993 — Silver proof	£30
*1994 Anniversary of the Normandy Landings	£5
1994 — Silver proof	£30
1995 50th Anniversary of Liberation	£5
1995 — Silver proof	£30
1995 — Silver Piedfort proof	£60

ONE POUND

1981	£3
1981 Gold proof	£85
1981 Gold piedfort	£250
1983 New specification, new reverse	£2
1985 New design (in folder)	£2
1995 Queen Mother's 95th Birthday. Silver proof	£25
1996 Queen's 70th Birthday. Silver proof	£25
1997 Royal Golden Wedding. Silver BU	£10
1997 — Silver proof	£25
1997 Castles of the British Isles—Tower of London. Silver proof only ...	£20
1998 Royal Air Force. Silver proof	£22
1999 Millennium. Silver proof (gold plated)	£30
1999 Wedding of Prince Edward and Sophie Rhys-Jones. Silver proof .	£25
1999 Queen Mother. Silver proof	£25

FIFTY PENCE

1969	£1
1970	£3
1971 Proof	£5
1981	£1
1982	£1
1985 New design	—

TWENTY-FIVE PENCE

1972 Royal Silver Wedding	£4
1972 — Silver proof	£12
1977 Royal Silver Jubilee	£1.50
1977 — Silver proof	£12
1978 Royal Visit	£1.50
1978 — Silver proof	£10
1980 Queen Mother's 80th birthday	£2
1980 — Silver proof	£12
1981 Royal Wedding	£1
1981 — Silver proof	£12

JERSEY

DATE	F	VF	EF	UNC

FIVE SHILLINGS
1966	—	£1	£1	£2
1966 Proof	—	£1	£2	£5

ONE QUARTER OF A SHILLING
1957	—	50p	£1	£2
1960 Proof	—	—	—	£5
1964	—	—	50p	£1
1966	—	—	50p	£1

ONE TWELFTH OF A SHILLING
1877H	50p	£1	£8	£30
1877H Proof in nickel	—	—	—	£1000
1877 Proof only	—	—	—	£350
1877 Proof in nickel	—	—	—	£1000
1881	£1	£2	£10	£40
1888	50p	£1	£8	£30
1894	50p	£1	£8	£30
1909	50p	£1	£10	£20
1911	50p	£1	£4	£18
1913	50p	£1	£4	£18
1923 Spade shield	50p	£1	£4	£18
1923 Square shield	50p	£1	£4	£16
1926	50p	£1	£5	£25
1931	50p	£1	£2	£5
1933	50p	£1	£2	£5
1935	50p	£1	£2	£5
1937	50p	£1	£2	£5
1946	50p	£1	£2	£4
1947	25p	£1	£2	£3
"1945" GVI	10p	25p	50p	£2
"1945" QE2	10p	25p	50p	£2
1957	10p	20p	40p	£1
*1960 1660–1960 300th anniversary	10p	15p	30p	75p
1960 Mule	—	—	—	£75
1966 "1066–1966"	—	—	50p	£1

ONE THIRTEENTH OF A SHILLING
1841	£2	£6	£28	£100
1844	£2	£7	£30	£120
1851	£3	£10	£40	£100
1858	£2	£7	£30	£100
1861	£3	£10	£40	£100
1865 Proof only	—	—	—	£550
1866 with LCW	£1	£3	£20	£55
1866 without LCW Proof only	—	—	—	£275
1870	£2	£6	£25	£55
1871	£2	£6	£25	£55

ONE TWENTY-FOURTH OF A SHILLING
1877H	£1	£2	£5	£25
1877 Proof only	—	—	—	£200
1888	£1	£2	£5	£20
1894	£1	£2	£5	£20
1909	£1	£2	£5	£18
1911	75p	£1.50	£3	£15
1913	75p	£1.50	£3	£15

DATE	F	VF	EF	UNC
1923 Spade shield	£1	£2	£5	£18
1923 Square shield	£1	£2	£4	£12
1926	£1	£2	£4	£12
1931	75p	£1.50	£3	£12
*1933	75p	£1.50	£3	£10
1935	75p	£1.50	£3	£10
1937	50p	£1	£2	£5
1946	50p	£1	£2	£6
1947	50p	£1	£2	£6

ONE TWENTY-SIXTH OF A SHILLING

1841	£3	£6	£20	£55
1844	£3	£6	£16	£50
1851	£2.50	£5	£15	£50
1858	£3	£7	£37	£100
1861	£2.50	£5	£15	£45
*1866	£2	£4	£15	£55
1870	£2	£4	£13	£35
1871	£2	£4	£13	£35

ONE FORTY-EIGHTH OF A SHILLING

1877H	£5	£10	£35	£75
1877 Proof only	—	—	—	£250

ONE FIFTY-SECOND OF A SHILLING

1841	£6	£17	£45	£100
1861 Proof only	—	—	—	£475

DECIMAL COINAGE

Ordinary circulating coinage from 1986 onwards is usually available in uncirculated condition at a small premium above face value thus it is not listed here.

ONE HUNDRED POUNDS
1995 50th Anniversary of Liberation. Gold Proof £400

FIFTY POUNDS
1995 50th Anniversary of Liberation. Gold Proof £300

TWENTY-FIVE POUNDS
1995 50th Anniversary of Liberation. Gold Proof £200

TEN POUNDS
*1990 50th Anniversary of the Battle of Britain. Gold Proof £150
1995 50th Anniversary of Liberation. Gold Proof £150

FIVE POUNDS
*1990 50th Anniversary of the Battle of Britain. Silver Proof (5 ounces) £85
1997 Royal Golden Wedding £10
1997 — Silver proof £38
1999 Millennium £45

(Reduced)

TWO POUNDS FIFTY PENCE
1972 Royal Silver Wedding £8
1972 — Silver proof £15

TWO POUNDS
(note all modern Proof coins have frosted relief)
1972 Royal Silver Wedding £7
1972 — Silver proof £10
1981 Royal Wedding, nickel silver (crown size) £3
1981— in presentation pack £5
1981 — Silver proof £16
1981 — Gold proof £300
1985 40th Anniversary of Liberation (crown size) £3
1985 — in presentation pack £4
1985 — Silver proof £23

(Enlarged)

DATE UNC

1985 — Gold proof	£950
1986 Commonwealth Games	£4
1986 — in presentation case	£5
1986 — .500 silver	£15
1986 — .925 silver proof	£23
1987 World Wildlife Fund 25th Anniversary	£4
1987 — Silver proof	£24
1989 Royal Visit	£4
1989 — Silver proof	£22
1990 Queen Mother's 90th Birthday	£4
1990 — Silver proof	£35
1990 — Gold proof	£400
1990 50th Anniversary of the Battle of Britain, silver proof	£32
1993 40th Anniversary of the Coronation	£5
1993 — Silver proof	£35
*1995 50th Anniversary of Liberation	£5
1995 — Silver Proof	£35
1996 HM the Queen's 70th Birthday	£5
1996 — Silver proof	£32
1997 Bimetal	£5
1997 — Silver proof	£25
1997 — new portrait	£5

ONE POUND

1972 Royal Silver Wedding	£4
1972 — Silver proof	£5
1981	£3
1981 Silver proof	£10
1981 Gold proof	£160
1983 New designs and specifications on presentation card (St Helier)	£3
1983 — Silver proof	£15
1983 — gold proof	£350
1984 Presentation wallet (St Saviour)	£3
1984 — Silver proof	£22
1984 — Gold proof	£350
1984 Presentation wallet (St Brelade)	£3
1984 — Silver proof	£22
1984 — Gold proof	£350
1985 Presentation wallet (St Clement)	£3
1985 — Silver proof	£22
1985 — Gold proof	£350
1985 Presentation wallet (St Lawrence)	£3
1985 — Silver proof	£22
1985 — Gold proof	£350
1986 Presentation wallet (St Peter)	£3
1986 — Silver proof	£22
1986 — Gold proof	£350
1986 Presentation wallet (Grouville)	£3
1986 — Silver proof	£22
1986 — Gold proof	£350
1987 Presentation wallet (St Martin)	£3
1987 — Silver proof	£22
1987 — Gold proof	£350
1987 Presentation wallet (St Ouen)	£3
1987 — Silver proof	£22
1987 — Gold proof	£350
1988 Presentation wallet (Trinity)	£3
1988 — Silver proof	£22
1988 — Gold proof	£350
1988 Presentation wallet (St John)	£3
1988 — Silver proof	£22
1988 — Gold proof	£350
1989 Presentation wallet (St Mary)	£3
1989 — Silver proof	£22
1989 — Gold proof	£350

DATE	UNC

1991 Ship Building in Jersey Series

1991 "Tickler" Silver proof	£36
1991 — Gold proof	£355
1991 "Percy Douglas" Silver proof	£28
1991 — Gold proof	£355
1992 "The Hebe" Silver proof	£22
1992 — Gold proof	£320
1992 "Coat of Arms" Silver proof	£22
1992 — Gold proof	£320
1993 "The Gemini" Silver proof	£22
1993 — Gold proof	£350
1993 "The Century" Silver proof	£22
1993 — Gold proof	£350
*1994 "Resolute" Silver proof	£25
1994 — Gold proof	£350

FIFTY PENCE

1969	£1.50
1972 Royal Silver Wedding	£2
1972 — Silver proof	£3
1983 New design	£1.50
1985 40th Anniversary of Liberation	£2

TWENTY-FIVE PENCE

1977 Royal Jubilee	£1.50
1977 — Silver proof	£12

TWENTY PENCE

1982 Date on rocks on rev. (cased)	£1
1982 — Silver proof piedfort	£36
1983 New obv. with date, rev. no date on rocks	—

ALDERNEY

DATE	UNC

ONE HUNDRED POUNDS
1994 50th Anniversary of D-Day Landings gold proof £450

FIFTY POUNDS
1994 50th Anniversary of D–Day Landing gold proof £250

TWENTY FIVE POUNDS
1993 40th Anniversary of Coronation gold proof £160
1994 50th Anniversary of D-Day Landings gold proof £175
1997 Royal Golden Wedding gold proof £200

TEN POUNDS
1994 50th Anniversary of D–Day Landing gold proof £55

FIVE POUNDS
1995 Queen Mother Cupro-Nickel Crown £8
1995 — Silver proof £32
1995 — Silver piedfort £60
1995 — Gold proof £800
1996 HM the Queen's 70th Birthday £8
1996 — Silver proof £32
1996 — Silver piedfort £60
1996 — Gold proof £800
1999 — Eclipse of the Sun. Silver proof with colour centre .... —

TWO POUNDS
1989 Royal Visit Cupro-Nickel Crown £5
1989 — Silver proof £26
1989 — Silver piedfort £55
1989 — Gold proof £900
*1990 Queen Mother's 90th Birthday £4
1990 — Silver proof £28
1990 — Silver piedfort £60
1990 — Gold proof £900
*1992 40th Anniversary of Accession £4
1992 — Silver proof £28
1992 — Silver piedfort £60
1992 — Gold proof £900
1993 40th Anniversary of Coronation £4
1993 — Silver proof £28
1993 — Silver piedfort £60
1994 50th Anniversary of D-Day Landings £5
1994 — Silver proof £30
1994 — Silver piedfort £60
1995 50th Anniversary of Return of Islanders £4
1995 — Silver proof £35
1995 — Silver piedfort £60
1995 — Gold proof £800
*1997 WWF Puffin £5
1997 — Silver proof £35
1997 Royal Golden Wedding £4
1997 — Silver proof £38

ONE POUND
1993 40th Anniversary of Coronation Silver proof £30
*1995 50th Anniversary of VE Day Silver proof £22
1995 — Gold proof £300

IRELAND

DATE	F	VF	EF	UNC

All copper unless otherwise stated

PENNIES

DATE	F	VF	EF	UNC
1805	£5	£15	£75	£150
1805 Proof	—	—	—	£150
1805 in Bronze Proof	—	—	—	£130
1805 in Copper Gilt Proof	—	—	—	£200
1805 in Silver Proof (restrike)	—	—	—	£1250
1822	£5	£15	£95	£200
1822 Proof	—	—	—	£300
1823	£5	£15	£95	£200
1823 Proof	—	—	—	£300

HALFPENNIES

DATE	F	VF	EF	UNC
1722 Holding Harp Left	£30	£85	£200	£500
1722 Holding Harp Right	£25	£75	£200	£400
1723/2 Harp Right	£25	£75	£200	£500
1723 Harp right	£10	£50	£100	£250
1723 Silver Proof	—	—	—	£1500
1723 Obv. R's altered from B's	£12	£60	£150	—
1723 No stop after date	£12	£60	£150	£250
1724 Rev. legend divided	£20	£70	£180	—
1724 Rev. legend continuous	£20	£70	£180	—
*1736	£10	£40	£100	£200
1736 Proof	—	—	—	£250
1736 Silver Proof	—	—	—	£600
1737	£10	£30	£100	—
1738	£15	£40	£120	—
1741	£15	£40	£120	—
1742	£15	£40	£120	—
1743	£15	£40	£120	—
1744/3	£15	£35	£100	—
1744	£15	£45	£125	—
1746	£15	£40	£120	—
1747	£15	£40	£120	—
1748	£15	£40	£120	—
1749	£15	£40	£120	—
1750	£15	£40	£120	—
1751	£15	£40	£120	—
1752	£15	£40	£120	—
1753	£15	£40	£120	—
1755	£20	£70	£200	—
*1760	£10	£30	£85	—
1766	£10	£30	£85	—
1769	£10	£30	£85	—
1769 Longer bust	£18	£45	£120	—
1774 Pattern only Proof	—	—	—	£900
1775	£10	£30	£100	—
1775 Proof	—	—	—	£300
1776	£25	£85	£200	—
1781	£15	£30	£75	£180
1782	£15	£30	£75	£180
1805	£3	£5	£30	£85
1805 Copper Proof	—	—	—	£100
1805 in Bronze	—	—	—	£75
1805 in Gilt Copper	—	—	—	£150
1805 in Silver (restrike)	—	—	—	£750

DATE	F	VF	EF	UNC
1822	£5	£10	£45	£140
1822 Proof	—	—	—	£250
1823	£5	£10	£45	£130
1823	—	—	—	£250

NB Prooflike Unirculated Pennies and Halfpennies of 1822/23 are often misdescribed as Proofs. The true Proofs are rare. Some are on heavier, thicker flans.

FARTHINGS

	F	VF	EF	UNC
1722 D.G. Rex Harp to left (Pattern)	£500	£1000	£1500	—
1723 D.G. Rex Harp to right	£65	£100	£250	—
1723 Dei Gratia Rex Harp to right	£12	£40	£100	£220
1723 — Silver Proof	—	—	—	£1000
1724 Dei Gratia Rex Harp to right	£40	£80	£200	£460
1737	£15	£35	£75	£160
1737 Proof	—	—	—	£200
1737 Silver Proof	—	—	—	£400
1738	£15	£35	£90	£185
1744	£15	£35	£90	£185
1760	£8	£16	£55	£125
*1806	£4	£10	£35	£75
1806 Copper Proof	—	—	—	£100
1806 Bronzed Copper Proof	—	—	—	£65
1806 Copper Gilt Proof	—	—	—	£100
1806 Silver Proof (restrike)	—	—	—	£500
1822 George IV (Pattern) Proof	—	—	—	£700

TOKEN ISSUES BY THE BANK OF IRELAND

FIVE PENCE IN SILVER

	F	VF	EF	UNC
1805	£6	£15	£34	£95
1806	£10	£30	£80	£150
1806/5	£25	£75	£225	£500

TEN PENCE IN SILVER

	F	VF	EF	UNC
1805	£7	£16	£35	£120
1806	£10	£30	£80	£150
*1813	£6	£15	£35	£100
1813 Proof	—	—	—	£250

THIRTY PENCE IN SILVER

	F	VF	EF	UNC
1808	£15	£45	£125	£250

SIX SHILLINGS

	F	VF	EF	UNC
*1804 in Silver	£65	£125	£250	£750
1804 Proof	—	—	—	£800
1804 in Copper (restrike)	—	—	—	£450
1804 Copper Gilt	—	—	—	£900
1804 in Gilt Silver	—	—	—	£1500

In this series fully struck specimens, with sharp hair curls, etc., are worth appreciably more than the prices quoted.

IRISH FREE STATE

DATE	F	VF	EF	UNC

TEN SHILLINGS

*1966 Easter Rising	—	£4	£6	£10
1966 Cased Proof	—	—	—	£12
1966 special double case	—	—	—	£35

HALF CROWNS

1928	£2	£5	£20	£35
1928 Proof	—	—	—	£35
1930	£5	£12	£80	£225
1931	£5	£20	£110	£280
1933	£5	£12	£100	£230
1934	£5	£7	£30	£95
1937	£35	£90	£325	£800
*1939	£2	£4	£14	£40
1939 Proof	—	—	—	£400
1940	£2	£4	£14	£38
1941	£3	£8	£16	£48
1942	£3	£5	£14	£35
1943	£60	£120	£500	£1200
1951	£1	£2	£5	£20
1951 Proof	—	—	—	£300
1954	£1	£2	£5	£20
1954 Proof	—	—	—	£300
1955	£1	£2	£4	£16
1955	—	—	—	£400
1959	£1	£2	£4	£12
1961	£1	£2	£10	£25
1961 Obv as 1928, rev. as 1951	£10	£15	£135	—
1962	£1	£2	£4	£10
1963	£1	£2	£3	£7
1964	£1	£2	£3	£5
1966	£1	£2	£3	£5
1967	£1	£2	£3	£5

FLORINS

1928	£2	£4	£10	£30
1928 Proof	—	—	—	£35
1930	£3	£10	£75	£225
1930 Proof				*Unique*
1931	£4	£15	£100	£275
1933	£3	£10	£75	£250
1934	£5	£80	£150	£400
1934 Proof	—	—	—	£1800
1935	£2	£9	£40	£100
1937	£5	£15	£85	£250
1939	£1	£3	£12	£20
1939 Proof	—	—	—	£400
1940	£2	£4	£14	£32
1941	£2	£4	£15	£35
1941 Proof	—	—	—	£500
1942	£3	£8	£16	£35
1943	£500	£1000	£2000	£4000
1951	50p	£1	£5	£14
1951 Proof	—	—	—	£300
1954	50p	£1	£4	£15
1954 Proof	—	—	—	£250
1955	—	50p	£3	£12

DATE	F	VF	EF	UNC
1955 Proof	—	—	—	£250
1959	35p	£1	£4	£10
1961	50p	£2	£8	£25
1962	35p	£1	£3	£10
1963	25p	£1	£2	£7
1964	25p	£1	£2	£5
1965	25p	£1	£2	£5
1966	25p	£1	£2	£4
1968	25p	£1	£2	£4

SHILLINGS

	F	VF	EF	UNC
1928	£1	£3	£6	£17
1928 Proof	—	—	—	£16
1930	£2	£10	£60	£175
1930 Proof	—	—	—	£600
1931	£2	£10	£60	£115
1933	£2	£10	£60	£150
1935	£2	£5	£25	£75
1937	£4	£40	£150	£700
1939	£1	£3	£10	£25
1939 Proof	—	—	—	£400
1940	£1	£3	£12	£24
1941	£2	£4	£15	£32
1942	£2	£3	£8	£22
1951	50p	£1	£4	£10
1951 Proof	—	—	—	£275
1954	50p	£1	£3	£8
1954 Proof	—	—	—	£300
1955	50p	£1	£4	£10
1959	50p	£1	£4	£15
1962	25p	£1	£2	£6
1963	25p	£1	£2	£4
1964	25p	£1	£2	£3
1966	25p	£1	£2	£3
1968	25p	£1	£2	£3

SIXPENCES

	F	VF	EF	UNC
1928	50p	£1	£5	£14
1928 Proof	—	—	—	£15
1934	50p	£2	£10	£55
1935	75p	£2	£18	£75
1939	50p	£1	£5	£32
1939 Proof	—	—	—	£400
1940	50p	£1	£5	£32
1942	50p	£1	£8	£34
1945	£1p	£3	£22	£68
1946	£1	£3	£45	£230
1947	£1	£2	£20	£55
1948	50p	£2	£10	£38
1949	50p	£1	£6	£27
1950	50p	£2	£18	£70
1952	50p	£1	£3	£15
1953	50p	£1	£3	£15
1953 Proof	—	—	—	£75
1955	50p	£1	£3	£15
1956	50p	£1	£2	£12
1956 Proof	—	—	—	£80
1958	£1	£2	£10	£42
1958 Proof	—	—	—	£250
1959	25p	50p	£2	£8
1960	25p	50p	£1	£5
1961	25p	50p	£1	£5

DATE	F	VF	EF	UNC
1962	£1	£3	£15	£40
1963	25p	£2	£5	£7
1964	25p	50p	£3	£5
1966	25p	50p	£3	£5
1967	25p	50p	£1	£3
1968	25p	50p	£1	£3
1969	£1	£2	£5	£8

THREEPENCES

	F	VF	EF	UNC
1928	£1	£2	£6	£10
1928 Proof	—	—	—	£15
1933	£2	£5	£40	£185
1934	50p	£1	£5	£35
1935	£1	£3	£12	£100
1939	£2	£6	£45	£225
1939 Proof	—	—	—	£725
1940	50p	£1	£5	£35
1942	25p	75p	£4	£25
1943	£1	£2	£8	£48
1946	25p	75p	£5	£24
1946 Proof	—	—	—	£155
1948	£1	£2	£18	£55
1949	25p	£1	£2	£20
1949 Proof	—	—	—	£155
1950	25p	£1	£2	£6
1950 Proof	—	—	—	£155
1953	25p	£1	£2	£7
1956	25p	£1	£2	£5
1961	25p	50p	£1	£3
1962	25p	50p	£1	£5
1963	25p	50p	£1	£5
1964	20p	50p	£1	£3
1965	20p	50p	£1	£2
1966	20p	50p	£1	£2
1967	20p	50p	£1	£2
1968	20p	40p	£1	£2

PENNIES

	F	VF	EF	UNC
1928	£1	£2	£6	£14
1928 Proof	—	—	—	£20
1931	£1	£3	£20	£70
1931 Proof	—	—	—	£750
1933	£1	£3	£25	£90
1935	50p	£1	£10	£30
1937	75p	£1	£15	£65
1937 Proof	—	—	—	£700
1938				*Unique*
1940	£2	£10	£80	—
1941	50p	£1	£5	£16
1942	25p	50p	£2	£10
1943	25p	£1	£3	£14
1946	25p	£1	£2	£9
1948	25p	£1	£2	£9
1949	25p	£1	£2	£9
1949 Proof	—	—	—	£250
1950	25p	75p	£2	£12
1952	25p	50p	£2	£4
1962	30p	75p	£2	£6
1962 Proof	—	—	—	£80
1963	10p	25p	£1	£3
1963 Proof	—	—	—	£70
1964	—	20p	50p	£2

DATE	F	VF	EF	UNC
1965	—	25p	50p	£3
1966	—	25p	50p	£3
1967	—	15p	25p	£2
1968	—	15p	25p	£2
1968 Proof	—	—	—	£155

HALFPENNIES

	F	VF	EF	UNC
1928	50p	£1	£5	£15
1928 Proof	—	—	—	£15
1933	£3	£10	£45	£320
1935	£2	£4	£20	£100
1937	£1	£3	£10	£45
1939	£2	£5	£25	£100
1939 Proof	—	—	—	£550
1940	50p	£2	£18	£100
1941	20p	50p	£3	£18
1942	20p	50p	£3	£18
1943	20p	50p	£5	£20
1946	50p	£1	£14	£50
1949	20p	50p	£4	£18
1953	10p	25p	£1	£6
1953 Proof	—	—	—	£350
1964	—	25p	50p	£2
1965	—	30p	75p	£3
1966	—	25p	50p	£2
1967	—	25p	50p	£2

FARTHINGS

	F	VF	EF	UNC
1928	50p	£1	£3	£6
1928 Proof	—	—	—	£12
1930	50p	£1	£4	£12
1931	£1	£2	£10	£20
1931 Proof	—	—	—	£550
1932	£1	£3	£12	£22
1933	50p	£1	£3	£10
1935	£1	£3	£10	£22
1936	£1	£3	£9	£20
1937	50p	£1	£3	£10
1939	50p	£1	£2	£4
1939 Proof	—	—	—	£400
1940	£1	£2	£5	£12
1941	50p	£1	£2	£5
1943	50p	£1	£2	£5
1944	50p	£1	£3	£7
1946	50p	£1	£2	£5
1949	£1	£2	£5	£12
1949 Proof	—	—	—	£250
1953	25p	50p	£1	£3
1953 Proof	—	—	—	£180
1959	50p	£1	£2	£3
1966	—	50p	£1.50	£3

For the 1928–50 coppper issues it is worth noting that UNC means UNC with some lustre. BU examples with full lustre are extremely elusive and are worth much more than the quoted prices.

Decimal issues are not included in this publication but it should be noted that many dates are virtually impossible to find in uncirculated grade. An example is the 1986 set which was sold exclusivly through souvenir shops and included the only specimens of the ½p for that year.

Official and semi-official commemorative
MEDALS

It is probably a strong love of history, rather than the strict discipline of coin collecting that make collectors turn to commemorative medals. The link between the two is intertwined, and it is to be hoped that collectors will be encouraged to venture into the wider world of medallions, encouraged by this brief guide, supplied by courtesy of Daniel Fearon, acknowledged expert and author of the *Catalogue of British Commemorative Medals*.

DATE	VF	EF
JAMES I		
1603 Coronation *(possibly by C. Anthony)*, 29mm, Silver	£300	£700
QUEEN ANNE		
1603 Coronation,29mm, AR	£350	£700
CHARLES I		
1626 Coronation *(by N. Briot)*, 30mm, Silver	£185	£500
1633 Scottish Coronation *(by N. Briot)*, 28mm, Silver	£145	£275
1649 Memorial *(by J. Roettier)*. Struck after the Restoration, 50mm, Bronze	£55	£175
CHARLES II		
1651 Scottish Coronation, in exile *(from design by Sir J. Balfour)*, 32mm, Silver	£350	£800
CROMWELL		
1651 Lord Protector *(by T. Simon)*, 38mm, Silver	£300	£700
— Cast examples	£80	£175
CHARLES II		
1661 Coronation *(by T. Simon)*, 29mm		
— Gold	£800	£1500
— Silver	£85	£200
1685 Death *(by N. Roettier)*, 39mm, Bronze	£75	£175

James I Coronation, 1603

Charles II Coronation, 1661

DATE	VF	EF

JAMES II
1685 Coronation *(by J. Roettier)*, 34mm
— Gold £850 £1600
— Silver £155 £285

MARY
1685 Coronation *(by J. Roettier)*, 34mm
— Gold £850 £1700
— Silver £125 £275

WILLIAM & MARY
1689 Coronation *(by J. Roettier)*, 32mm
— Gold £750 £1600
— Silver £85 £200
1689 Coronation, "Perseus" *(by G. Bower)*,
   38mm, Gold £650 £1500

MARY
1694 Death *(by N. Roettier)*, 39mm, Bronze £45 £150

WILLIAM III
1697 "The State of Britain" *(by J. Croker)*, 69mm,
   Silver £350 £800

ANNE
1702 Accession, "Entirely English" *(by J. Croker)*, 34mm
— Gold £650 £1500
— Silver £70 £150
1702 Coronation *(by J. Croker)*, 36mm
— Gold £550 £1500
— Silver £75 £175
1707 Union with Scotland *(by J. Croker, rev. by S. Bull)*, 34mm
— Gold £500 £850
— Silver £55 £120
1713 Peace of Utrecht *(by J. Croker—issued in gold to Members
of Parliament)*, 34mm
— Gold £450 £900
— Silver £55 £120

Charles II Coronation, 1661

GEORGE I
1714 Coronation *(by J. Croker)*, 34mm
— Gold £650 £1650
— Silver £80 £160
1727 Death *(by J. Dassier)*, 31mm, Silver £60 £120

GEORGE II
1727 Coronation *(by J. Croker)*, 34mm
— Gold £600 £1600
— Silver £80 £160

QUEEN CAROLINE
1727 Coronation *(by J. Croker)*, 34mm
— Gold £600 £1650
— Silver £80 £160
1732 The Royal Family *(by J. Croker)*, 70mm
— Silver £150 £350
— Bronze £75 £175

George III, Coronation, 1761

DATE	VF	EF

GEORGE III
1761 Coronation *(by L. Natter)*, 34mm
— Gold £650 £1800
— Silver £100 £250
— Bronze £45 £100

QUEEN CHARLOTTE
1761 Coronation *(by L. Natter)*, 34mm
— Gold £650 £1850
— Silver £110 £260
— Bronze £45 £100
1810 Golden Jubilee, "Frogmore", 48mm, Silver £80 £175
— Bronze £45 £100

GEORGE IV
1821 Coronation *(by B. Pistrucci)*, 35mm
— Gold £400 £750
— Silver £50 £100
— Bronze £25 £65

WILLIAM IV
1831 Coronation *(by W. Wyon; rev.shows
    Queen Adelaide)*, 33mm
— Gold £350 £700
— Silver £50 £100
— Bronze £25 £65

QUEEN VICTORIA
1838 Coronation *(by B. Pistrucci)*, 37mm
— Gold £380 £800
— Silver £60 £140
— Bronze £25 £65

George IV Coronation, 1841

Queen Victoria Coronation, 1838

DATE	VF	EF

Queen Victoria Diamond Jubile 1897

1887 Golden Jubilee *(by J. E. Boehm, rev. by Lord Leighton)*
— Gold, 58mm	£750	£1100
— Silver, 78mm	£75	£175
— Bronze, 78mm	£35	£85

1897 Diamond Jubilee *(by T. Brock),*
— Gold, 56mm	£750	£900
— Silver, 56mm	£25	£65
— Bronze, 56mm	£10	£25
— Gold, 21mm	£120	£160
— Silver, 21mm	£10	£25

EDWARD VII
1902 Coronation (August 9) *(by G. W. de Saulles)*
— Gold, 56mm	£750	£900
— Silver, 56mm	£25	£65
— Bronze, 56mm	£12	£30
— Gold, 31mm	£130	£175
— Silver, 31mm	£12	£25

Some rare examples of the official medal show the date as June 26, the original date set for the Coronation which was postponed because the King developed appendicitis.

GEORGE V
1911 Coronation *(by B. Mackennal)*
— Gold, 51mm	£750	£1000
— Silver, 51mm	£25	£75
— Bronze, 51mm	£12	£28
— Gold, 31mm	£135	£180
— Silver, 31mm	£12	£30

1935 Silver Jubilee *(by P. Metcalfe)*
— Gold, 58mm	£750	£1000
— Silver, 58mm	£25	£65
— Gold, 32mm	£120	£160
— Silver, 32mm	£12	£30

George V Silver Jubilee, 1937

DATE	VF	EF

PRINCE EDWARD
1911 Investiture as Prince of Wales *(by W. Goscombe John)*

— Gold, 31mm	£220	£350
— Silver, 31mm	£30	£50

EDWARD VIII
1936 Abdication *(by L. E. Pinches)*, 35mm

— Gold	£300	£550
— Silver	£25	£55
— Bronze	£10	£25

GEORGE VI
1937 Coronation *(by P. Metcalfe)*

— Gold, 58mm	£800	£1100
— Silver, 58mm	£25	£70
— Gold, 32mm	£120	£160
— Silver, 32mm	£10	£20
— Bronze, 32mm	£5	£12

ELIZABETH II
1953 Coronation *(by Spink & Son)*

— Gold, 57mm	£660	£850
— Silver, 57mm	£25	£60
— Bronze, 57mm	£15	£25
— Gold, 32mm	£120	£155
— Silver, 32mm	£15	£25
— Bronze, 32mm	£10	£15

*The gold medals are priced for 18ct—they can also be found as 22ct and 9ct, and prices should be adjusted accordingly.

PRNCE CHARLES
1969 Investiture as Prince of Wales *(by M. Rizello)*

— Silver, 57mm	—	£30
— Bronze gilt, 57mm	—	£25
— Silver, 45mm	—	£20
— Gold, 32mm	—	£85
— Silver, 32mm	—	£20
— Bronze, 32mm	—	£10

1977 Silver Jubilee *(by A. Machin)*

— Silver, 57mm	—	£25
— Silver, 44mm	—	£20

QUEEN ELIZABETH QUEEN MOTHER
1980 80th Birthday *(by L. Durbin)*

— Silver, 57mm	—	£30
— Silver, 38mm	—	£20
— Bronze, 38mm	—	£10

N.B.—Official Medals command a premium when still in their original cases of issue.

Edward, Prince of Wales, 1911

Edward VIII Abdication, 1936

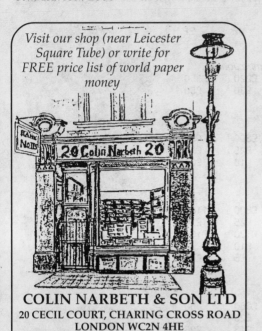

English
BANK NOTE
price guide

This price guide, supplied by courtesy of Pam West of British Notes, is by no means definitive. It is possible to buy notes for less than listed here, just as some may cost more. The prices quoted are for VF to EF up to the end of Peppiatt and EF and Uncirculated from O'Brien, which is usually considered to be the start of the modern period. Obviously notes in current circulation can be obtained at face value and it is always a good idea to put an uncirculated note away occasionally. Sometimes they may have "half moon" machine cutting marks, though they have never been circulated.

TREASURY NOTES

ISSUE	VF	EF
1st ISSUE		
T1 Bradbury £1	£900	£1650
T2 Bradbury £1	£900	£1650
T3 Bradbury £1 5/6 digit	£250	£550
T4 Bradbury £1	£550	£1150
T5 Bradbury £1	£650	£1350
T6 Bradbury £1	£400	£950
T7 Bradbury £1	—	
T8 Bradbury 10/-	£400	£950
T9 Bradbury 10/-	£190	£450
T10 Bradbury 10/-	£650	£1250
2nd ISSUE		
T11 Bradbury £1	£120	£340
T12 Bradbury 10/-	£95	£250
T13 Bradbury 10/-	£100	£275
T14 Bradbury £1 Dardenelles	£2100	£4500
T15 Bradbury 10/- Dardenelles	£450	£1000
3rd ISSUE		
T16 Bradbury £1	£60	£125

ISSUE	VF	EF
T16 with Anchor on rev. A1/B1 prefix	£150	£450
T17 Bradbury 10/-	£170	£300
T18 Bradbury 10/-	£140	£300
T19 Bradbury 10/-	£950	£1500
T20 Bradbury 10/-	£95	£195
1st ISSUE		
T24 Fisher £1	£35	£70
T25 Fisher 10/-	£65	£170
T26 Fisher 10/-	£55	£145
2nd ISSUE		
T30 Fisher 10/-	£60	£145
T31 Fisher £1	£45	£85
T32 Fisher £1	£65	£1165
3rd ISSUE (NORTHERN IRELAND)		
T33 Fisher 10/-	£65	£135
T34 Fisher £1	£40	£85
T35 Fisher £1	£70	£165

BANK OF ENGLAND WHITE £5 NOTES

ISSUE	EF
B208b Nairne	£300
B209a Harvey	£200
B215 Mahon	£160
B228 Catterns	£190
B241 Peppiatt	£110

ISSUE	EF
B255 Peppiatt	£80
B264 Peppiatt	£90
B270 Beale	£75
B275 O'Brien	£75
B276 O'Brien	£80

White notes in better grades are becoming difficult to obtain thus earlier rarer dates and notes in exceptional condition can command a premium.

BANK OF ENGLAND ISSUES

	VF	EF
SERIES A—BRITANNIA		
B210 Mahon 10/-	£55	£90
B212 Mahon £1	£20	£55
B223 Catterns 10/-	£30	£80
B225 Catterns £1 LNN	£10	£25
B226 Catterns £1 NNL	£60	£100
1st PERIOD		
B235 Peppiatt 10/- LNN	£18	£50
B236 Peppiatt 10/- NNL	£20	£50
B238 Peppiatt £1 NNL	£12	£25
B239 Peppiatt £1 LNNL	£10	£20
2nd PERIOD		
B248 Peppiatt £1 Blue	£5	£20
B249 Peppiatt £1 Blue	£3	£9
B251 Peppiatt 10/- Mauve	£12	£25
3rd PERIOD		
B256 Peppiatt 10/-	£20	£40
B258 Peppiatt £1	£15	£25
B258 Peppiatt £1 S--A	£20	£30
4th PERIOD (THREADED)		
B260 Peppiatt £1	£8	£15
B261 Peppiatt £1 ®	£35	£140
B262 Peppiatt 10/-	£8	£20
B263 Peppiatt 10/- ®	£350	£650
B265 Beale 10/- NNL	£5	£10
B266 Beale 10/- LNNL	£10	£18
B267 Beale 10/- ®	£60	£105
B268 Beale £1	£3	£8
B269 Beale £1 ®	£25	£35
B271 O'Brien 10/-	£8	£15
B272 O'Brien 10/- ®	£45	£70
B273 O'Brien £1	£3	£6
B274 O'Brien £1 ®	£20	£35
B274 O'Brien £1 ® S--T	£20	£30

	EF	UNC
SERIES B—HELMETED BRITANNIA		
B277 O'Brien £5 Shaded Symbol	£20	£35
— A01 (first)	£65	£180
B280 O'Brien £5 White Symbol	£20	£35

	VF	EF
SERIES C—PORTRAIT		
B281 O'Brien £1 LNN	£3	£5
B282 O'Brien £1 LNNL	£3	£5
B283 O'Brien £1 "R" EXP LNNL	£130	£280
B284 O'Brien £1 LNNL	£10	£20
B285 O'Brien £1 ®	£10	£30
B286 O'Brien 10/-	£3	£6
B287 O'Brien 10/- ®	£12	£30
B288 Hollom £1 LNNL	£2	£5
B289 Hollom £1 R LNN	£15	£30
B290 Hollom £1 R NNL	£12	£20
B291 Hollom £1 R LNNL	£18	£70
B292 Hollom £1 G	£2	£6
B293 Hollom £1 G ®	£14	£28
B294 Hollom 10/- LNN	£2	£5
B295 Hollom 10/- NNL	£2	£4
B296 Hollom 10/- ®	£20	£35

	EF	UNC
B297 Hollom £5	£12	£20
B298 Hollom £5 ®	£60	£100
B299 Hollom £10	£12	£30
B301 Fforde £1	£2	£4
B302 Fforde £1 R	£20	£40
B303 Fforde £1 G	£2	£8
B304 Fforde £1 G ®	£20	£40
B305 Fforde £1	£2	£5
B306 Fforde £1 ®	£14	£20 (types)
— R01M (first)	£65	£150
— Mid	£8	£15
— S01M (first)	£65	£150
B307 Fforde £1 G	£3	£10
B308 Fforde £1 G ®	£15	£40
B308 — T--M G	£60	£180
B309 Fforde 10/- LLN	£2	£5
B310 Fforde 10/- LNNL	£2	£4
B311 Fforde 10/- R	£4	£10
B312 Fforde £5 LNN	£12	£22
B313 Fforde £5 ®	£60	£90
B314 Fforde £5 NNL	£12	£30
B315 Fforde £5 ®	£50	£130
B316 Fforde £10	£18	£35
B318 Fforde £20 ®	£60	£140
B319 Fforde £20 ®	£100	£250
B320 Page £1 LNNL	£2	£4
B321 Page £1 ®	£10	£20
B322 Page £1 LLNN	£2	£4
B323 Page ®	£5	£10
B324 Page £5	£14	£30
B325 Page £5 ®	£80	£150
B326 Page £10	£18	£30
B327 Page £10 ®	£28	£35
SERIES D—PICTORIAL		
B328 Page £20	£28	£60
B329 Page £20 ®	£50	£90
B330 Page £10	£20	£32
B331 Page £10 ®	£55	£95
B332 Page £5 LNN no "L" on reverse	£15	£20
B333 Page £5 ®	£80	£120
B334 Page £5 NNL	£14	£20
B335 Page £5 ®	£70	£120
B336 Page £5 LLNN	£8	£15
B337 Page £1 LNN	£2	£4
B338 Page £1 ®	£170	£250
B339 Page £1 NNL	£2	£4
B339a Page £1 8l .. various	£50	£120
B340 Page £1 LNNL W	£4	£8
B341 Somerset £1 W	£3	£4
B342 Somerset £1 EXP	£350	£650
B343 Somerset £5	£10	£18

The B343 series starts DN01 and runs through a variety of prefixes to end at LZ90, although a sub-series exists of NA01 to NC90.

	EF	UNC
— DN01	£60	£125
— NA01	£100	£250
— NC90	£10	£35
— Mid on NB	£12	£20
B344 Somerset £5 OCR EXP	£450	£800

	EF	UNC
B345 Somerset £5 Wide Thread	£10	£15
B346 Somerset £10 LNN	£25	£40
B347 Somerset £10 NNL	£18	£32
B348 Somerset £10 LLNN with "L"	£18	£30
B349 Somerset £10 Window Thread	£14	£30
B350 Somerset £20 LNN	£30	£50
B351 Somerset £20 NNL Window Thread	£35	£45
B352 Somerset £50	£65	£95
B353 Gill £5	£10	£18
—SE90 (last)	£40	£80
B354 Gill £10	£14	£20
B355 Gill £20	£22	£40
— 01L (first)	£40	£90
— 20X (last)	£90	£150
B356 Gill £50 Window Thread	£60	£95
— E01	£65	£110

SERIES E—HISTORICAL

	EF	UNC
B357 Gill £5	—	£9
B358 Gill £20	—	£35

SERIES D

	EF	UNC
B359 Kentfield £10	—	£30
B360 Kentfield £50	—	£95

SERIES E

	EF	UNC
B361 Kentfield £5 MKI LNN	—	£9
— W18 (last)	£20	£45
B362 Kentfield £5 MKII LNN	—	£9
— AA01 (first)	£8	£16
B363 Kentfield £5 MKIII LLNN	—	£10
B364 Kentfield £10 MKI LNN	—	£15
B365 Kentfield "B" Ream £10 M/Y/Z LNN	—	£35
B366 Kentfield £10 MKII LLNN	—	Face
B367 Kentfield £20 LNN	—	£30
B368 Kentfield "B" Ream £20 A/B LNN	—	£60
& M/Z LNN	—	£60
B369 Kentfield £20 MKII LNN	—	£30
B370 Kentfield £20 MKII LLNN	—	£25
B371 Kentfield £50 LNN	—	Face
— A01	—	£95
DA01 Lowther £20 nos. under 1000	—	£65

Only some prices for true firsts and lasts, i.e. A01s–Z99s, have been quoted as often the price is dictated by availability of the notes which on earlier and some modern material, are often in short supply. Some low numbers on firsts command higher prices.

There is a series of unissued fractional notes, printed during the two wars, which are very scarce and not generally found for anything less than £2,000 in EF. These include Bradbury T21 5/–, T22 2/6, T23 1/–, Fisher T27 5/–, T28 2/6, T29 1/–, Peppiatt B253 5/–, B254 2/6.

Abbreviations

®	Replacement	OCR	Optical Character Recognition
"R"	Research	L	Letter (of serial number)
EXP	Experimental	N	Number (of serial number)
G	Goebel		i.e. LNNL = letter, number, number, letter
W	Webb Off-set	"B"	B Ream

Why not
BANK
NOTES?

Millions of pounds worth of banknotes exchange hands every day, and yet most of us pay little attention to the coloured pieces of paper we are about to part with. To a collector however, they are to be studied and enjoyed. Sometimes they can be worth many times their face value. A historian, with careful study, can discover much about a county's history from prosperity through war, siege and its inflationary periods. Banknotes have also been used for spreading propaganda. The Gulf war is a recent example. Many banknotes still survive long after the country of issue has disappeared.

So how do you start and where can you get advice on forming a collection? The answers, together with a few interesting facts about paper money can be found here. But remember, this feature can only scratch the surface of this fascinating subject; its aim is to inspire and surprise you.

Paper money is not a modern phenomenon. Its origins can be found in China during the second century BC. Emperor Wu (140–86BC), frustrated with the time taken for heavily laden wagons of copper coins to complete their journey, used deerhide as a kind of tax money. Skins from white stags were cut into pieces each a foot square. The borders were decorated with designs of water plants and each skin was given a value of 40,000 copper coins. Around 105 AD paper, made from broken down plant fibres and old cotton textiles was invented by a Chinese minister of Agriculture. However, true paper money didn't appear in China until the Tang Dynasty somewhere between 650–800 AD. The earliest Chinese notes collectors are likely to come across are from the Ming Dynasty. Made from mulberry bark paper, these notes measure 230mm x 330mm. Although over six hundred years old, these notes can be bought for around £500. An interesting factor is that Asia was using paper money while Britain and Europe were still in the dark ages.

The first European bank to be established was in Stockholm, Sweden in July 1661. Unfortunately its banknotes were not government backed and the

enterprise was forced to close within a few years.

On July 27, 1694 the Bank of England was founded by Royal Charter; the first European bank to survive to the present day. From its temporary offices at the Mercers' Hall, Cheapside, London, the

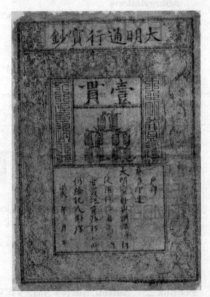

China is credited with issuing the earliest notes, very few of which survive today.

Bank set to work producing its first issues. These have become known as running cash notes. At first they were written out entirely by hand on paper bought by the Bank's staff from local stationers. Forgery however, soon put a stop to this practice. Each note was made out to the bearer for the amount they had on deposit. Although there was no guarantee of conversion into gold, the notes could be cashed in for part of their original value. This led to endorsements appearing on the notes stating the date and amount paid off. The notes would change hands for payment of goods or services just as our modern banknotes do today.

During the last century many private banks were set up in towns and cities throughout Britain. The notes they issued were usually well printed and many carry a motif or vignette identifying with the place of issue. For example coats of arms

Notes issued in Revolutionary France are important historical documents—mostly inexpensive and well worth looking out for.

Provincial banknotes are eagerly sought after by collectors of local history.

often appear, so too do famous buildings. Others simply have embellished initials. It is these simple features that help to make these provincial notes popular with collectors today, coupled with the interest of owning a banknote actually issued in your town! Unfortunately most of these banks went into liquidation and many investors lost their money—it is quite common to find provincial notes with the bankruptcy court stamp or other marks on the reverse. Notes are also encountered which have been rejoined with paper strips as it was often the practice to cut notes in half—sending half by one means and the second portion at a later date, to be joined with its counterpart before it could be redeemed. This lessened the risk of the note being stolen or lost in transit.

The expression "Safe as the Bank of England" is held in high regard today. In reality the Bank has almost collapsed on at least two occasions, and in 1696 it had its first major crisis. An act

passed by parliament ordered the recoinage of all metallic currency. As the notes circulated by the Bank had status of legal tender and therefore not legally convertible into gold, people naturally had more confidence in metal currency. Accounts submitted by the Bank to parliament in December of that year showed £764,000 worth of notes in circulation. These were backed by just under £36,000 worth of gold.

The second emergency for the Bank came in 1720 after the "bursting" of the South Sea Bubble. Holding the monopoly of trade with South America, the South Sea Company offered to take on the national debt in return for further concessions. Company shares soared but when the collapse came it was found that government ministers were deeply involved and a political crisis followed. Bankruptcy was rife and people naturally wished to obtain their money. The queue of those wanting to withdraw gold from the Bank of England stretched down Ludgate Hill into Fleet Street.

Notes of the old British Commonwealth are becoming difficult to find in good condition.

The Bank managed to save the situation by employing it own staff to join the queue posing as customers. Each would withdraw large quantities of money and then take it round to the back of the Bank where is was redeposited. This meant the tills were kept opened until the public alarm subsided.

One modern day crisis for the Bank came during the Second World War when Germany decided to forge the large white Bank of England notes in current circulation at the time, in huge quantities. This operation called for around 150 prisoners, each hand picked for their skills in engraving, printing and paper making. The original idea was to drop the undetectable forgeries on the British Isles and neutral nations in an effort to destroy Britain's economy but the plan never came to fruition, although millions of pounds in face value were produced. Most of the notes were dumped into Lake Toplitz, but many have since been recovered and often appear on the market today. When encountering forgeries, collectors are in a difficult position. If they hold a note, knowing it to be a forgery, they are breaking the law. If they have the note checked, they run the risk of having it confiscated!

A banknote need not be old to be worth collecting. Many interesting notes have been issued throughout the world each with their own story to tell. In 1954 the Canadian Central Bank issued notes in which the portrait of the Queen had what appeared to be the hidden face of the Devil in the folds of her hair. The public refused to handle them and the notes were withdrawn. To this day it is not known whether the engraving was done intentionally or not.

Most countries suffer from inflation but in 1923, Germany saw one of the biggest inflationary periods of modern times. On November 1 of that year the average wage packet was 28 million marks, equivalent to 1.3 million pounds at the 1913 exchange rate. This huge sum would not have been enough to buy a newspaper, which would have cost around 3,000 million marks. This period left a legacy of hundreds of different notes for the collector today.

Unlike coins, collecting of paper money is still in its infancy. It is still possible to obtain notes from many different countries for a modest outlay. Some dealers sell starter packs that include 50 uncirculated notes from 50 different counties, all for under £30. One reason why some notes are so cheap is that many countries devalue their currency. When a new set of notes are issued, the old set after a period, become worthless. Dealers can acquire large quantities of these notes for less than the original face value. New collectors will find many books on the subject of paper money. For a detailed look into Treasury and Bank of England issues, including a comprehensive price guide, *English Paper Money* by Vincent Duggleby is essential. The best way to meet fellow collectors is to join an organisation. The International Bank Note Society (IBNS) has over 2,000 members world wide; full details can be obtained from the Assistant General Secretary: Mrs Sally Thowney, 36B Dartmouth Park HIll, London NW5 1HN.

COIN NEWS is also a useful way of keeping in touch with the every day events of the banknote world. There is a dedicated banknote section in the magazine every month often giving vital pieces of information, for example the latest auction prices realised, forthcoming events and fairs and there are also informative articles designed to be of appeal to experienced collectors as well as newcomers.

Coincraft purchased the biggest-ever hoard of banknotes when they bought over 8 tons of British Armed Forces Special Vouchers at auction in 1991. Despite the quantity, these notes are still highly collectable and have all vanished into collections!

Directory section

ON the following pages will be found the most useful names and addresses needed by the coin collector.

At the time of going to press with this edition of the YEARBOOK the information is correct, as far as we have been able to ascertain. However, people move and establishments change, so it is always advisable to make contact with the person or organisation listed before travelling any distance, to ensure that the journey is not wasted.

Should any of the information in this section not be correct we would very much appreciate being advised in time for the preparation of the next edition of the COIN YEARBOOK.

MUSEUMS and LIBRARIES

Listed below are the Museums and Libraries in the UK which have coins or items of numismatic interest on display or available to the general public.

A

Anthropological Museum, University of Aberdeen, Broad Street, **Aberdeen,** AB9 1AS (01224 272014).

Curtis Museum (1855), High Street, **Alton,** Hants (01420 2802). *General collection of British coins.*

Ashburton Museum, 1 West Street, **Ashburton,** Devon. *Ancient British and Roman antiquities including local coin finds.*

Ashwell Village Museum (1930), Swan Street, **Ashwell,** Baldock, Herts. *Roman coins from local finds, local trade tokens, Anglo-Gallic coins and jetons.*

Buckinghamshire County Museum (1862), Church Street, **Aylesbury,** Bucks (01296 88849). *Roman and medieval English coins found locally, 17th/18th century Buckinghamshire tokens, commemorative medals.*

B

Public Library and Museum (1948), Marlborough Road, **Banbury,** Oxon (01295 259855). *Wrexlin Hoard of Roman coins.*

Museum of North Devon (1931), The Square, **Barnstaple,** EX32 8LN (01271 46747). *General coin and medal collection, including local finds. Medals of the Royal Devonshire Yeomanry.*

Roman Baths Museum, Pump Room, **Bath,** Avon (01225 461111 ext 2785). *Comprehensive collection of Roman coins from local finds.*

Bagshaw Museum and Art Gallery (1911), Wilton Park, **Batley,** West Yorkshire (01924 472514). *Roman, Scottish, Irish, English hammered, British and foreign coins, local traders' tokens, political medalets, campaign medals and decorations.*

Bedford Museum (1961), Castle Lane, **Bedford** (01234 353323). *Collections of the Bedford Library and Scientific Institute, the Beds Archaeological Society and Bedford Modern School (Pritchard Memorial) Museum.*

Ulster Museum (1928), Botanic Gardens, **Belfast** BT9 5AB (01232 381251). *Irish, English and British coins and commemorative medals.*

Berwick Borough Museum (1867), The Clock Block, Berwick Barracks, Ravensdowne, **Berwick.** TD15 1DQ (01289 330044). *Roman, Scottish and medievial coins.*

Public Library, Art Gallery and Museum (1910), Champney Road, **Beverley,** Humberside (01482 882255). *Beverley trade tokens, Roman, English, British and foreign coins.*

Bignor Roman Villa (1811), **Bignor,** nr Pulborough, West Sussex (017987 202). *Roman coins found locally.*

City Museum and Art Gallery (1861), Chamberlain Square, **Birmingham** B3 3DH (0121 235 2834). *Coins, medals and tokens, with special emphasis on the products of the Soho, Heaton, Birmingham and Watt mints.*

Blackburn Museum, Museum Street, **Blackburn,** Lancs (01254 667130). *Incorporates the Hart (5,000 Greek, Roman and early English) and Hornby (500 English coins) collections, as well as the museum's own collection of British and Commonwealth coins.*

Museum Collection, Town Hall, **Bognor Regis,** West Sussex. *Roman, English and British coins and trade tokens.*

Museum and Art Gallery,(1893), Civic Centre, **Bolton,** Lancashire (01204 22311 ext 2191). *General collection of about 3000 British and foreign coins, and over 500 British medals. Numismatic library.*

Art Gallery and Museum, Central Library, Oriel Road, **Bootle,** Lancs. *Greek, Roman, English, British and some foreign coins, local trade tokens.*

Roman Town and Museum (1949) Main Street, **Boroughbridge,** N. Yorks. YO2 3PH (01423 322768). *Roman coins.*

The Museum (1929), The Guildhall, **Boston,** Lincs (01205 365954). *Small collection of English coins.*

Natural Science Society Museum (1903), 39 Christchurch Road, **Bournemouth,** Dorset (01202 553525). *Greek, Roman and English hammered coins (including the Hengistbury Hoard), local trade tokens.*

Bolling Hall Museum (1915), Bolling Hall Road, **Bradford,** West Yorkshire BD4 7LP (01274 723057). *Some 2,000 coins and tokens, mostly 18th–20th centuries.*

Cartwright Hall Museum and Art Gallery (1904), Lister Park, **Bradford,** West Yorkshire BD9 4NS (01274 493313). *Roman coins found locally.*

Museum and Art Gallery (1932), South Street, **Bridport,** Dorset (01308 22116). *Roman coins, mainly from excavations at Claudian Fort.*

The City Museum (1820), Queen's Road, **Bristol** BS8 1RL (0117 9 27256). *Ancient British, Roman (mainly from local hoards), English hammered coins, especially from the Bristol mint, and several hundred local trade tokens.*

District Library and Museum (1891), Terrace Road, **Buxton,** Derbyshire SK17 6DU (01298 24658). *English and British coins, tokens and commemorative medals. Numismatic library.*

C
Segontium Museum (1928), Beddgelert Road, **Caernarfon,** Gwynedd (01286 675625) *Roman coins and artifacts excavated from the fort.*

Fitzwilliam Museum (1816), Department of Coins and Medals, Trumpington Street, **Cambridge** (01223 332900). *Ancient, English, medieval European, oriental coins, medals, plaques, seals and cameos.*

National Museum & Galleries of Wales, Cathays Park, **Cardiff** (029 20397951). *Greek, Celtic, Roman and British coins and tokens with the emphasis on Welsh interest. Also military, civilian and commemorative medals.*

Guildhall Museum (1979), Greenmarket, **Carlisle,** Cumbria (01228 819925). *General collection of coins and medals.*

Tullie House (1877), Castle Street, **Carlisle,** Cumbria (01228 34781). *Roman, medieval and later coins from local finds, including medieval counterfeiter's coin-moulds.*

Gough's Caves Museum (1934), The Cliffs, **Cheddar,** Somerset (01934 343). *Roman coins.*

Chelmsford and Essex Museum (1835), Oaklands Park, Moulsham Street, **Cheltenham,** Glos CM2 9AQ (01245 353066). *Ancient British, Roman, medieval and later coins mainly from local finds, local medals.*

Town Gate Museum (1949), **Chepstow,** Gwent. *Local coins and trade tokens.*

Grosvenor Museum (1886), Grosvenor Street, **Chester** (01244 21616). *Roman coins from the fortress site, Anglo-Saxon, English medieval and post-medieval coins of the Chester and Rhuddlan mints, trade tokens of Chester and Cheshire, English and British milled coins.*

Public Library (1879), Corporation Street, **Chesterfield,** Derbyshire (01246 2047). *Roman coins from local finds, Derbyshire trade tokens, medals, seals and railway passes. Numismatic library. Numismatic library and publications.*

Red House Museum (1919), Quay Road, **Christchurch,** Dorset (01202 482860). *Coins of archaeological significance from Hampshire and Dorset, notably the South Hants Hoard, ancient British, Armorican, Gallo-Belgic, Celtic and Roman coins, local trade tokens and medals.*

Corinium Museum (1856), Park Street, **Cirencester,** Glos (01285 655611). *Roman coins from archaeological excavations.*

Colchester and Essex Museum (1860), The Castle, **Colchester,** Essex (01206 712931/2). *Ancient British and Roman coins from local finds, medieval coins (especially the Colchester Hoard), later English and Essex trade tokens, commemorative medals.*

D
Public Library, Museum and Art Gallery (1921), Crown Street, **Darlington,** Co Durham (01325 463795). *General collection of coins, medals and tokens.*

Borough Museum (1908), Central Park, **Dartford,** Kent (01322 343555). *Roman, medieval and later English hammered coins, trade tokens and commemorative medals.*

Dartmouth Museum (1953), The Butterknowle, **Dartmouth,** Devon (01803 832923). *Coins and medals of a historical and maritime nature.*

Museum and Art Gallery (1878), The Strand, **Derby** (01332 255586). *Roman coins, English silver and copper regal coins, Derbyshire tradesmen's tokens, British campaign medals and decorations of the Derbyshire Yeomanry and the 9/12 Royal Lancers.*

Museum and Art Gallery (1909), Chequer Road, **Doncaster,** South Yorkshire (01302 734293). *General collection of English and foreign silver and bronze coins. Representative collection of Roman imperial silver and bronze coins, including a number from local hoards. English trade tokens, principally of local issues, medals.*

Dorset County Museum(1846), **Dorchester,** Dorset (01305 262735). *British, Roman, medieval and later coins of local interest.*

Central Museum (1884), Central Library, St James's Road, **Dudley,** West Midlands (01384 453576). *Small general collection of coins, medals and tokens.*

Burgh Museum (1835), The Observatory, Corberry Hill, **Dumfries** (01387 53374). *Greek, Roman, Anglo-Saxon, medieval English and Scottish coins, especially from local hoards. Numismatic library.*

Dundee Art Galleries and Museums (1873). Albert Square, **Dundee** DD1 1DA (01382 23141). *Coins and medals of local interest.*

The Cathedral Treasury (995 AD), The College, **Durham** (0191-384 4854). *Greek and Roman coins bequeathed by Canon Sir George Wheeler (1724), general collection of medals from the Renaissance to modern times, medieval English coins, especially those struck at the Durham ecclesiastical mint.*

Durham Heritage Centre, St Mary le Bow, North Bailey, **Durham** (0191-384 2214). *Roman, medieval and later coins, mainly from local finds.*

E
Royal Museum of Scotland (1781), Queen Street, **Edinburgh** EH1 (0131 225 7534). *Roman, Anglo-Saxon, Englsh and Scottish coins, trade tokens, commemorative medals and communion tokens. Numismatic library. Publications.*

Royal Albert Memorial Museum (1868), Queen St, **Exeter** EX4 3RX (01392 265858). *Roman and medieval. Coins of the Exeter Mint.*

G

Hunterian Museum (1807), Glasgow University, University Avenue, **Glasgow** G12 8QQ (041 339 8855). *Greek, Roman, Byzantine, Scottish, English and Irish coins, Papal and other European medals, Indian and Oriental coins, trade and communion tokens.*

Art Gallery and Museum (1888), Kelvingrove, **Glasgow** G3 (0141 357 3929). *General collection of coins, trade tokens, communion tokens, commemorative and military medals.*

Museum of Transport (1974), Kelvin Hall, Bunhouse Road, **Glasgow** G3 (0141 357 3929). *Transport tokens and passes, commemorative medals, badges and insignia of railway companies and shipping lines.*

City Museum and Art Gallery (1859), Brunswick Road, **Gloucester** (01452 524131). *Ancient British, Roman, Anglo-Saxon (from local finds), early medieval (from local mints), Gloucestershire trade tokens.*

Guernsey Museum and Art Gallery, St Peter Port, **Guernsey** (01481 726518). *Armorican, Roman, medieval and later coins, including the coins, medals, tokens and paper money of Guernsey.*

Guildford Museum (1898), Castle Arch, **Guildford,** Surrey GU1 3SX (01483 444750). *Roman and medieval coins and later medals.*

H

Gray Museum and Art Gallery, Clarence Road, **Hartlepool,** Cleveland (01429 268916). *General collection, including coins from local finds.*

Public Museum and Art Gallery (1890), John's Place, Cambridge Road, **Hastings,** East Sussex (01424 721952). *General collection of English and British coins, collection of Anglo-Saxon coins from Sussex mints.*

City Museum (1874), Broad Street, **Hereford** (01432 268121 ext 207). *Coins from the Hereford mint and local finds, Herefordshire trade tokens, general collection of later coins and medals.*

Hertford Museum (1902), 18 Bull Plain, **Hertford** (01992 582686). *British, Roman, medieval and later English coins and medals.*

Honiton and Allhallows Public Museum (1946), High Street, **Honiton,** Devon (01404 44966). *Small general collection, including coins from local finds.*

Museum and Art Gallery (1891), 19 New Church Road, **Hove,** East Sussex (01273 779410). *English coins, Sussex trade tokens and hop tallies, campaign medals, orders and decorations, commemorative medals.*

Tolson Memorial Museum (1920), Ravensknowle Park, **Huddersfield,** West Yorkshire (01484 541455). *Representative collection of British coins and tokens, Roman and medieval coins, mainly from local finds.*

Hull and East Riding Museum (1928), 36 High Street, **Hull** (01482 593902). *Celtic, Roman and medieval coins and artifacts from local finds. Some later coins including tradesmen's tokens.*

I

The Manx Museum, Douglas, **Isle of Man** (01624 675522). *Roman, Celtic, Hiberno-Norse, Viking, medieval English and Scottish coins, mainly from local finds, Manx traders' tokens from the 17th to 19th centuries, Manx coins from 1709 to the present day.*

J

Jersey Museum, Weighbridge, St Helier, **Jersey** (01534 30511). *Armorican, Gallo-Belgic, Roman, medieval English and French coins, coins, paper money and tokens of Jersey.*

K

Dick Institute Museum and Art Gallery (1893), Elmbank Avenue, **Kilmarnock,** Ayrshire (01563 26401). *General collection of coins and medals, and the Hunter-Selkirk collection of communion tokens.*

L

City Museum (1923), Old Town Hall, Market Square, **Lancaster** (01524 64637). *Roman, Anglo-Saxon, medieval English coins, provincial trade tokens, medals of the King's Own Royal Lancaster Regiment.*

City Museum (1820), Municipal Buildings, The Headrow, **Leeds,** West Yorkshire (01532 478279). *Greek, Roman, Anglo-Saxon, English medieval, Scottish, Irish, British, Commonwealth and foreign coins. Several Roman and Saxon hoards. The Backhouse collection of Yorkshire banknotes, the Thornton collection of Yorkshire tokens, British and foreign commemorative medals.*

Leicester Museum and Art Gallery (1849), New Walk, **Leicester** (01533 554100). *Roman, medieval and later coins, mainly from local finds, tokens, commemorative medals, campaign medals and decorations.*

Pennington Hall Museum and Art Gallery, **Leigh,** Lancashire. *General collection of Roman, English and British coins and medals.*

Museum and Art Gallery (1914), Broadway, **Letchworth,** Herts (01462 65647). *Ancient British coins minted at Camulodunum, Roman, medieval and English coins, Hertfordshire trade tokens, commemorative and campaign medals.*

City Library, Art Gallery and Museum (1859), Bird Street, **Lichfield,** Staffs (01543 2177). *Roman, medieval and later English coins, Staffordshire trade tokens and commemorative medals.*

Liverpool Museum (1851), William Brown Street, **Liverpool** L3 8EN (0151 207 0001). *General collection of Roman, medieval and later British coins, tokens.*

Bank of England Museum, Threadneedle Street, **London** EC2 (020-7601 5545). *Exhibits relating to gold bullion, coins, tokens and medals, the design and manufacture of banknotes, and a comprehensive collection of bank notes dating from the 17th century to the present day.*

British Museum (1752), HSBC Coin Gallery, Great Russell Street, **London** WC1 (020-7636 1555). *Almost a million coins, medals, tokens and badges of all period from Lydia, 7th century BC to the present time. Extensive library of books and periodicals.*

British Numismatic Society (1903), Warburg Institute, Woburn Square, **London** WC1. *Library containing over 5,000 volumes, including sale catalogues, periodicals and pamphlets. Open to members only.*

Cuming Museum (1906), Walworth Road, **London** SE17 (020-7703 3324/5529). *Some 8,000 items, including Greek, Roman, medieval English and modern British coins, English tokens and commemorative medals.*

Gunnersbury Park Museum (1927), Acton, **London** W3. *Ancient British, Greek, Roman, medieval English, British and some foreign coins, tradesmen's tokens and commemorative medals, including local finds. Small numismatic library.*

Horniman Museum and Library (1890), **London** Road, Forest Hill, London SE23 (020-7699 2339). *General collection, primitive currency, some tokens.*

Imperial War Museum, Lambeth Road, **London** SE1 6HZ (020-7416 5000). *Emergency coinage of two world wars, occupation and invasion money, extensive collection of German Notgeld, commemorative, propaganda and military medals, badges and insignia.*

Sir John Soane's Museum (1833), 13 Lincoln's Inn Fields, **London** WC2 (020-7405 2107). *Napoleonic medals and medallic series of the late 18th and early 19th centuries.*

National Maritime Museum, Romney Road, Greenwich, **London** SE10 (020-8858 4422). *Commemorative medals with a nautical or maritime theme, naval medals and decorations.*

Victoria and Albert Museum (1852), South Kensington, **London** SW7 (020-7938 8441). *Byzantine gold and medieval Hispano-Mauresque coins (Department of Metalwork), large collection of Renaissance and later medals (Department of Architecture and Sculpture). Library of numismatic books.*

Ludlow Museum (1833). The Assembly Rooms. Castle Square, **Ludlow** (01584 873857). *Roman and medieval coins from local finds.*

Luton Museum and Art Gallery (1927), Wardown Park, **Luton**, Beds (01582 36941). *Coins, tokens and medals.*

M

Museum and Art Gallery (1858), **Maidstone**, Kent (01622 754497). *Ancient British, Roman, Anglo-Saxon and medieval coins found in Kent, modern British coins, Kent trade tokens, banknotes, hop tallies and tokens, primitive currency, collections of Kent Numismatic Society.*

The Manchester Museum (1868), The University, **Manchester** M13 (0161-275 2634). *Very fine collections of Greek and Roman coins, comprehensive collections of English, European and Oriental coins, over 30,000 in all.*

Margate Museum (1923), The Old Town Hall, Market Place, **Margate**, Kent (01843 225511 ext 2520). *Small collection of coins, including Roman from local finds.*

Montrose Museum and Art Gallery (1836). Panmure Place, **Montrose**, Angus DD10 8HE (01674 73232). *Scottish and British coins.*

N

Newark-on-Trent Museum (1912), Appleton Gate, **Newark**, Notts (01636 702358). *Siege pieces, trade tokens and coins from local finds and hoards.*

Newbury District Museum, The Wharf, **Newbury**, Berkshire (01635 30511). *Ancient British, Roman and medieval coins and artifacts, later coins and tokens.*

The Greek Museum, Percy Building, **Newcastle-upon-Tyne** (0191 2226000 ext 7966). *Ancient coins.*

O

Heberden Coin Room, Ashmolean Museum (1683), **Oxford** (01865 278000). *Extensive collections of all periods, notably Greek, Roman, English and Oriental coins, Renaissance portrait and later medals, tokens and paper money. Large library. Numerous publications.*

P

Peterborough Museum (1881), Priestgate, **Peterborough**, Cambs (01733 340 3329). *Roman (mainly from local hoards and finds), Anglo-Saxon, medieval English, British and modern European coins, English and British commemorative medals and tokens.*

City Museum and Art Gallery (1897), Drake Circus, **Plymouth**, Devon (01752 264878). *General collections of British and Commonwealth coins and tokens, Devon trade tokens and Plymouth tradesmen's checks, Ancient British and Roman coins from local sites.*

Waterfront Museum, 4 High Street, **Poole**, Dorset (01202 683138). *General collection of British and foreign coins, medals and tokens (view by appointment).*

City Museum (1972), Museum Road, Old **Portsmouth** PO1 (023 80827261). *Roman, medieval and later coins mainly from local finds and archaeological excavation, British coins, trade tokens of Hampshire, commemorative medals.*

Harris Museum and Art Gallery (1893), Market Square, **Preston**, Lancashire (01772 58248). *English and British coins, tokens and medals.*

R

Reading Museum and Art Gallery, (1883) Blagrave Street, **Reading**, Berks (01734 399809). *British, Roman and medieval English coins, mostly from local finds, tradesmen's tokens and commemorative medals.*

Rochdale Museum (1905), Sparrow Hill, **Rochdale**, Lancs (01706 41085). *Roman and medieval coins from local finds, Rochdale trade tokens, miscellaneous British and foreign coins and medals.*

Municipal Museum and Art Gallery (1893), Clifton Park, **Rotherham** (01709382121). *Roman coins from Templeborough Forts, medieval English coins from local hoards and a general collection of British coins.*

S

Saffron Walden Museum (1832) (1939), Museum Street, **Saffron** Walden, Essex (01799 522494). *Ancient British, Roman, medieval and later coins, mainly from local finds and archaeological excavation, trade tokens and commemorative medals.*

Verulamium Museum, St Michael's, **St Albans**, Herts (01727 819339). *Coins and artifacts excavated from the Roman town.*

Salisbury and South Wiltshire Museum (1861), The Cathedral Close, **Salisbury,** Wilts (01722 332151). *Collection of coins minted or found locally, including finds of Iron Age, Roman, Saxon and medieval coins, as well as 18th and 19th century tradesmen's tokens.*

Richborough Castle Museum (1930), **Sandwich,** Kent (0304 612013). *Roman coins of 1st–5th centuries from excavations of the Richborough site.*

Scarborough Museum (1829), The Rotunda, Vernon Road, **Scarborough**, North Yorkshire (01723 374839). *Over 4,000 Roman coins, 1,500 English and 600 coins from local finds, siege pieces and trade tokens.*

Shaftesbury and Dorset Local History Museum (1946), 1 Gold Hill, **Shaftesbury**, Dorset (01747 52157). *Hoard of Saxon coins.*

City Museum (1875), Weston Park, **Sheffield** (0114 2 768588). *Over 5,000 coins of all periods, but mainly English and modern British. European coins, imperial Roman (including three hoards of about 500 coins each), Yorkshire trade tokens, British historical medals, campaign medals. Library.*

Rowley's House Museum, Barker Street, **Shrewsbury**, Salop (01743 361196). *Coins minted at Shrewsbury 925-1180, Civil War coinage of 1642, Shropshire tradesmen's tokens, English coins and medals.*

Museum of Archaeology (1951), God's House Tower, Town Quay, **Southampton**, Hants (023 8022 0007). *Main emphasis lies in Ancient British, Roman and medieval English coins from local archaeological excavations. General collection of later coins and medals.*

Atkinson Art Gallery (1878), Lord Street, **Southport,** Lancs (01704 533133). *Roman coins.*

Botanic Gardens Museum, Churchtown, **Southport,** Lancs (01704 87547). *English and British coins and medals, military medals and decorations.*

Southwold Museum (1933), St Bartholomew's Green, **Southwold**, Suffolk (01502 722375). *General collection of coins, specialised Suffolk trade tokens.*

Stamford Museum (1961), Broad Street, **Stamford**, Lincs (01780 66317). *General collection of coins, medals and tokens, including a selection from the Stamford mint.*

Municipal Museum (1860), Vernon Park, Turncroft Lane, **Stockport**, Cheshire (0161 474 4460) *Miscellaneous general collection of coins, tokens and medals.*

Stroud Museum (1899), Lansdown, **Stroud**, Glos (01453 376394). *Ancient British, Roman, Saxon, Norman, later medieval English, British coins and Gloucestershire trade tokens.*

Museum and Art Gallery (1846), Borough Road, **Sunderland,** Tyne & Wear (0191 514 1235). *Roman imperial, medieval and later English, including examples of the pennies minted at Durham, modern British and foreign coins, 17th-19th century tradesmen's tokens, local medallions and campaign medals.*

Swansea Museum (1835), Victoria Road, **Swansea**, W. Glamorgan, SA1 1SN (0792 653765). *Coins and medals of local interest.*

T

Tamworth Castle and Museum (1899), The Holloway, **Tamworth**, Staffs (01827 63563). *Anglo-Saxon coins, medieval English including coins of the Tamworth mint, later English and British coins, tokens, commemorative medallions and medals.*

Somerset County Museum, Taunton Castle, **Taunton**, Somerset (01823 255510/320200). *Celtic, Roman, Anglo-Saxon, early Medieval, tokens, medallions and banknotes. Strong emphasis on locally-found items.*

Thurrock Local History Museum (1956), Civic Square, **Tilbury**, Essex (01375 390000 ext 2414). *Roman coins.*

Royal Cornwall Museum (1818), River Street, **Truro**, Cornwall (01872 72205). *Coins, tokens and medals pertaining principally to the county of Cornwall.*

W

Wakefield Museum (1919), Wood Street, **Wakefield,** West Yorkshire (01924 295351). *Roman and medieval English silver and copper coins.*

Epping Forest District Museum, 39/41 Sun Street, **Waltham Abbey**, Essex EN 9. *Ancient British, Roman and medieval coins, Essex tradesmen's tokens of local interest.*

Warrington Museum and Art Gallery (1848). Bold Street, **Warrington**, Cheshire, WA1 1JG (01925 30550). *Coins, medals and tokens.*

Worcester City Museum (1833), Foregate Street, **Worcester** (01905 25371). *Roman, medieval and later coins and tokens. Coins of the Worcester mint.*

Wells Museum (18903), 8 Cathedral Green, **Wells,** Somerset (01749 3477). *Ancient and modern British and world coins, local trade tokens and medals.*

Municipal Museum and Art Gallery (1878), Station Road, **Wigan**, Lancashire. *British, Commonwealth and foreign coins from about 1660 to the present. Roman coins from local sites, commemorative medals.*

City Museum (1851), The Square, **Winchester**, Hants (01962 848269). *Roman and medieval coins chiefly from local hoards and finds. Hampshire tradesmen's tokens and commemorative medals. Small reference library.*

Wisbech and Fenland Museum (1835), Museum Square, **Wisbech**, Cambridgeshire (01945 583817), *British Roman, medieval and later coins, medals and tokens.*

Y

The Museum of South Somerset (1928), Hendford, **Yeovil**, Somerset (01935 24774). *Roman coins from local sites, medieval English, modern British coins and medals and a fine collection of tokens (particularly 17th century Somerset).*

Castle Museum (1938), **York** (01904 653611). *English and British coins, campaign medals, orders and decorations, comemorative medals.*

Jorvik Viking Centre (1984), Coppergate, **York** (01904 643211). *Coins and artefacts pertaining to the Viking occupatio of York.*

The Yorkshire Museum (1823), **York** (01904 629745). *Roman imperial, medieval English and later coins, about 12,000 in all.*

CLUB
directory

Details given here are the name of the Numismatic Club or Society, its date of foundation, its venue, days and times of meetings. Meetings are monthly unless otherwise stated. Finally, the telephone number of the club secretary is given; the names and addresses of club secretaries are withheld for security reasons, but full details may be obtained by writing to the Secretary of the British Association of Numismatic Societies, Philip Mernick, c/o Bush Boake Allen Ltd, Blackhorse Lane, London E17 5QP.

Banbury & District Numismatic Society (1967). Banbury British Rail Working Mens Club. 2nd Mon (exc Jul & Aug), 19.45. (01295 254451).

Bath & Bristol Numismatic Society (1950). Ship Inn, Temple Street, Keynsham, Bristol. 2nd Thu, 19.30. (01275 472385).

Bedford Numismatic Society (1966). RAF Association Club, 93 Ashburnham Road, Bedford MK40 1EA. 3rd Mon, 19.30. (01234 228833/358369).

Bexley Coin Club (1968). St Martin's Church Hall, Erith Road, Barnehurst, Bexleyheath, Kent. 1st Mon (exc Jan & Aug), 20.00. (0181 303 0510).

Birmingham Numismatic Society (1964). Friend's Meeting House, 40 Bull Street, Birmingham. 1st Wed, 19.30. (0121 308 1616).

Matthew Boulton Society (1994). PO Box 395, Birmingham B31 2TB (0121 781 6558 fax 0121 781 6574).

Bradford & District Numismatic Society (1967). East Bowling Unity Club, Leicester Street, Bradford, West Yorkshire. 3rd Mon, 19.00. (01532 677151).

Brighton & Hove Coin Club (1971). Methodist Church Hall, St Patrick's Road, Hove, East Sussex. Last Wed (exc Dec), 20.00. (01273 419303).

British Cheque Collectors' Society (1980). John Purser, 71 Mile Lane, Cheylesmore, Coventry, West Midlands CV3 5GB.

British Numismatic Society (1903). Warburg Institute, Woburn Square, London WC1H 0AB. Monthly (exc Jul, Aug & Dec), 18.00. Graham Dyer, Royal Mint, Llantrisant, Pontyclun, Mid Glamorgan CF7 8YT (01443 222111).

Cambridgeshire Numismatic Society (1946). Friends' Meeting House, 12 Jesus Lane (entrance in Park Street), Cambridge, CB5 8BA. 3rd Mon, Sept–June, 19.30. (01767 312112).

Chester & North Wales Coin & Banknote Society (1996). Liver Hotel, 110 Brook Street, Chester. 1st Tue, 20.00. (0151 478 4293)

Cheltenham Numismatic Society, The Reddings & District Community Association, North Road, The Reddings, Cheltenham. 3rd Mon, 19.45 (01242 673263)

Coin Correspondence Club (1988). Postal only. A.H. Chubb, 49 White Hart Lane, Barnes, London SW13 0PP. (0181-878 0472).

Cornwall Collectors' Club (1990). The Swan Inn, 40 Bosvigo Road, Truro. 1st Wed, 20.00. (01872 73376).

Crawley Coin Club (1969). Furnace Green Community Centre, Ashburnham Road, Furnace Green, Crawley, West Sussex. 1st Tue, 20.00. (01293 548671).

Crewe & District Coin & Medal Club (1968). Memorial Hall, Church Lane, Wistaston, Crewe, 2nd Tue (exc Jan & July), 19.30. (01270 69836).

Darlington & District Numismatic Society (1968). Darlington Arts Centre, Vane Terrace, Darlington, Co Durhm. 3rd Wed, 19.30. (01609 772976).

Derbyshire Numismatic Society (1964). The Friends' Meeting House, St Helens Street, Derby. 3rd Mon (exc August), 19.45. (01283 211623).

Devon & Exeter Numismatic Society (1965). Red Cross Centre, Butts Road, Heavitree, Exeter, Devon. 3rd Tue, 19.30. (01392 461013).

Edinburgh Numismatic Society (1996). Department of History and Applied Arts, Royal Museum of Scotland, Chambers Street, Edinburgh EH1 1JF. 3rd Mon, 19.30. (0131 225 7534).

Enfield & District Numismatic Society (1969). Millfield House Arts Centre, Silver Street,

Edmonton, London N18 1PJ. 3rd Mon, 20.00. (0181-340 0767).

Essex Numismatic Society (1966). Chelmsford & Essex Museum, Moulsham Street, Chelmsford, Essex. 4th Fri (exc Dec), 20.00. (01376 21846).

Glasgow & West of Scotland Numismatic Society (1947). The College Club, University of Glasgow, University Avenue, Glasgow G12. 2nd Thu, Oct-May, 19.30. (0141 633 5422).

Harrow & North West Middlesex Numismatic Society (1968). YMCA, 51 Sheepcote Road, Harrow, Middlesex. 2nd Thu and 4th Tue, 20.00. (020 8952 8765).

Havering Numismatic Society (1967). Fairkytes Arts Centre, Billet Lane, Hornchurch, Essex. 1st Tue, 19.30. (01708 704201).

Hayes & District Coin Club. The United Reformed Church Hall, Swakeleys Road, Ickenham, Middlesex. 3rd Thu, 19.45. (0181-422 9178).

Horncastle & District Coin Club (1963). Bull Hotel, Bull Ring, Horncastle, Lincs. 2nd Thu (exc Aug), 19.30. (01754 2706).

Huddersfield Numismatic Society (1947). Tolson Memorial Museum, Ravensknowle Park, Huddersfield, West Yorkshire. 1st Mon (exc Jul & Aug), 19.30. (01274 876443).

Hull & District Numismatic Society (1967). The Young People's Institute, George Street, Hull. Monthly (exc Aug & Dec), 19.30. (01482 441933).

International Bank Note Society (1961). Victory Services Club, 63–79 Seymour Street, London W1. Last Thu (exc Dec), 18.00. (020-8969 9493).

International Bank Note Society, Scottish Chapter (1995). West End Hotel, Palmerston Place, Edinburgh. Last Sat (exc Dec), 14.30.

Ipswich Numismatic Society (1966). Ipswich Citizens Advice Bureau, 19 Tower Street, Ipswich, Suffolk. 3rd Wed, 19.30. (01473 626950).

Kent Towns Numismatic Society (1913). Adult Education Centre, 9 Sittingbourne Road (Maidstone) and King's School Preparatory School, King Edward Road (Rochester). 1st Fri of month, 19.30 alternately at Maidstone and Rochester. (01622 843881).

Kingston Numismatic Society (1966). King Athelstan's School, Villiers Road, Kingston-upon-Thames, Surrey. 3rd Thu (exc Jan), 19.30. (020-8397 6944).

Lancashire & Cheshire Numismatic Society (1933). Manchester Central Library, St Peter's Square, Manchester M2 5PD. Monthly, Sep-June, Wed (18.30) or Sat (14.30). (0161 445 2042).

Lincolnshire Numismatic Society (1932). Grimsby Bridge Club, Bargate, Grimsby, South Humberside. 4th Wed (exc Aug), 19.30.

London Numismatic Club (1947). Institute of Archaeology, 31–34 Gordon Square, London WC1H 0PY. Monthly, 18.30.

Loughborough Coin & Search Society (1964). Wallace Humphry Room, Shelthorpe Community Centre, Loughborough, Leics. 1st Thu, 19.30. (01509 261352).

Merseyside Numismatic Society (1947). The Lecture Theatre, Liverpool Museum, William Brown Street, Liverpool L3 8EN. Monthly (exc July & Aug), 19.00. (0151-929 2143).

Mid Lanark Coin Circle (1969). Hospitality Room, The Civic Centre, Motherwell, Lanarkshire. 4th Thu, Sep–Apr (exc Dec), 19.30. (0141-552 2083).

Monmouthshire Numismatic Society. W. R. Lysaght Institute, Corporation Road, Newport. 2nd Wed, 19.30. (029 20 561564)

Morecambe & Lancaster Numismatic Society. Monthly, 19.30. (01524 411036).

Newbury Coin & Medal Club (1971). Monthly, 20.00. (01635 41233).

Northampton Numismatic Society (1969). Old Scouts RFC, Rushmere Road, Northampton. 3rd Mon, 20.00.

Norwich Numismatic Society (1967). Assembly House, Theatre Street, Norwich, Norfolk. 3rd Mon, 19.30. (01493 651577).

Nottinghamshire Numismatic Society (1948). The Meeting Room, County Library, Angel Row, Nottingham NG1 6HP. 2nd Tue (Sep-Apr), 19.30. (0115 9257674).

Nuneaton & District Coin Club (1968). United Reformed Church Room, Coton Road, opposite Council House, Nuneaton, Warwickshire. 2nd Tue, 19.30. (01203 371556).

Orders & Medals Research Society (1942). National Army Museum, Royal Hospital Road, Chelsea, London SW3. Monthly, 14.30. (020-8680 2701).

Ormskirk & West Lancashire Numismatic Society (1970). Greyhound Inn, Aughton Street, Ormskirk. Lancs. 1st Thu, 20.15. (01704 531266).

Peterborough Coin & Medal Club (1967). The Club Room, APV-Baker Social Club, Alma Road, Peterborough, Cambs. Last Tue (exc July & Aug), 19.30.

Plymouth Coin & Medal Club (1970). RAFA Club, 5 Ermington Terrace, Mutley Plain, Plymouth, Devon. 4th Wed (exc Dec), 19.30. (01752 663803).

Preston & District Numismatic Society (1965). Eldon Hotel, Eldon Street, Preston, Lancs. 1st and 3rd Tue, 20.00. (012572 66869).

Reading Coin Club (1964). Reading Library, Abbey Square, Reading. 1st Tue, 20.00. (0118 9332843).

Redbridge Numismatic Society (1968). Gants Hill Library, Cranbrook Road, Ilford, Essex. 4th Wed, 19.30. (020-8554 5486).

Rochford Hundred Numismatic Society. Civic Suite, Rayleigh Town Hall, Rayleigh, Essex. 2nd Thu, 20.00. (01702 230950).

Romsey Numismatic Society (1969). Romsey WM Conservative Club, Market Place, Romsey, Hants SO5 8NA. 4th Fri (exc Dec), 19.30. (01703 253921).

Rotherham & District Coin Club (1982). Rotherham Art Centre, Rotherham, South Yorkshire. 1st Wed, 19.00. (01709 528179).

Royal Mint Coin Club, PO Box 500, Cardiff CF1 1HA (01443 222111).

Royal Numismatic Society (1836). Society of Antiquaries, Piccadilly, London W1. Monthly (Oct-June), 17.30. Joe Cribb, Coins and Medals, British Museum, London WC1B 3DG (020-7323 8585).

Rye Coin Club (1955). Rye Further Education Centre, Lion Street, Rye, East Sussex. 2nd Thu (Oct-Dec, Feb-May), 19.30. (01424 422974).

St Albans & Hertfordshire Numismatic Society (1948). St Michael's Parish Centre, Museum Entrance, Verulamium Park, St Albans, Herts AL3 4SL. 2nd Tue (exc Aug), 19.30. (01727 862060).

Sheffield Numismatic Society. Telephone for venue. 2nd Wed, 19.00. (0114 2817129)

South East Hants Numismatic Society. Different locations. 1st Fri. Contact: Tony Matthews, 8 King George Road, Totton, Southampton SO4 3FE.

South Manchester Numismatic Society (1967). Nursery Inn, Green Lane, Heaton Mersey, Stockport. Fortnightly Mon, 20.00. (0161-485 7017).

South Wales & Monmouthshire Numismatic Society (1958). The W. R. Lysaght Institute, Corporation Road, Newport. 2nd Wed, 19.30. (029 20561564).

Thurrock Numismatic Society (1970). Stanley Lazell Hall, Dell Road, Grays, Essex. 3rd Wed, 19.00.

Torbay & District Coin Club (1967). British Rail Social Club, Brunel Road, Newton Abbott, Devon TQ12 4PB. 1st Tue, 1945. (01803 326497).

Tyneside Numismatic Society (1954). RAFA Club, Eric Nelson House, 16 Berwick Road, Gateshead, Tyne & Wear. 2nd Wed, 19.30. (0191 372 2266).

Wessex NS (1948). Hotel Bristowe, Grange Road, Southbourne, Bournemouth, Dorset. 2nd Thurs (exc Aug), 19.45. (01590 682 662).

Wiltshire Numismatic Society (1965). Raven Inn, Poulshot, Nr Devizes, Wiltshire. 3rd Mon, Mar-Dec, 20.00. (01225 703143).

Worthing & District Numismatic Society (1967). Kingsway Hotel, Marine Parade, Worthing, West Sussex BN11 3QQ. 3rd Thu, 19.30. (01903 241503).

Yorkshire Numismatic Society (1909). Leeds Museum, The Headrow , Leeds. 1st Sat (exc Jan, Aug & Dec) (0113 286 4914).

Club Secretaries: if your details as listed are incorrect please let us know in time for the next edition of the COIN YEARBOOK

IMPORTANT ORGANISATIONS

**ADA
The Antiquities
Dealers Association**

*Secretary: Susan Hadida, Duke's Court,
32 Duke Street, London SW1Y 6DU*

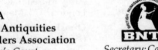

**BNTA
The British Numismatic
Trade Association**

*Secretary: Carol Carter, PO Box 474A, Thames Ditton,
Surrey KT7 0WJ*

**ANA
The American
Numismatic
Association**

*818 North Cascade Avenue, Colorado Springs, CO
80903-3279, USA*

**IAPN
International
Association of
Professional Numismatists**

*Secretary: Jean-Luc Van der Schueren, 14 Rue de la
Bourse, B–1000, Brussels.*

**IBNS
International Bank Note Society**
*Membership Secretary: Mrs Sally Thowney,
36B Dartmouth Park Hill, London NW5 1HN*

Directory of AUCTIONEERS

Listed here are the major UK auction houses which handle coins, medals, banknotes and other items of numismatic interest. Many of them hold regular public auctions, whilst others handle numismatic material infrequently. A number of coin companies also hold regular Postal Auctions—these are marked with a P.

Baldwin's Auctions Ltd

11 Adelphi Terrace, London WC2N 6BJ (020-7930 6879 fax 020-7930 9450).

Banking Memorabilia

PO Box 14, Carlisle CA3 8DZ (0169 7476465).

A. F. Brock & Company

269 London Road, Hazel Grove, Stockport, Cheshire SK7 4PL (0161-456 5050/5112).

Bonhams

Montpelier Street, London SW7 1HH (020-7584 9161 fax 020-7589 4072).

Christie, Manson & Wood Ltd

8 King Street, St James's, London SW1Y 6QT (020-7 839 9060).

Christie's Scotland Ltd

164–166 Bath Street, Glasgow G2 4TG (0141-332 8134 fax 0141-332 5759).

Classical Numismatic Group Inc (Seaby Coins)

14 Old Bond Street, London W1X 4JL (020-7495 1888 fax 020-7499 5916). **P**

Corbitts

5 Moseley Sreet, Newcastle upon Tyne NE1 1YE (0191-232 7268 fax 0191-261 4130).

Croydon Coin Auctions

272 Melfort Road, Thornton Heath, Surrey CR7 7RR (020-8656 4583/020-8684 6515 fax 020-8656 4583).

Dix Noonan Webb

1 Old Bond Street, London W1XZ 3TD (020 7499 5022 fax 020 7499 5023)

Edinburgh Coin Shop

11 West Crosscauseway, Edinburgh EH8 9JW (0131 668 2928 fax 0131 668 2926). **P**

Fellows & Sons

Augusta House, 19 Augusta Street, Hockley, Birmingham B18 6JA (0121-212 2131).

B. Frank & Son

3 South Avenue, Ryton, Tyne & Wear NE40 3LD (0191 413 8749 fax 0191 413 2957).

T. Gillingham

42 Highbury Park, Warminster, Wilts BA12 9JF (01985 216486).

Gillio Coins International

1013 State Street, Santa Barbara, CA 93101, USA (805 9631345—London contact Eric Green 020-7586 3964).

Glendining & Co

101 New Bond Street, London W1Y 9LG (020 7 493 2445 fax 020 7491 9181).

Graves, Son & Pilcher Fine Arts

71 Church Road, Hove, East Sussex BN3 2GL (01273 735266 fax 01273 723813).

Hoods Postal Coin Auctions

23 High Street, Kilbirnie, Ayrshire KA25 7EX (fax/tel 01505 682157). **P**

Kleeford Coin Auctions

19 Craythorns Crescent, Dishforth, Thirsk YO7 3LY. (tel/fax 01845 577977).

W. H. Lane & Son

65 Morrab Road, Penzance, Cornwall TR18 2QT (01736 61447 fax 0736 50097) also: Trafalgar House, Malpas Road, Truro, Cornwall TR1 1QH (0872 223379).

Lawrence Fine Art Auctioneers

South Street, Crewkerne, Somerset TA18 8AB (01460 73041).

David Lay

The Penzance Auction House, Alverton, Penzance, Cornwall TR18 4RE (01736 61414 fax 01736 60035).

Lockdale Coins

36 Upper Orwell Street, Ipswich IP4 1BR. (01473 218588).

London Coin Auctions

31 Reigate Way, Wallington, Surrey SM6 8NU (020 8 688 5297).

Neales

192–194 Mansfield Road, Nottingham NG1 3HU (0115 9624141 fax 0115 9856890).

Phillips

101 New Bond Street, London W1Y 9LG (020-7629 1877 fax 020-7409 3466).

R & W Coin Auctions

307 Bretch Hill, Banbury, Oxon OX16 0JD (01295 275128).

Sheffield Coin Auctions

7 Beacon Close, Sheffield S9 1AA (0114 2 490442).

Simmons Gallery

53, Lamb's Conduit Street, Holborn, London WC1N 3NB (020 7831 2080 fax 020 7831 2090.   P

Sotheby's

34–35 New Bond Street, London W1Y 2AA (020-7408 5312/4 fax 020-7493 6863) (Coins).

Henry Spencer & Sons

20 The Square, Retford, Notts DN22 6BX (01777 708633 fax 01777 709299).

Spink & Son Ltd

5–7 King Street, St James's, London SW1Y 6QS (020 7930 7888 fax 020 7839 4853).

Sussex Auction Galleries

59 Perrymount Road, Haywards Heath, West Sussex RH16 3DS (01444 414935 fax 01444 450402).

Italo Vecchi

35 Dover Street, London W1X 3RA (020 7491 7048 fax 020 7409 7835).

Wallis & Wallis

West Street, Lewes, East Sussex (01273 480208 fax 01273 476562).

Warwick & Warwick

Chalon House, Scarbank, Millers Road, Warwick CV34 5DB (01926 499031 fax 01926 491906)

Whytes

30 Marlborough Street, Dublin 1, Republic of Ireland (3531 874 6161 fax 874 6020).

Directory of
DEALERS

The dealers listed below have comprehensive stocks of coins and medals, unless otherwise stated. Specialities, where known, are noted. Many of those listed are postal dealers only, so to avoid disappointment always make contact by telephone or mail in the first instance, particularly before travelling any distance.

Abbreviations:
ADA—Antiquities Dealers Association
ANA—American Numismatic Association
BADA—British Antique Dealers Association
BNTA—British Numismatic Trade Association
IAPN—International Association of Professional Numismatists
IBNS—International Bank Note Society
P—Postal only
L—Publishes regular lists

A. Ackroyd (IBNS)
62 Albert Road, Parkstone, Poole, Dorset BH12 2DB (tel/fax 01202 739039). *P. L. Banknotes, cheques and related collectables.*

Airedale Coins (ANA, BNTA)
PO Box 7, Oakwood Park, Lady Lane, Bingley, West Yorkshire, BD16 4ST (01274 563869 fax 01274 563869). *P. L. British and modern coins of the world.*

David Allen Coins and Collectables
PO Box 125, Pinner, Middlesex HA5 2TX (020 866 6796). *P. L. British and world coins, tokens, banknotes.*

Joan Allen Electronics Ltd
190 Main Road, Biggin Hill, Kent TN16 3BB (01959 71255). Mon-Sat 09.00–17.00. *Metal detectors.*

Ancient Forum (ADA)
PO Box 356, Christchurch, Dorset BH23 2YD (01202 478592). *P. L. Greek, Roman and medieval antiquities with occasional groups of coins.*

Ancient World
16 High Petergate, York, YO1 2EH (01904 624062) 10.30–17.00 weekdays. *Greek, Roman, Celtic and medieval coins, also antiquities.*

Antiquarius—Collectors Centre
237 Mansfield Road, Nottingham (0115 9417268). *Coins, banknotes, militaria, books.*

Antique Boutique
54–59 Merrion Centre, Leeds, West Yorkshire (01132 444174). 09.30–17.30 (Wed 09.30–13.30).

Keith Austin (IBNS)
PO Box 89, Carlise, Cumbria CA3 0GH (01228 819149). L. *Banknotes.*

N. J. Aves
PO Box 811, Yeovil, Somerset (01935 72368). P. *Coins, tokens and medals.*

Mark Bailey
120 Sterte Court, Sterte Close, Poole, Dorset BH15 2AY (01202 674936). *P. L. Ancient, modern, world coins and antiquities.*

Baird & Co
304 High Street, Stratford, London E15 1AJ (020 8555 5217). 09.00–17.30 weekdays. *Bullion and World coins.*

A. H. Baldwin & Sons Ltd (ANA, BADA, BNTA, IAPN)
11 Adelphi Terrace, London WC2N 6BJ. 09.00–17.00 weekdays. *Coins, tokens, commemorative medals, war medals and decorations, numismatic books.*

Banking Memorabilia (IBNS)
PO Box 14, Carlisle, Cumbria (0169 96465). 09.00–18.00 (not Sun). *Cheques, banknotes, related ephemera. auctions.*

D. G. Barney
Greenfield, Colyton Hill, Colyton, Devon EX24 6HY (01297 552 702). *British and world coins, tokens and banknotes.*

G. Barrington Smith
Cross Street, Oadby, Leicestershire LE2 4DD (01533 712114). 08.30–17.15 weekdays. *Albums, catalogues and accessories.*

Bath Stamp and Coin Shop (BNTA)
Pulteney Bridge, Bath, Avon BA2 4AY (01225 463073). Mon-Sat 09.30–17.30. *British and world coins.*

Baxters Coin & Stamp Exchange
20–22 Hapworths Arcade, Silver Street, Hull, North Humberside, HU1 1JU (01482 223875). 10.00–17.00 (closed Thurs). *British and world coins.*

Michael Beaumont
PO Box 8, Carlton, Notts NG4 4QZ (0115 9878361). *P. Coins, medals and tokens of the world.*

Beaver Coin Room (BNTA)
57 Philbeach Gardens, LondonSW5 9ED (020 7373 4553). *P. European coins and medals.*

R. P. & P. J. Beckett
Maesyderw, Capel Dewi, Llandyssul, Dyfed SA44 4PJ. *P. World crowns, coin sets and banknotes.*

Lloyd Bennett (BNTA)

PO Box 2, Monmouth, Gwent NP5 3YE (01600 890634). Abergavenny Market (Tue), Monmouth Market (Fri–Sat) 09.00–16.00. *English hammered, milled and coins of the world.*

Berkshire Coin Centre

35 Castle Street, Reading, Berkshire RG1 7SB (01734 575593). 10.00–16.00 weekdays, half-day Sat. *British and world coins.*

Beron Coins

64 Rosewood Close, Glascote, Tamworth, Staffs B77 3PD (01827 54541). *P. L. British and world coins.*

Stephen J. Betts

4 Victoria Street, Narborough, Leics LE9 5DP (0116 2864434). *P. L. Medieval and modern coins, counters, jetons and tokens, countermarks and medals.*

Birchin Lane Gold Coin Company

6 Castle Court, St Michael's Alley (off Cornhill), London EC3V 9DS (020 7621 0370 and 020 7263 3981). Mon-Fri 10.00–16.30. *Gold and bullion coins.*

Barry Boswell

24 Townsend Lane, Upper Boddington, Daventry, Northants NN11 6DR (01327 61877). *P. L. British and world banknotes.*

James & C. Brett

17 Dale Road, Lewes, East Sussex BN7 1LH. *P. L. British and world coins.*

J. Bridgeman Coins

129a Blackburn Road, Accrington, Lancs (01254 384757). 09.30–17.00. *British & World coins.*

Brighton Coin Company (ANA, BNTA)

36 Ship Street, Brighton, Sussex BN1 1AB (01273 733365). Mon-Fri 9.45–17.30, Sat 9.45–15.30. *World coins.*

Britannia Jewellery Co

234 Yorkshire Street, Rochdale, Lancs OL16 2DP (01706 341046/55507. Mon-Sat 10.00–17.00.

BRM Coins

3 Minshull Street, Knutsford, Cheshire WA16 6HG (01565) 651480 and 0606 74522). Mon-Sat 10,00–17.00. *British coins.*

Peter F. Broadbelt

10 Dragon Road, Harrogate, North Yorkshire HG1 5DF (01423 562037). Mon-Sat 11–18.00. *Specialist in Foreign coins.*

A. F. Brock & Company

269 London Road, Hazel Grove, Stockport, Cheshire SK7 4PL (0161 456 5050/5112. Mon-Sat 09.30–17.30.

E. J. & C. A. Brooks (BNTA, IBNS)

44 Kiln Road, Thundersley, Essex SS7 1TB (01268 753835). Any time up to 23.00. *L. British coins and banknotes.*

Iain Burn

2 Compton Gardens, 53 Park Road, Camberley, Surrey GU15 2SP (01276 23304).

Butler & Co

111 Promenade, Cheltenham, Glos GL50 1NN (01242 522272). Sat only. *World coins.*

BBM Coins

8–9 Lion Street, Kidderminster, Hereford & Worcester, DY10 1PT (01562 744118). Mon, Wed-Sat 10.00–17.00. *World coins.*

Cambridge Stamp Centre Ltd

9 Sussex Street, Cambridge CB4 4HU (01223 63980). Mon-Sat 09.00–17.30. *British coins.*

Castle Coins

47a High Street South, Dunstable, Beds LU6 3RZ (01582 602778). Mon-Sat 10.00–17.00. *English coins.*

Castle Curios

165 Wellgate, Rotherham, South Yorkshire S60 4DT. Wed-Sat 11.00–17.00. *English coins.*

Castle Galleries

81 Castle Street, Salisbury, Wiltshire SP1 3SP (01722 333734). Tue, Thu Fri 09.00–17.00, Sat 09.30–16.00. *British coins, medals and tokens.*

Cathedral Coins

23 Kirkgate, Ripon, North Yorkshire HG4 1PB (01765 701400). Mon-Sat 10.00–17.00.

David L. Cavanagh

49 Cockburn Street, Edinburgh EH1 1PB (0131 226 3391). Mon-Sat 10.30–17.00. *British coins.*

Cavendish Coins

14 Longfields, Ongar, Essex CM5 9BZ. *P. Modern crown-sized coins.*

CCC Coins

PO Box 192, Peterborough, PE2 5DT. *P. L. Roman, hammered and English milled silver.*

Lance Chaplin

17 Wanstead Lane, Ilford, Essex IG1 3SB (020 8554 7154). *P. L. Roman, Greek, Celtic, hammered coins and antiquities.*

Chelsea Coins Ltd (BNTA)

PO Box 2, Fulham Road, London SW10 9PQ. (020 8870 5501 Fax 020 8875 1459). *P. World coins.*

Nigel A. Clark

28 Ulundi Road, Blackheath, London SE3 7UG (020 8858 4020). *P. L. Mainly 17th century tokens.*

Classical Numismatic Group

14 Old Bond Street, London W1X 4JL. (020 7495 1888 Fax 020 7499 5916). *P. Ancient and world coins. Publishers of the Classical Numismatic Review.*

Paul Clayton (BNTA)

PO Box 21, Wetherby, West Yorkshire LS22 5JY. (01937 72441). *Modern gold coins.*

André de Clermont (BNTA)

PO Box 3615, London, SW10 0YD. (020 7351 5727, Fax 020 7352 8127). *World coins, especially Islamic & Oriental coins, Latin America.*

M. Coeshaw

PO Box 115, Leicester LE3 8JJ (01533 873808). *P.*

Philip Cohen Numismatics (ANA, BNTA)

20 Cecil Court, Charing Cross Road, London WC2N 4HE (020 7379 0615). Mon-Sat 10.30–17.30 (half-days Mon and Sat).

Coin & Collectors Centre

PO Box 22, Pontefract, West Yorkshire WR8 1YT (01977 704112). *P. British coins.*

Coincraft (ANA, IBNS)

44/45 Great Russell Street, London WC1B 3LU (020 7636 1188 and 020 7637 8785 fax 020 7323 2860). Mon-Fri 09.30–17.00, Sat 10.00–14.30. *L (newspaper format). Coins and banknotes.*

Coinote Services Ltd

PO Box 53, Sorting Office, Clarke Street, Hartlepool TS26 NYL (01429 273044/272411). *P. L. Coins and banknotes 1615 todate. Accessories and books.*

Coins of Beeston

PO Box 19, Beeston, Notts BG9 2NE. *P. L. Tokens, medals and paranumismatics.*

Coins of Canterbury

PO Box 47, Faversham, Kent ME13 7HX (01795 531980). *P. English coins.*

Coliseum Coins

30 Staunton Avenue, Hayling Island, Hants PO11 0EN (01705 464332). *P. Greek, Roman, Oriental coins.*

Collecta Coins Limited

PO Box 101, Northampton NN1 3LT (01604 766607/ 27076). Mon-Sat 09.00–21.00. *World coins.*

The Collector

242 High Street, Orpington, Kent BR6 0LZ (01689 890045). Mon-Sat 09.30–17.00 (closed Tue). *Coins, medals, banknotes, badges, militaria, cigarette cards etc*

3CO

PO Box 27, Manchester, M23 9UJ. *English milled coinage.*

Collectors' Corner

East Street, Crescent Road, Faversham, Kent ME13 8AD (01795 539721). Mon-Fri 10.00–15.00 (half-day Mon, Thu). *Coins and medals.*

Collectors' Corner

Watford Market (off High Street), Watford, Herts (020 8904 0552). Tue, Fri, Sat 09.00-17.00. *World coins.*

Collectors' Forum

237 South Street, Romford, Essex RM1 2BE (01708 723357). Mon-Sat 09.30-18.00 Thu 09.30-14.00. *British coins and medals.*

Collectors Gallery (BNTA, IBNS)

6 & 7 Castle Gates, Shrewsbury SY1 2AE (01743 272140 fax 01743 366041). Mon-Fri 09.00–18.00, half-day Sat. *Coins, medals and banknotes. Numismatic accessories and related books. Agents for the Abafil range of coin cases.*

Constantia CB

15 Church Road, Northwood, Middlesex HA6 1AR. *P. Roman and medieval hammered coins.*

Colin Cooke

257 Brooklands Road, Manchester M23 9HF (0161 973 2395 fax 0161 962 2864). *L. British coins.*

Corbitts (BNTA)

5 Mosley Street, Newcastle Upon Tyne NE1 1YE (0191 232 7268 fax: 0191 261 4130). *Dealers and auctioneers of all coins and medals.*

G. D. Courtenay

58 New Peachey Lane, Uxbridge, Middlesex UB8 3SX. *P. L. Coins, medals, tokens and banknotes.*

David Craddock

PO Box 3785, Camp Hill, Birmingham B11 2NF. *L. Crown to farthings. Copper and bronze specialist. Some foreign.*

K. A. Cudworth

8 Park Avenue, Clayton West, Huddersfield, West Yorkshire HD8 9PT (01484 862679). *P. British and world coins.*

John Cummings Ltd (BNTA)

Parthenon Gallery, 25 Bury Place, WC1A 2JH (020 7242 5656). *P. Greek, Roman, Byzantine, Celtic, Saxon, Viking and English hammered coins. Quarterly catalogue.*

Mark Davidson

PO Box 197, South Croydon, Surrey CR3 0ZD (020 8651 3890). *Ancient, hammered coinage.*

Davidson Monk Fairs

PO Box 201, Croydon, Surrey CR9 7AQ (020 8656 4583). *Organiser of monthly fairs at the Commonwealth Institute, Kensington High Street, London W8.*

Paul Davies Ltd (ANA, BNTA, IAPN)

PO Box 17, Ilkley, West Yorkshire LS29 8TZ (01943 603116). *P. World coins.*

Paul Davis

PO Box 418, Birmingham B17 0RZ (0121 427 7179). *P. Hammered gold and silver coins.*

DD Coins of Windsor

24–28 St Leonards Road, Suite 100, Windsor, Berks SL4 3BB. (01753 739487). *L. GB milled list.*

B. J. Dawson (Coins) (BNTA)

52 St Helens Road, Lancs BL3 3NH (01204 63732). Mon Tue Sat 09.30–16.00, Thu Fri 09.30–17.30, Wed 09.30–13.00. *L. Ancient, hammered and milled coins, tokens and banknotes.*

Patrick Deane

PO Box 76, Orpington, Kent BR6 0UB. (01689 812222). By appointment only. *British coins.*

Decus Coins

The Haven, Brockweir, Chepstow, Gwent NP6 7NN (01291 689216). *P.*

Dei Gratia

PO Box 3568, Buckingham MK18 4ZS (01280 848000). *P. L. Pre-Roman to modern coins, antiquities, banknotes.*

Den of Antiquity

26 West End, Haddenham, Ely, Cambs CB6 3TE (01353 741759).

Clive Dennett (BNTA)

66 St Benedicts Street, Norwich, Norfolk NR2 4AR (01603 624315). Mon-Fri 09.00–17.30, Sat 09.00–16.00 (closed Thu). *L. World paper money.*

C. J. Denton (ANA, BNTA, FRNS)

PO Box 25, Orpington, Kent BR6 8PU (01689 873690). *P. World coins.*

Michael Dickinson (ANA, BNTA)

Ramsay House, 825 High Road Finchley, London N12 8UB (0181 441 7175). *P. British and world coins.*

Dolphin Coins (ANA)

2c Englands Lane, Hampstead, London NW3 4TG (020 7722 4116 fax 020 7483 2000). Mon-Fri 09.30–17.00. Sat appt only. *L. British and world coins.*

Dorset Coin Co Ltd (BNTA)

193 Ashley Road, Parkstone, Poole, Dorset BH14 9DL (01202 739606, fax 01202 739230). *P. L. Separate coin and banknote lists.*

Drizen Coins

1 Hawthorns, Leigh-on-Sea, Essex SS9 4JT (01702 521094). *P. L. British, Commonwealth and world coins.*

Dyas Coins & Medals

30 Shaftmoor Lane, Acocks Green, Birmingham B27 7RS (0121 707 2808). Fri 10.30–18.30, Sun 10.30–13.00. *World coins and medals.*

Eagle Coins

Winterhaven, Mourneabbey, Mallow, Co. Cork, Ireland (010 35322 29385). *P. L. Irish and English coins.*

East Kent Coins

PO Box 106, Herne Bay, Kent CT6 6GN (01227 365073). *P. L. World coins*

Eden Coins

PO Box 73, Oldbury, Warley, West Midlands B68 0BT (0121 422 5357). *P. English coins, tokens and medals.*

Edinburgh Coin Shop (ANA)

11 West Crosscauseway, Edinburgh EH8 9JW (0131 668 2928 fax 0131 668 2926). Mon-Sat 10.00–17.30. *L. World coins and medals. Postal auctions.*

Christopher Eimer (ANA, BNTA)

PO Box 352 London NW11 7SU (020 8458 9933). *P. Commemorative medals.*

Elm Hill Stamps & Coins

27 Elm Hill, Norwich, Norfolk NR3 1HN (01603 627413). Mon-Fri 09.00–16.45, half-day Sat. *British and world coins.*

ELM

15 Phillimore Walk, Kensington, London W8 7SA (020 7937 8484)P. *Egyptian Banknotes.*

Ely Stamp & Coin Shop

27 Fore Hill, Ely, Cambs CB7 1AA (01353 663919). Mon, Wed-Sat 09.30–17.30. *World coins, medals and stamps.*

Europa Numismatics (ANA, BNTA)

PO Box 119, High Wycombe, Bucks HP11 1QL (01494 437307). *P. European coins.*

Tim Everson

40 Woodlands Avenue, New Malden, Surrey KT3 3UQ (020 8949 7739) *P. L. Early British coinage.*

Evesham Stamp & Coin Centre

Magpie Antiques, Paris House, 61 High Street, Evesham, Worcs WR11 4DA (01386 41631). Mon-Sat 09.00–17.30. *British coins.*

Michael E. Ewins

Meyrick Heights, 20 Meyrick Park Crescent, Bournemouth, Dorset BH3 7AQ (01202 290674). *P. World coins.*

I. Fine & Son Ltd

Victoria House, 93 Manor Farm Road, Wembley, Middlesex HA10 1XB (020 8997 5055). *P. British & World coins.*

Patrick Finn (BNTA)

PO Box 26, Kendal, Cumbria LA9 7AB (01539 730008, fax 01539 721800). *P. L. Early British, Irish, Scottish and Anglo-Gallic coins.*

Robin Finnegan Stamp Shop

83 Skinnergate, Darlington, Co Durham DL3 7LX (01325 489820/357674). Mon-Sat 10.00–17.30 (closed Wed). *World coins.*

Richard N. Flashman

54 Ebbsfleet Walk, Gravesend, Kent, DA11 9EW. *L. P. British banknotes.*

David Fletcher (Mint Coins) (ANA, BNTA)

PO Box 64, Coventry, Warwickshire CV5 6SN (024 7671 5425, Fax 024 7667 7985). *P. World new issues*

Folley Island Coins

PO Box 361, Dunstable, Bedfordshire LU5 4YU. (01582 667734). *World and English coins.*

Format of Birmingham Ltd (ANA, BNTA, IAPN, IBNS)

18-19 Bennetts Hill, Birmingham B2 5QJ (0121 643 2058). Mon-Fri 09.30-7.00. *L. Coins, tokens and medals.*

Fox & Co (BNTA)

30 Princes Street, Yeovil, Somerset BA20 1EQ (01935 72323). Mon-Sat 09.00-17.30. *British and world coins, numismatic books.*

B. Frank & Son (ANA, IBNS)

3 South Avenue, Ryton, Tyne & Wear NE40 3LD (0191 413 8749). *P. L. Banknotes and cheques, coins of the world. Organiser of the North of England fair.*

Frank Milward (BNTA)

2 Ravensworth Road, Mortimer, Berks, RG7 3UU (01734 332843). Mon-Sat 09.00-18.00. *British and World coins.*

Dennis Fudge Coins

127 Hadrian Road, Jarrow, Tyne & Wear NE32 3TS (0191 421 6221). *P. L. Ancient coins.*

Galata Coins Ltd (ANA, BNTA)

The Old White Lion, Market Street, Llanfylin, Powys SY22 5BX (01691 648 765). *P. British and world coins.*

G. Gant

Glazenwood, 37 Augustus Way, Witham, Essex CM8 1HH. *P. British and Commonwealth coins.*

James Garriock

38 Hazel Close Bemerton Heath, Salisbury, Wiltshire SP2 977 (01722 500590). *P. L. Mainly hammered coins.*

John Gaunt

21 Harvey Road, Bedford MK41 9LF (01234 217685). By appointment. *Numismatic books.*

Alistair Gibb (IBNS)

5 West Albert Road, Kirkcaldy, Fife KY1 1DL (01592 269045). *P. L. Banknotes and books on banking.*

A. & S. Gillis

20 Howard Street, Darfield, Barnsley, South Yorkshire S73 9JD. *P. L. Ancient and medieval coins.*

Glance Back Books

17 Upper Street, Chepstow, Gwent NP6 5EX (01291 626562). 10.30–17.30. *World coins, medals, banknotes.*

Glendining's (ANA, BNTA)

101 New Bond Street, London W1Y 9LG (020 7493 2445). Mon-Fri 08.30-17.00, Sat 08.30–13.00. *Auctioneers.*

Phil Goodwin (ANA)

PO Box 69, Portsmouth, Hants PO1 5SH (01705 752 006 or evenings 01705 423 267). *P or by appointment. L. Ancient coins and antiquities.*

K. Goulborn

44 Highfield Park, Rhyl, LL18 3NH (01745 338112 or 01745 344856). *P. L. British coins and banknotes.*

Granta Stamp & Coin Shop

28 Magdalene Street, Cambridge CB3 0AF (01223 315044) Mon-Sat 10.30-18.30. *English coins and medals.*

Grantham Coins (BNTA)

PO Box 60, Grantham, Lincs (01476 870565). *P. L. English coins and banknotes.*

Eric Green—Agent in UK for Ronald J. Gillio Inc, 1013 State Street, Santa Barbara, California, USA 93101 (020 8907 0015, Mobile 0468 454948). *Gold coins, medals and paper money of the world.*

Grove Philatelics, Coins & Antiquities

Suite 4, Grove House, Blackheath Grove, London SE3 0DG (020 8463 0063). *P. British coins.*

R. I. Groves

82 Burntscarth Green, Locharbriggs, Dumfries DG1 1UL (01387 710636). *P. World, esp. Scandinavian coins.*

Ian Haines

PO Box 45, Hereford, HR2 7YP (01432 268178). *P. L. British and foreign coins and banknotes.*

Anthony Halse

The Headlands, Chepstow Road, Langstone, Newport, Gwent NP6 2JN (01633 413238). *P. L. English and foreign coins and tokens.*

A. D. Hamilton & Co (ANA, BNTA)

7 St Vincent Place, Glasgow G1 5JA (0141 221 5423, fax 0141 248 6019). Mon-Sat 09.00-17.30. *British and World coins.*

Peter Hancock

40 West Street, Chichester, West Sussex PO19 1RP (01243 786173). Mon-Sat. *World coins.*

P. Hanson

160 Princess Road, Buckhurst Hill, Essex IG9 5DJ. *P. L. Inexpensive world coins.*

J. Hardiman & Son

PO Box 151, London SE20 7YL (020 8778 2678/4159). *P. Quality world coins, all periods.*

Craig Holmes

6 Marlborough Drive, Bangor, Co Down BT19 1HB. *P. L. Low cost banknotes of the world.*

R. G. Holmes

11 Cross Park, Ilfracombe, Devon EX34 8BJ (01271 864474). *P. L. Coins, modern world crowns and foreign banknotes.*

John L. Homan

Oxford Grange, Marsh Lane, Barrow Haven, Barrow-on-Humber, South Humberside DN19 7ER (01469 32109). *P. Greek, Roman and Byzantine coins.*

Homeland Holding Ltd (IBNS)

Homeland, St John, Jersey, Channel Islands JE3 4AB (01534 65339). Mon-Fri 09.00-2.00. *World coins.*

HTSM Coins

26 Dosk Avenue, Glasgow G13 4LQ. *P. L. British and foreign coins and banknotes.*

T. A. Hull

15 Tangmere Crescent, Hornchurch, Essex RM12 5PL. *P. L. British coins, farthings to crowns, tokens.*

Humber Coins (BNTA) PO Box 16, Scunthorpe, South Humberside DN15 7AA (01724 763990). *P. British coins.*

J. Hume

107 Halsbury Road East, Northolt, Middlesex UB5 4PY (020 8864 1731). *P. L. Chinese coins.*

D. D. & A. Ingle

380 Carlton Hill, Nottingham (0115 9873325). Mon-Sat 09.30–17.00. *World coins.*

Rendal Ingram Coins (English)

206 Honeysuckle Road, Bassett, Southampton, Hants SO16 3BU. *P. L. English milled and modern coins.*

Intercol London (ANA, BNTA, IBNS)

43 Templars Crescent, London N3 3QR (020 7349 2207). *P. Paper money of the world.*

Peter Ireland Ltd (BNTA, IBNS)

31 Clifton Street, Blackpool, Lancs FY1 1JQ (01253 21588 fax 0253 300232). Mon-Sat 09.00-17.30. *British and world coins, medals and tokens.*

JAK (IBNS)

31 Vapron Road, Mannamead, Plymouth, Devon PL3 5NJ (01752 665405). *P. L. GB and Common. banknotes.*

F. J. Jeffery & Son Ltd

61 Locking Close, Melksham, Wiltshire SN12 6XS (01225 703143). *P. British, Commonwealth and foreign coins.*

Richard W. Jeffery

Trebehor, Porthcurno, Penzance, Cornwall TR19 6LS (01736 871263). *P. Britishand world coins.*

Jersey Coin Co Ltd

26 Halkett Street, St Helier, Jersey, Channel Islands (01534 25743). Mon-Sat 09.00–17.00. *World coins.*

John of Satin

27 Osborne Road, Cale Green, Stockport, Cheshire SK2 6RQ (0161 477 1064). *P. L. British coins.*

Ian Johnson

PO Box 28, Swinton, Manchester M27 3FR (01204 393944). *P. L. Ancient European and Oriental coins.*

I. L. Johnson

63, Sedley Close, Parkwood, Kent ME8 9QZ. (01634 261037) *P. L. English coins 1672–1967.*

Robert Johnson Coin Co

PO Box 194, 15 Bury Place, London WC1A 2JN (020 7831 0305). Mon-Fri 10.30-18.00, Sat 10.30-15.00. *British and world coins.*

Ian Jull

PO Box 594, Harrow, Middx, HA2 7SG. (020 8429 3988 fax: 020 8248 1714). *British coins and medals.*

Jumbo Coins

22 Woodend Lane, Stalybridge, Cheshire SK15 2SR (0161 338 5741). Fri-Sat 14.00-19.00. *World coins, medals and tokens.*

KB Coins (BNTA)

50 Lingfield Road, Martins Wood, Stevenage, Herts SG1 5SL (01438 312661). 09.00–18.00 by appointment only. *L. Mainly British coins.*

Knightsbridge Coins (ANA, BNTA, IAPN)

43 Duke Street, St James's, London SW1Y 6DD (020 7930 8215/7597 Fax 020 7930 8214). Mon-Fri 10.00–17.30. *Quality coins of the world.*

Lancashire Coin & Medal Co

31 Adelaide Street, Fleetwood, Lancs FY7 6AD (01253 779308). *P. British coins and medals.*

Lennox Gallery Ltd

K12/13, 4 Davies Mews, London, W1Y 1AR. (020 7629 9119 fax 020 7629 9119). *Ancient coins.*

Peter Licence

31 Reigate Way, Wallington, Surrey SM6 8NU (020 8688 5297). *P. British and World coins.*

Lighthouse Publications (UK)

4 Beaufort Road, Reigate, Surrey RH2 9DJ (01737 244222 Fax 0737 24743). *L. Manufacturers and stockists of coin albums, cabinets and accessories.*

Lindner Publications Ltd

13 Fore Street, Hayle, Cornwall TR27 4DX (01736 751914 fax: 01736 751911. Mon–Fri 09.00–13.00. *L. Manufacturers of coin albums, cabinets and accessories.*

Jan Lis (BNTA)

Beaver Coin Room, 57 Philbeach Gardens, London SW5 9ED (020 7373 4553 fax 020 7373 4555). *By appointment only. European coins.*

Keith Lloyd

45 Bramblewood, The Beeches, Ipswich, Suffolk IP8 3RS (01473 603067). *P. L. Greek, Roman coins.*

Lockdale Coins

36 Upper Orwell Street, Ipswich. (01473 218588). L. (Shop open 9.30–4.30 Mon–Sat). *World coins, medals, banknotes and accessories.*

Stephen Lockett

59 Cedar Drive, Sutton at Hone, Kent DA4 9EW (01322 861 228). *British and world coins.*

Mike Longfield Detectors

83 Station Road, Balsall Common, nr Coventry, Warwickshire CV7 7FN (01676 533274). Mon-Sat 09.30-17.00. *Metal detectors.*

Richard M. Lubbock (ANA, BNTA, IAPN, IBNS)

315 Regent Street, London W1R 7YB (020 7580 9922, 020 7637 7922 fax 020 7637 7602). *By appointment only. World coins and medals.*

Don MacRae Coins

PO Box 233, Uxbridge, Middlesex UB9 4HY (01895 832625). *P. British and world coins.*

Mannin Collections Ltd

5 Castle Street, Peel, Isle of Man (01624 843897). Mon-Sat 10.00-17.00. Half-day Thu. *British and Isle of Man coins.*

I. Markovits

1-3 Cobbold Mews, London W12 9LB (020 8749 3000). *Enamelled coins.*

Marron Coins

7 Beacon Close, Sheffield, South Yorkshire S9 1AA (0114 2433500). *P. English coins.*

C. J. Martin (Coins) Ltd (BNTA)

85 The Vale, Southgate, London N14 6AT (020 8882 1509). P. L. Bi-monthly catalogue. *Greek, Roman and English hammered coins.*

Clive Maxwell-Yates

21 Nicolas Road, Chorlton Manchester, M21 1LG (0161 881 7015). *P. L. World banknotes.*

Michael Coins

6 Hillgate Street, London W8 7SR (020 7727 1518). Mon-Fri 10.00-17.00. *World coins and banknotes.*

Midland Medals

12 Commerce House, Vicarage Lane, Water Orton, Birmingham B46 1RR (0121 7475983 fax 01564 784245). *P. Commemorative medals.*

David Miller Coins & Antiquities (ANA, BNTA)

PO Box 711, Hemel Hempstead, HP2 4UH (tel/fax 01442 251492). *Ancient and hammered English coins.*

Frank Milward (ANA, BNTA)

2 Ravensworth Road, Mortimer, Berkshire RG7 3UU (01734 322843). *P. European coins.*

Modern Coins & Stamps

24 Market Hall, Arndale Centre, Luton, Beds LU1 2TA (01582 412839). Mon-Sat 09.00-17.00. Half-day Wed. *Modern world coins.*

Graeme & Linda Monk (ANA, BNTA)

PO Box 201, Croydon, Surrey, CR9 7AQ (020 8656 4583 fax 020 8656 4583). *P. Fair organisers.*

Mike Morey

9 Elmtrees, Long Crendon, Bucks HP18 9DG. *P. L. British coins, halfcrowns to farthings.*

Peter Morris

1 Station Concourse, Bromley North Station, Bromley, BR1 1NN or PO Box 223, Bromley, BR1 4EQ (020 8466 1762, 020 8313 3410). Mon-Fri 10.00–18.00, Sat 0900-14.00 or by appointment. *L. British and world coins, proof sets and numismatic books.*

James Murphy

PO Box 122, Chorley, Lancashire PR7 2GE. *(01257 274 381). P. L. Ancient coins and antiquities.*

Colin Narbeth & Son Ltd (ANA, IBNS)

20 Cecil Court, Leicester Square, London WC2N 4HE (020 7379 6975). Mon-Sat 10.30-17.00. *World banknotes.*

New Forest Leaves

Bisterne Close, Burley, Ringwood, Hants BH24 4BA (014253 3315). *Publishers of numismatic books.*

Wayne Nicholls

PO Box 44, Bilston, West Midlands. (01902 495735) *L. Choice English coins*

North Wales Coins Ltd (BNTA)

1b Penrhyn Road, Colwyn Bay, Clwyd (01492 533023/532129). Mon-Sat (closed Wed) 09.30–17.30. *British coins.*

Notability (IBNS)

'Mallards', Chirton, Devizes, Wilts SN10 3QX (01380 723961). *P. L. Banknotes of the world.*

N P Collectables

9 Main Street, Gedney Dyke, Spalding, Lincs PE12 0AJ (01406 365211Ireland (010 35322 29385). *P. L. English Hammered and Milled coins.*

The Numismery

89b Oxford Road, Reading, Berks RG1 7UZ (01734 582145). Mon-Sat 11.00–20.30. *World coins.*

Glenn S. Ogden

Duncraig, Canada Hill, Ogwell, Newton Abbot, Devon TQ12 6AF. (01626 331663) *P. L. English milled.*

John Ogden Coins

Hodge Clough Cottage, Moorside, Oldham OL1 4JW (0161 678 0709) *P. L. Ancient and hammered coins.*

Michael O'Grady (IBNS)

PO Box 307, Pinner, Middlesex HA5 4XT (020 8428 4002). *P. British and world paper money.*

Colin James O'Keefe

5 Pettits Place, Dagenham, Essex RM10 8NL. *P. British and European coins.*

Don Oliver Gold Coins
The Coin Gallery, Stanford House, 23 Market Street, Stourbridge, West Midlands DY8 1AB (01384 373899). Mon-Fri 10.00–17.00, Sat 10.00-13.00 (closed Thu). *Gold coins of the world.*

Ongar Coins
14 Longfields, Marden Ash, Ongar, Essex IG7 6DS. *P.World coins.*

Tim Owen Coins
63 Allerton Grange Rise, Leeds 17, West Yorkshire (0113 2688015). *P. L. Quality hammered coins.*

Oxford Coins
25, Weldon Road, New Marston, Oxford OX3 0HP (01865 726939). *British coins.*

Penrith Coin & Stamp Centre
37 King Street, Penrith, Cumbria CA11 7AY (01768 64185). Mon-Sat 09.00–17.30. *World coins.*

Pentland Coins (IBNS)
Pentland House, 92 High Street, Wick, Caithness KW14 L5. *P. British and world coins and world banknotes.*

Phil Phipps
PO Box 31, Emsworth, Hants PO10 8XA (tel/fax 01243 376086). *P. L. World and German banknotes.*

David C. Pinder
20 Princess Road West, Leicester LE1 6TP (0116 2702439). *P. Greek, Roman and Byzantine coins.*

Pobjoy Mint Ltd (ANA)
Millennium House, Kingswood Park, Bonsor Drive, Kingswood, Surrey KT20 6AY (01737 818181 fax 01737 818199). Mon-Fri 09.00–17.00. *Europe's largest private mint. New issues.*

S. R. Porter (ANA)
18 Trinity Road, Headington Quarry, Oxford OX3 8LQ (01865 766851). *P. L. Ancient and British coins, some foreign, tokens, banknotes and accessories.*

David Pratchett
Trafalgar Square Collectors Centre, 7 Whitcombe Street, London WC2H 7HA. (020 7930 1979). Mon-Fri 10.00–7.30. *Specialist in gold and silverworld coins.*

Tony Radman
Westfield House, 2G Westfield Road, Witney, Oxon OX8 5JG (01993 772 705). Mon-Sat 10.00-17.00. *Ancient and World coins.*

George Rankin Coin Co Ltd (ANA, BNTA)
325 Bethnal Green Road, London E2 6AH (020 7729 1280 fax 020 7729 5023). Mon-Sat 10.00-18.00 (half-day Thu). *World coins.*

Mark T. Ray (formerly MTR Coins)
22a Kingsnorth Close, Newark, Notts NG24 1PS. (01636 703152). *P. British coins.*

Regton Ltd
82 Cleveland Street, Birmingham B1 3SN (0121 359 2379). Mon-Sat 09.30-17.00. *Metal detectors.*

Rhyl Coin & Stamp Centre 12 Sussex Street, Rhyl, Clwyd (01745 338112). Mon-Sat 10.00-17.30. *World coins.*

Chris Rigby
PO Box 181, Worcester WR1 1YE (01905 28028. *P. L. Modern British coins.*

Roderick Richardson
The Old Granary Antiques Centre, King's Staithe Lane, King's Lynn, Norfolk. (01553 670833) *L. Mainly British Milled coins.*

F. J. Rist
Rectory Lane, Nailstone, Nuneaton, Warwickshire CV13 0QQ (01530 60009). *P. L. Ancient and medieval coins, British coins and antiquities.*

Ian Robinson
PO Box 929, Burgess Hill, West Sussex RH15 9FN (01444 242215). *P. L. Quality English milled coins.*

S. J. Rood & Co Ltd
52–53 Burlington Arcade, London W1V 9AE (0171 493 0739). Mon-Sat 09.30-17.00. *World gold coins.*

Bill Rosedale
17 Priory JClose, Abbots Park, Chester CH1 4BX (01244 382554) *P. L. World paper money*

Royal Mint Coin Club
PO Box 500, Cardiff CF1 1YY (01433 223366). *P. New issues struck by the Royal Mint.*

Colin de Rouffignac (BNTA)
57, Wigan Lane, Wigan, Lancs WN1 2LF (01942 237927) *P. English and Scottish hammered.*

Chris A. Rudd (IAPN)
PO Box 222, Aylsham, Norfolk, NR11 6TY (01263 735007). *P. L. Celtic coins.*

Colin Rumney (BNTA)
26 Caer Felin, Llanrheadr, Denbigh, Clwyd LL16 4PR (074 578621). *All world including ancients.*

R & J Coins
21b Alexandra Street, Southend-on-Sea, Essex SS1 1DA (01702 345995). Mon-Sat 10.00–16.00 (closed Wed). *World coins.*

RJB Coins (BNTA)
R. J. Bayliss, PO Box 95, Cheltenham GL51 9SF (01242 680652). *P. General world coins, especially Western Europe.*

R & L Coins (BNTA)
521 Lytham Road, Blackpool, Lancs FY4 1RJ (01253 43081). Mon-Sat 09.00–17.00 by appointment only. *British, Commonwealth and European coins.*

Safe Albums (UK) Ltd
Freepost (RG 1792), Wokingham, Berks RG11 1BR (01734 328976 fax 01734 328612). *P. Stackable coin drawers, coin holders, etc.*

Saltford Coins
Boyds Paddock, Grange Road, Saltford, Bristol, Avon BS18 3AQ (01225 873512). *P. British, Commonwealth and world coins.*

I. S. Sandiford & Co Ltd
3 Marriotts Court, Brown Street, Manchester M2 1EA (0161 834 9346). Mon-Sat 09.00-16.30. *British and world coins.*

Schwer Coins (ANA, BNTA)
6 South Hill, Felixstowe, Suffolk, IP11 8AA (01394 278580 fax 0394 271348). *P. World coins.*

Seaford Coins
PO Box 2016, Seaford, East Sussex BN25 2PW (01323 491646). *P. L. British and foreign coins.*

David Seaman
60/64 Matthias Road, London N16 8QD (0171 241 1931). *P. L. Hammered, Milled, Maundy.*

Patrick Semmens

3 Hospital Road, Half Key, Malvern, Worcs WR14 1UZ (0886 33123). *P. European and British coins.*

Mark Senior

553 Falmer Road, Woodingdean, Brighton, Sussex (01273 309359). *By appointment only. P. L. Saxon, Norman and English hammered coins.*

S. E. Sewell

PO Box 104, Ipswich, Suffolk IP5 7QL (01473 626 950). *Mainly British milled coins.*

T. Sexton (IBNS)

19 Great Western Avenue, Bridgend, Mid Glamorgan CF31 1NN (01656 4861). *P. World coins.*

R. D. Shah (BNTA)

9 Lansdowne Grove, Neasden, London NW10 1LP (020 8452 5160). *Ancient India and Indian states.*

Robert Sharman Numismatist (ANA)

36 Dairsie Road, Eltham, London SE9 1XH (020 8850 6450). *P. British coins.*

Shepshed Coins & Jewellery

24 Charnwood Road, Shepshed, Leics LE12 9QF (01509 502511). Mon, Wed-Sat 09.15-16.30. *British coins.*

Simmons Gallery (ANA, BNTA, IBNS)

53 Lamb's Conduit Street, London WC1N 3NB (020 7831 2080 fax 020 7831 2090). *Organisers of the London Coin Fair, Cumberland Hotel, Marble Arch, London W1. L. Coins, tokens and medals.*

Raymond J. Sleet (BNTA)

11 Seagull Close, Kempshott, Basingstoke, Hants RG22 5QR (01256 53256 fax 01256 63525) *General world coins and tokens.*

E. Smith (ANA, IBNS)

PO Box 348, Lincoln LN6 0TX (01522 684681 fax 01522 689528). *P. Organisewr of the Morley, Leeds, monthly coin fair. World coins and paper money.*

J. Smith (BNTA)

47 The Shambles, York YO1 2LX (01904 654769). Mon-Sat 09.30-17.00. *World coins.*

Val Smith

170 Derby Road, Nottingham NG7 1LR (0115 9781194). Mon-Sat 11.00-16.30 (cl. Thu). *British and world coins.*

Jim Smythe

PO Box 6970, Birmingham B23 7WD (e-mail Jimdens@aol.com). *P. L. 19th/20th century British and world coins.*

S & B Coins

Grass Walk, Wood Lane, South Heath, Great Missenden, Bucks HP16 0RB (01494 862161). *P. L. British coins and medallions.*

Southern Coins

51 Beach Road, Selsey, West Sussex PO20 0LT (01243 606698). *P. British and world coins.*

George Sowden

Coins Galore, The Lizard, nr Helston, Cornwall TR12 7NU (01326 290300). *P. British and European coins.*

Spink & Son Ltd (ANA, BNTA, IAPN, IBNS)

5–7 King Street, St James's, London SW1Y 6QS (020 7930 7888 fax 020 7839 4853), Mon-Sat 09.30–17.30. *Ancient, medieval and modern world coins, orders, medals and decorations, banknotes and numismatic books—new and secondhand.*

SPM Jewellers (BNTA)

9 Bedford Place, Southampton, Hants SO1 2DB (01703 223255/227923). Tue-Sat 09.15–17.00, Sat 09.15–16.00. *World coins and medals.*

The Stamp & Coin Shop

3 Norman Road, St Leonards on Sea, East Sussex TN37 6HH (01424 436682). Mon-Sat 09.00–18.00. World coins. *Manufacturers of coin and medal cabinets.*

Stamp & Collectors Centre

404 York Town Road, College Town, Camberley, Surrey GU15 4PR (01276 32587 fax 01276 32505). Mon, Tue, Thu, Sat 09.00–17.00, Wed, Fri 09.00–1900. *World coins and medals.*

Sterling Coins & Medals

2 Somerset Road, Boscombe, Bournemouth, Dorset BH7 6JH (01202 423881). Mon-Sat 09.30–16.30 (closed Wed). *World coins and medals.*

Strawbridge

Tanglewood, Ivy Tree Hill, Stokeinteignhead, Newton Abbott, Devon TQ12 4QH (01626 873783). *P. L. Coins, tokens, medals, banknotes.*

Studio Coins (ANA, BNTA)

16 Kilham Lane, Winchester, Hants SO22 5PT (01962 853156). *P. English coins.*

Surena Numismatics (BNTA)

PO Box 2194, London NW8 6QQ (0831 220010). *P. Parthian, Sassanian, Islamic coins.*

Stuart J. Timmins

Smallwood Lodge Bookshop, Newport, Salop (01952 813232). Mon-Sat 09.30–17.00. *Numismatic literature.*

R. Tims

39 Villiers Road, Watford, Herts WD1 4AL. *P. L. Uncirculated world banknotes.*

Trafalgar Square Collectors' Centre (ANA, BNTA, LM, OMRS)

7 Whitcomb Street, Trafalgar Square, London WC2H 7HA (020 7930 1979). Mon-Fri 10.00–17.30. *World coins and commemorative medals. War medals and decorations.*

D. A. Travis

8 Cookridge Drive, Leeds LS16 7LT. *P. L. US coins.*

Michael Trenerry Ltd (BNTA)

PO Box 55, Truro, Cornwall TR1 2YQ (01872 277977 fax 01872 225565). By appointment only. *L. Roman, Celtic and English hammered coins, trade tokens.*

Vera Trinder Ltd

38 Bedford Street, Strand, London WC2E 9EU (020 7836 2365/6). Mon-Fri 08.30-17.30. *L. Coin catalogues and books, albums, envelopes, cases and accessories.*

Robert Tye

Poll Toran, Loch Eynort, South Uist PA81 5SJ. *P. European and Oriental hammered coins.*

Vale (ADA BNTA)

21 Tranquil Vale, Blackheath, London SE3 0BU (020 8852 9817. Mon-Sat 10.00–17.30 (closed Thu). *British coins and medals.*

Tony Vaughan Collectables

PO Box 364, Wolverhampton, WV3 9PW (01902 27351). *P. L. World coins and medals.*

Italo Vecchi Ltd (BNTA, IAPN)

35, Dover Street, London W1X 3RA (020 7491 7048) . *Ancient, medieval and modern up to 1900.*

Victory Coins

184 Chichester Road, North End, Portsmouth, Hants PO2 0AX (01705 751908/663450). Mon-Sat 09.15–17.30. *British and world coins.*

Mark J. Vincenzi (BNTA)

Rylands, Earls Colne, Essex. CO6 2LE (01787 222555). *P. Greek, Roman, Hammered.*

Mike Vosper

PO Box 2874, Colchester CO4 5UR (01206 752110). *Retail premises: Essex Antiques Centre, Unit 11, Priory Street, Colchester. L. Ancient and English coins.*

Wallis & Wallis

West Street Auction Galleries, Lewes, East Sussex BN7 2NJ (01273 476562). Mon-Fri 09.00–17.30. *Regular auctions of coins, medals and militaria.*

B. M. & S. A. Weeks

PO Box 1447, Salisbury, Wilts SP5 2YG (01725 510311). *L. British coins, world crowns and medals.*

John Welsh

PO Box 150, Burton-on-Trent, Staffs DE13 7LB (01543 73073 fax 0543 473234). *P. L. British coins.*

Wessex Numismatics Ltd

PO Box 13, Eastleigh, Hants. *P. British, European and world coins.*

Pam West (IBNS)

PO Box 257, Sutton, Surrey SM3 9WW (020 8641 3224). *P. L. English banknotes.*

West Cornwall Stamp Centre

13 Fore Street, Hayle, Cornwall TR27 4DX (01736 751910 fax: 01736 751911. *L. Coin Accessories.*

West Essex Coin Investments (BNTA, IBNS)

Croft Cottage, Station Road, Alderholt, Fordingbridge, Hants SP6 3AZ (01425 656 459). *P. L. British and World coins and paper money.*

R & J White (IBNS)

29 Shortacre, Basildon, Essex SS14 2LR (01268 522923). *P. L. Banknotes and world ephemera.*

Whitmore (BNTA)

Teynham Lodge, Chase Road, Upper Colwall, Malvern, Worcs WR13 6DT (01684 40651). *P. World coins, tokens and medals.*

J. L. Williams

502 Clive Court, Maida Vale, London W9 1SG (020 7286 3461). *P. L. Wholesaler—dealers only.*

A. G. Wilson (BNTA)

PO Box 864, Eastbourne, BN21 4YR (01323 738591 fax 0323 737936). *Rare and choice coins of the world*

World Coins

35–36 Broad Street, Canterbury, Kent CT1 2LR (01227 68887). Mon-Sat 09.30–17.30 (half-day Thu). *World coins.*

World Treasure Books

PO Box 5, Newport, Isle of Wight PO30 5QE (01983 740712). *L. Coins, books, metal detectors*

Barry Wright,

54 Dooley Drive, Bootle, Merseyside. L3O 8RT. *P. L. World banknotes.*

B. N. Yarwood (ANA) Yarwood Hall, Luttongate Road, Sutton St Edmund, Spalding, Lincs PE12 0LH. *P. British and US coins.*

Banks, Mints and Numismatic
BUREAUX
of the world

Many national banks and mints operate numismatic bureaux and sales agencies from which coins, medals and other numismatic products may be obtained direct. The conditions under which purchases may be made vary considerably. In many cases at the present time bureaux will accept orders from overseas customers quoting their credit card number and its expiry date; but in others payment can only be made by certified bank cheque, or international money order, or by girobank. Cash is seldom, if ever, acceptable. It is best to write in the first instance to enquire about methods of payment.

A

National Mint, Baghe Arg, Kabul, Afghanistan

Bank Mille Afghan, Kabul, Afghanistan

Banque d'Algerie, Sucursale d'Alger, 8 Boulevard Carnot, Alger, Algeria

Banco de Angola, Luanda, Daroal, Angola

Casa de Moneda de la Nacion, Avenida Antartica, Buenos Aires, BA, Argentina

Royal Australian Mint, Department of the Treasury, Canberra, ACT, Australia

GoldCorp Australia, Perth Mint Buildings, GPO Box M924, Perth, Western Australia 6001

Oesterreichsiches Hauptmunzamt, Am Heumarkt 1, A-1031 Wien, Postfach 225, Austria

Oesterreichische Nationalbank, A-1090 Wien, Otto Wagner-platz 3, Austria

B

Treasury Department, PO Box 557, Nassau, Bahamas (*coins*)

Ministry of Finance, PO Box 300, Nassau, Bahamas (*banknotes*)

Bank of Bahrain, PO Box 106, Manama, Bahrain

Eastern Bank, PO Box 29, Manama, Bahrain

Monnaie Royale de Belgique, Avenue de Pacheco 32, B-1000 Bruxelles, Belgium

Banque Nationale de Belgique SA, Caisse Centrale, Bruxelles, Belgium

Banque de Bruxelles SA, 2 Rue de la Regence, Bruxelles 1, Belgium

Casa de la Moneda, Potosi, Bolivia

Banco Central de Bolivia, La Paz, Bolivia

Casa da Moeda, Praca da Republica 173, Rio de Janeiro, Brazil

Hemus FTO, 7 Vasil Levski Street, Sofia C-1, Bulgaria

Banque de la Republique, Bujumbura, Burundi

C

Banque Centrale, Douala, Boite Postale 5.445, Cameroun

Royal Canadian Mint, 320 Sussex Drive, Ottawa 2, Ontario, Canada K1A 0G8

Casa de Moneda, Quinta Normal, Santiago, Chile

Casa de Moneda, Calle 11 no 4-93, Bogota, Colombia

Numismatic Section, The Treasury, Avarua, Rarotonga, Cook Islands

Banco Centrale de Costa Rica, Departamento de Contabilidad, San Jose, Costa Rica, CA

Central Bank of Cyprus, PO Box 1087, Nicosia, Cyprus

Artia, Ve Smekach 30, PO Box 790, Praha 1, Czech Republic

D

Den Kongelige Mønt, Amager Boulevard 115, København S, Denmark

Danmarks Nationalbank, Holmens Kanal 17, 1060 København K, Denmark

Banco Central de Santo Domingo, Santo Domingo, Dominican Republic

E

Banco Central, Quito, Ecuador

Mint House, Abbassia, Cairo, Egyptian Arab Republic

Exchange Control Department, National Bank of Egypt, Cairo, Egyptian Arab Republic

Banco Central de la Republica, Santa Isabel, Equatorial Guinea

Commercial Bank of Ethiopia, Foreign Branch, PO Box 255, Addis Ababa, Ethiopia

F

Currency Board, Victoria Parade, Suva, Fiji

Suomen Rahapaja, Katajanokanlaituri 3, Helsinki 16, Finland

Suomen Pankki, PO Box 10160, Helsinki 10, Finland

Hotel de Monnaie, 11 Quai de Conti, 75-Paris 6e, France

G

Banque Centrale Libreville, Boite Postale 112, Gabon

Verkaufstelle fur Sammlermunzen, D-638 Bad Homburg vdH, Bahnhofstrasse 16–18, Germany

Staatliche Munze Karlsruhe, Stephanienstrasse 28a, 75 Karlsruhe, Germany

Staatliche Munze Cannstatt, Taubenheimerstrasse 77, 7 Stuttgart-Bad, Germany

Bayerisches Hauptmunzamt, Hofgraben 4, 8 Munich, Germany

Hamburgische Munze, Norderstrasse 66, 2 Hamburg 1, Germany

Bank of Ghana, PO Box 2674, Accra, Ghana

Pobjoy Mint, Mint House, 92 Oldfields Road, Sutton, Surrey SM1 2NW

Royal Mint, Llantrisant, Mid Glamorgan, Wales, CF7 8YT

Royal Mint Coin Club, PO Box 500, Cardiff, CF1 1HA

Bank of Greece, Treasury Department, Cash, Delivery & Despatch Division, PO Box 105, Athens, Greece

Casa Nacional de Moneda, 6a Calle 4-28, Zona 1, Ciudad Guatemala, Republica de Guatemala CA

States Treasury, St Peter Port, Guernsey, Channel Islands

Bank of Guyana, PO Box 658, Georgetown, Guyana

H

Banque Nationale de la Republique d'Haiti, Rue Americaine et Rue Fereu, Port-au-Prince, Haiti

Banco Central de Honduras, Tegucigalpa DC, Honduras CA

State Mint, Ulloi utca 102, Budapest VIII, Hungary

Artex, PO Box 167, Budapest 62, Hungary

Magyar Nemzeti Bank, Board of Exchange, Budapest 54, Hungary

I

Sedlabanki Islands, Reykjavik, Iceland

Indian Government Mint, Bombay 1, India

Arthie Vasa, Keabajoran Baru, Djakarta, Indonesia

Perum Peruri, Djakarta, Indonesia

National Mint, Tehran, Iran

Bank Markazi Iran, Tehran, IranCentral Bank of Iraq, PO Box 64, Baghdad, Iraq

Central Bank of Ireland, Dublin 2, Republic of Ireland

The Treasury, Government Buildings, Prospect Hill, Douglas, Isle of Man

Israel Stamp and Coin Gallery, 4 Maze Street, Tel Aviv, Israel

Istituto Poligraphico e Zecca dello Stato, Via Principe Umberto, Roma, Italy

J

Decimal Currency Board, PO Box 8000, Kingston, Jamaica

Mint Bureau, 1 Shinkawasakicho, Kita-ku, Osaka 530, Japan

Numismatic Section, Treasury Department, St Helier, Jersey

Central Bank of Jordan, Amman, Jordan

Banque Nationale du Liban, Rue Masraf Loubnan, Beirut, Lebanon

K

Central Bank, PO Box 526, Kuwait

L

Bank of Lithuania, Cash Department, Gedimino av. 6, 2001 Vilius, Lithuania

Caisse Generale de l'Etat, 5 Rue Goethe, Luxembourg-Ville, Grande Duche de Luxembourg

M

Institut d'Emission Malgache, Boite Postale 205, Tananarive, Madagascar

Central Bank of Malta, Valletta 1, Malta

Casa de Moneda, Calle del Apartado no 13, Mexico 1, DF, Mexico

Le Tresorier General des Finances, Monte Carlo, Principaute de Monaco

Banque de l'Etat du Maroc, Rabat, Morocco

Banco Nacional Ultramarino, Maputo, Republica de Mocambique

British Bank of the Middle East, Muscat

N

Royal Mint, Dharahara, Katmandu, Nepal

Nepal Rastra Bank, Katmandu, Nepal

Rijks Munt, Leidseweg 90, Utrecht, Netherlands

Hollandsche Bank-Unie NV, Willemstad, Breedestraat 1, Curacao, Netherlands Antilles

Central Bank of Curacao, Willemstad, Curacao, Netherlands Antilles

The Treasury, Private Bag, Lambton Quay, Wellington, New Zealand

Banco de Nicaragua, Departamento de Emison, La Tresoria, Apartada 2252, Managua, Nicaragua

Nigerian Security Printing and Minting Corporation, Ahmadu Bello Road, Victoria Island, Lagos, Nigeria

Central Bank of Nigeria, Tinubu Square LB, Lagos, Nigeria

Norges Bank, Oslo, Norway

Den Kongelige Mynt, Hyttegaten, Konigsberg, Norway

P

Pakistan State Mint, Baghban Pura, Lahore 9, Pakistan

National Development Bank, Asuncion, Paraguay

Casa Nacional de Moneda, Calle Junin 791, Lima, Peru

Central Bank of the Philippines, Manila, Philippines

Bank Handlowy w Warszawie, Ul. Romuald Traugutta 7, Warsaw, Poland

Desa Foreign Trade Department, Al. Jerozolimskie 2, Warszawa, Poland

Casa da Moeda, Avenida Dr Antonio Jose de Almeida, Lisbon 1, Portugal

R

Cartimex, 14-18 Aristide Briand St, PO Box 134-135, Bucharest, Roumania

Bank of Foreign Trade, Commercial Department, Moscow K 16, Neglinnaja 12, Russian Federation

Banque Nationale du Rwanda, Boite Postale 351, Kigali, Republique Rwandaise

S

Numismatic Section, Box 194, GPO, Apia, Samoa

Azienda Autonoma di Stato Filatelica-Numismatica, Casalla Postale 1, 47031 Repubblica di San Marino

Banque Internationale pour le Commerce, 2 Avenue Roume, Dakar, Senegal

Bank of Yugoslavia, PO Box 1010, Belgrade, Serbia

The Treasury, PO Box 59, Victoria, Seychelles

Bank of Sierra Leone, PO Box 30, Freetown, Sierra Leone

The Singapore Mint, 249 Jalan Boon Lay, Jurong, Singapore

South African Mint, PO Box 464, Pretoria, South Africa

Government Printing Agency, 93 Bukchang Dong, Chungku, Seoul, Republic of South Korea

Fabrica Nacional de Moneda y Timbre, Jorge Juan 106, Madrid 9, Spain

Bank of Sri Lanka, PO Box 241, Colombo, Sri Lanka

Hong Kong and Shanghai Banking Corporation, PO Box 73, Colombo 1, Sri Lanka

Sudan Mint, PO Box 43, Khartoum, Sudan

Bank of Sudan, PO Box 313, Khartoum, Sudan

Bank of Paramaribo, Paramaribo, Suriname

Kungelige Mynt och Justeringsverket, Box 22055, Stockholm 22, Sweden

Eidgenossische Staatskasse, Bundesgasse 14, CH-3003, Berne, Switzerland

Central Bank of Syria, Damascus, Syrian Arab Republic

T

Central Mint of China, 44 Chiu Chuan Street, Taipei, Taiwan, ROC

Royal Thai Mint, 4 Chao Fah Road, Bangkok, Thailand

Numismatic Section, The Treasury, Nuku'alofa, Tonga

Central Bank of Trinidad and Tobago, PO Box 1250, Port of Spain, Trinidad

Banque Centrale de Tunisie, Tunis, Tunisia

State Mint, Maliye Bakanligi Darphane Mudurlugu, Istanbul, Turkey

U

Bank of Uganda, PO Box 7120, Kampala, Uganda

Numismatic Service, US Assay Office, 350 Duboce Avenue, San Francisco, CA, 94102, USA

Office of the Director of the Mint, Treasury Department, Washington, DC, 20220, USA

Philadelphia Mint, 16th and Spring Garden Streets, Philadelphia, PA, 19130, USA

Franklin Mint, Franklin Center, Pennsylvania, 19063, USA

Banco Central del Uruguay, Cerrito 351, Montevideo, RO del Uruguay

V

Ufficio Numismatico, Governatorato dello Stato della Citta de Vaticano, Italy

Banco Central de Venezuela, Caracas, Venezuela

Y

Yemen Bank, Sana'a, Yemen.

Z

Bank of Zambia, PO Box 80, Lusaka, Zambia

Chief Cashier, Reserve Bank, PO Box 1283, Harare, Zimbabwe

Numismatics and
THE LAW

Counterfeit Currency

A counterfeit is a forgery or imitation of a coin or banknote produced with the intention of defrauding the revenue of the State or deceiving members of the public. By the Coinage Offences Act (1861) it was a felony to counterfeit gold or silver coins. Lesser offences included the gilding of farthings and sixpences to pass them off as half-sovereigns, the possession of moulds, machines or tools clandestinely removed from the Royal Mint, the impairment or diminution of gold or silver coins by filing or clipping (or even the possession of such filings and clippings).

The Coinage Act of 1870 made provision for the counterfeiting of base-metal coins, or the stamping of letters or words on coins of any kind, or the forging of colonial coinage. The most celebrated prosecution under this Act occurred in 1930 when Martin Coles Harman was convicted and fined £5 for issuing bronze coins resembling the British penny and halfpenny for the island of Lundy of which he was then the proprietor. Interestingly, no attempt was made to prosecute the Birmingham Mint which actually struck the coins (prudently omitting the H mintmark).

The making of medals or coins resembling current coin became a misdemeanour under the Counterfeit Medal Act of 1883. This Act is invoked from time to time against manufacturers or distributors of medallic pieces or coin jewellery. Such pieces, often struck in 9 carat gold, are deemed to infringe the Act if, for example, they have a figure even vaguely resembling St George and the Dragon on one side. The use of the royal effigy, however, without due authorisation, is regarded as a misdemeanour punishable by an unlimited fine and the confiscation of tools, dies and instruments. At the present time it is a serious offence to make a counterfeit of a currency note or coin with the intention of passing it off or tendering it as genuine. This offence carries a maximum penalty of ten years' imprisonment or an unlimited fine, or both. Making a counterfeit of a currency note or coin without lawful authority incurs a penalty up to two years' imprisonment or an unlimited fine, or both.

Passing or tendering as genuine anything which is known or believed to be a counterfeit of a currency note or coin renders the criminal on conviction to a term of ten years' imprisonment or an unlimited fine, or both. The mere possession of any forged note or coin is itself a criminal offence. Possessing counterfeits without authority or permission so to do, and doing so knowingly, renders the possessor liable to two years' imprisonment or an unlimited fine, or both. The Act also stipulates that the reproduction of a current banknote—of the Bank of England or of the Scottish and Northern Irish banks is a serious offence. This clause covers even such apparently innocent acts as making a photocopy (whether in black and white or full colour) of a current banknote, the photography of such a note or the illustration of such a note in any book, magazine or newspaper. Strict regulations are laid down concerning the legitimate illustration of notes, whether current or not, in books and periodicals; such illustrations must be either greatly reduced or enlarged *and* must bear a prominent defacement, such as SPECIMEN or CANCELLED. It is also a serious offence to utilise a reproduction of a current British banknote in any medium. Theoretically this includes such things as tea-towels, T-shirts, mugs, plates and other souvenirs in glass or ceramics, but in practice the law seems to turn a blind eye to such practices. Imitations and parodies of notes and coins are also regarded as infringements of the law, but in these instances prosecution of the offender seldom proceeds; a warning is generally regarded as sufficient, provided that the offending article or articles are withdrawn and suppressed.

The advent of high-definition colour photocopying in recent years has brought the offence of reproduction into prominence once more. The regulations have been tightened considerably and there have been several cases of successful prosecution. In each case, however, the intent deliberately to deceive the public by uttering a colour photocopy as a genuine note was proved.

Technically the offence takes places as soon as the photocopy is made, for whatever purpose, but as a rule only those cases in which an element of fraudulent deception subsequently arose were pursued with the full rigour of the law. The law is quite clear, however, and it is a criminal offence to make a colour photocopy or photograph of any current British note unless permission to do so has been obtained from the Treasury. The maximum penalty on conviction is an unlimited fine.

The note-issuing banks have, of course, taken steps in recent years to incorporate further security devices into their notes, notably the use of latent images and underprints in colours which are difficult, if not impossible to photocopy accurately. At the same time, the adoption of metal strips and more complex watermark devices has theoretically made the task of the forger much more difficult. If, by some unlucky chance, someone passes a dud note on to you, you must make no attempt to pass it in turn. To do so renders you liable to prosecution for uttering a forgery. Forged notes must be handed over to the police as soon as possible. If you receive a forged note in payment for goods or services you are entitled to claim its face value from the person who gave it to you. Even if the person giving you the note did not realise that it was counterfeit, it is assumed in law that he or she represented to you that the note was worth its face value at the time the note was passed. If the tenderer knew that the note was forged, he can be prosecuted; but at the end of the day he is still liable to you for the fraud and can be sued in the civil courts for the recovery of the sum involved. If, on the other hand, you received the money as a gift, you have no legal claim against the person who gave it to you. If you pay someone with a counterfeit note or coin unknowingly, you have committed no offence, but you must pay again. The degree of culpability is often difficult to prove or disprove, but it is unlikely that a prosecution would be initiated on the basis of a single note or a solitary coin.

It is also a serious offence to manufacture blanks, discs or washers which are intended to defraud the proprietors of vending machines, or to possess tools and equipment for the dishonest manufacture or alteration of such blanks for this purpose. Under the Gold and Silver Export Control Act (1920) melting down gold or silver coins to extract their precious metal content is an offence punishable by a fine of £100 or two years' imprisonment, or both.

Legal Tender

The dictionary defines this as currency which a creditor is bound by law to accept as payment of a money debt. Debts and purchases must be paid for in cash of legal tender unless the creditor or seller is willing to accept payment in another form, such as a postal order, money order, cheque or, nowadays, credit card. Bank of England notes of any denomination are legal tender in England and Wales. Formerly Bank of England pound notes (but no other) were legal tender in Scotland. Technically, since the demise of the pound note, no Bank of England notes are legal tender in Scotland, although in practice they circulate freely north of the Border. Even more surprisingly, Scottish banknotes are not legal tender anywhere, not even in Scotland! The subtle difference is reflected in the actual wording of the promise on English and Scottish banknotes. Thus English notes are inscribed *"I promise to pay the bearer on demand the sum of . . ."* without stipulating any specific place, the promise being made by the Chief Cashier. Scottish notes, on the other hand, have the promise in the third person. It is the bank itself which makes the promise *"to pay the bearer on demand . . . pounds sterling at their head office here in Edinburgh, by order of the Board"*. In practice, however, Scottish banknotes are accepted without question, not only throughout Scotland but also in parts of England, and are generally accepted in London, although there is no obligation on the part of a creditor so to do.

Apart from gold coins, the base-metal pound coin is legal tender for payment of any amounts. So, too, presumably, are the various two-pound and five-pound base-metal coins of recent years, even though they have been struck as commemoratives and not intended for general circulation in the ordinary sense. Smaller denominations are only legal tender up to a maximum value in each case. In the case of 50p coins, 25p crowns and 20p coins, they may be used alone, or in combination with each other, in payment of amounts up to £10. 10p and 5p coins, alone or in combination, may be used for sums up to £5. Bronze 1p and 2p coins, however, can only be used for payment of amounts up to 20p. In practice, of course, you can probably get away with making payment in larger quantities (within reason!) although strictly speaking there is no obligation on the part of your creditor to accept them.

An Offence to Possess Legal Tender Coins

From the foregoing it will be seen that gold coins are, and always have been, legal tender. Since 1817 the legal tender gold coin of the United Kingdom has been the sovereign (with its sub-division and multiples). Yet there have been times when actual possession of these legal tender coins has been, *per se*, an illegal act. The first attempt to regulate the movement and possession of gold coins arose in 1947 with the passage of the Exchange Control Act which made it illegal to buy, borrow, lend or sell any gold or foreign currency, unless authorised to deal in gold. Moreover it was stipulated that *"any person possessing gold should offer it for sale to an authorised dealer at a price not exceeding the authorised price, unless the Treasury consented to this retention of the gold"*. The serious implications of this Act were mitigated in the case of numismatists by the Exchange Control (Collectors' Pieces Exemption) Order 1947, which allowed collectors to hold on to *"any gold coin which was minted in 1816 or earlier, and any gold coin which was minted after 1816 and which has a numismatic value greater than the value of the gold content which would have been received if the coin had been sold to an authorised (bullion) dealer"*. In effect this meant that numismatists and coin dealers were not hindered from buying and selling gold coins as long as the coins were in collectable condition and possessed numismatic interest. This loophole was brazenly breached in the 1960s and led to the Exchange Control (Gold Coins Exemption) Order of 1966 which aimed to prevent the loss of currency reserves caused by the import of gold coins from abroad, and to eliminate the hoarding of gold by speculators. By the terms of this Order no one was permitted to hold more than four gold coins minted after 1837 unless he had received express permission from the Treasury. The maximum was set at four coins so that people who had one or two sovereigns as mementoes could keep them without breaking the law. Numismatists who possessed more than four post-1837 gold coins on April 27, 1966 had to apply to the Treasury for permission to retain them. To do so they had to prove that they were *bona fide* collectors by completing form GC 1, providing a detailed list of the coins in their possession—not only in gold, but also in silver (pre-1816, 1816–1919 and post-1919) and base metals (before and after 1860). Several individuals were successfully prosecuted under this draconian legislation and their holdings of gold sovereigns confiscated, although no one was imprisoned or heavily fined as the legislation provided. The 1966 order was rescinded in 1970, re-imposed in a modified form in 1975, and finally revoked in 1979. Since that date numismatists and speculators alike have been free to collect (or hoard) gold to their hearts' content.

Value Added Tax

This is a matter which primarily concerns dealers, but it also applies to those who dabble in coins on a part-time basis, and has implications for collectors at all levels. Briefly, anyone conducting a business,

or in self-employment, who has a turnover in excess of £43,000 per annum, must register with HM Customs and Excise for the collection and payment of Value Added Tax. Anyone whose turnover is less than £43,000 is exempt from the obligation to register, but is at liberty to register if he or she feels that this would be advantageous. It is nice to think that there is an element of choice in this, although one would be hard pressed to think why anyone would voluntarily register for VAT unless they absolutely had to! Incidentally, the government raised the VAT registration level by 40 per cent to £35,000 in March 1991 with the avowed intention of relieving a large number of businesses from this burden, at a time when the rate of tax was increased from 15 per cent to 17.5 per cent. Assuming that you are a dealer with a turnover above the magic limit, then you are committing a serious offence if you fail to register. Registration then lays you open to the full machinery of the system. You have to charge VAT on all goods and services, issuing VAT invoices and receipts and keeping detailed accounts which are liable to snap inspection at any time. You have to make quarterly returns to Customs and Excise of the amount of tax you have collected. From this you are allowed to deduct the VAT which you yourself have paid out in the course of your business, and you then have to remit the difference to the VAT collector. Of course, should the amount you have paid exceed the tax you have collected, you receive a repayment in due course. This arises in businesses which handle zero-rated goods and services, but coins and medals do not come within that category.

For dealers in gold bullion, coins or medals, there is a special VAT leaflet which covers regulations specific to such matters. In general the supply and importation of gold and gold coins is subject to the standard rate of 17.5 per cent, but antique gold coins and medals (more than a hundred years old) are exempt from VAT upon importation, but when sold by a VAT-registered dealer, VAT at the standard rate needs to be accounted for on the profit margin. It is vital therefore to maintain accurate records of all buying and selling, and which coins and medals are subject to VAT and which are exempt. Furthermore, the onus is on you to ensure that the source of the gold you bring into the country is impeccable. There are extremely heavy penalties for smuggling gold, and ignorance of the law, or apparently innocent handling of smuggled gold subsequently, are no defence.

From January 1, 1995 the special margin scheme of accounting for VAT currently available for certain second-hand goods, such as cars, was extended to almost all second-hand goods. The scheme allows businesses buying and selling eligible goods to account for VAT only on the difference between the buying and selling prices of these items.

A special system of accounting has recently been introduced which enables some dealers to account for VAT without the need to keep a detailed record of every transaction. Certain works of art, antiques and collector's items, including "secondhand" coins, defined in Notice 712 *Secondhand goods*, were exempt from VAT at import. From January 1, 1996 these items became subject to VAT at import at an effective rate of 2.5 per cent.

Export and Import

Some coins do require an export licence before they can be taken out of the country and unfortunately these controls have been extended during the past year. Following the lifting of the export regulations relating to gold coins in 1979, then prior to April 1, 1993 the only coins which required any export licence were those with a value in excess of £35,000. However the agreement by the UK to implement an EC directive on the removal of cultural goods has resulted in a fresh interpretation of previous UK legislation on these coins which are on the market as a result of an archaeological find. Therefore as from April 1, 1993, any coin *whatever its value* which has come from an archaeological source within the UK will require an export licence even to take it to another EC country. Certain other coins of EC provenance other than the UK will now require an EC export licence. The value limit for non-archaeological source coins has been increased to £39,600 (Ecu 50,000). Both types of licence are issued by the Department of National Heritage, 2–4 Cockspur Street, Trafalgar Square, London SW1Y 5DH who can also supply a handy flow-chart to enable you to tell at a glance whether a licence is needed and what type. These new regulations are imposing an enormous additional burden on the trade and the British Numismatic Trade Association has held numerous meetings with the authorities in an attempt to reduce to a minimum the number of licence applications needed. Hopefully, by next year's edition there will be better news.

The restrictions applied to the importation of gold coins were removed in 1979, as previously mentioned. Coins of any kind are now permitted under Open General Import licence from any country and a specific or individual licence is no longer required. Details of any duties which may be payable on imported coins can be obtained from HM Customs and Excise, King's Beam House, Southwark, London SE1 or any local Customs and Excise office. Until recently, the only gold coins

under embargo were Krugerrands. This was a political decision, aimed at tightening sanctions against South Africa, and applied to the importation of new gold coins from that country, but not to Krugerrands which had been brought into the United Kingdom, or any of the countries of the European Community, prior to the imposition of sanctions. In practice, it was very difficult to regulate the movement, let alone the importation, of Krugerrands, and with the relaxation of Apartheid this regulation has been lifted.

Importing Coins by Mail

Elsewhere in this volume will be found the names and addresses of mints, banks and numismatic bureaux around the world from whom it may be possible to obtain currency direct. It is a wise precaution to write to these bodies in the first instance for details of their sales and distribution. In some cases they appoint a dealer in Britain as an agent and this is a method of purchase that removes a great deal of the hassle and red tape. Nowadays, however, many mints and banks are quite happy to use the credit card system to make it easy to part you from your money. The problem arises, however, when the coins are despatched. As a rule, banks and mints stipulate quite clearly that they will not accept orders prepaid in cash, and it is an offence to send coins or banknotes out of the country as payment, except through banks authorised for this purpose. Cheques drawn on British banks should not be used. Indeed, this may be actively discouraged by the imposition of heavy clearance and handling charges at the other end. The converse is also true, although Americans seem to think that dollar cheques drawn on some obscure mid-West bank will be eagerly accepted here, and are consequently aggrieved when it is tactfully pointed out to them that this creates enormous problems— to say nothing of the swingeing bank charges incurred in converting such cheques to sterling. Other than credit cards, the Girobank system is probably the best method of remitting currency from one country to another; full details may be obtained from any post office. Details on the preferred method of sending remittances, or transferring cash to another country, as well as the transmission of coins by post to different countries, will be found in the *Royal Mail International Service Guide*. This also lists, among the prohibitions pertaining to each country, which countries accept gold or silver, and which ban the transmission of precious metals by post.

The receipt of postal packets containing coins from abroad makes you liable for Value Added Tax on their importation. As a rule, the despatching mint or bank will have affixed a Customs declaration to the packet, listing the contents, their weight and value, and it is on that basis that VAT will be calculated. The position regarding the import and export of coins by post is more complicated, and applies also to goods sent on approval. In such cases you must consult your Customs and Excise office who will advise you on the correct procedure and what your liabilities will be to tax in either case. This also applies to dealers taking stock out of the country to a coin show and then re-importing the unsold stock afterwards, or importing material purchased at the show.

Buying and Selling

When goods are sold, the seller and the buyer enter into a contract which confers rights and imposes obligations on both parties. The contract need not be in writing. There is no law governing the quality of goods sold by a private individual. If you purchase a coin from a fellow-collector as a result of an informal meeting at the local numismatic society it is incumbent on you to ensure that what you buy is what you think you are buying. If you purchase something from a dealer or shopkeeper, however, you are entitled under the Sale of Goods Act to goods of "merchantable quality" which means that they must be reasonably fit for their purpose. Items sold under a specific description, on the other hand, must correspond exactly with that description. If they do not, the seller *even a private individual* can be sued under the Sale of Goods Act. This is an important distinction because there is an erroneous notion that the Act does not apply to transactions between private individuals. If A sells a coin to B, purporting it to be a rare date, and B subsequently discovers that the date has been deliberately altered, then B can sue A. Even if A claims that he made the sale in good faith, believing the coin to be a genuine rare date, he will still be liable for restitution (giving B his money back) and may also face a claim for damages. The Sale of Goods Act thus overturns the traditional adage *caveat emptor* which, in its full formula, translates as "let the buyer beware for he ought not to be ignorant of the nature of the property which he is buying from another party". Traditionally this was the maxim applicable at auctions. Once the auctioneer's gavel had dropped, the successful bidder had, in effect, made a contract with the vendor and was bound to pay for the lot, even if he subsequently discovered that what he had purchased was not what he had imagined. The view was that it was up to the purchaser to ensure beforehand that what he purchased was genuine and answered the description in the sale catalogue.

Because of vexatious disputes arising from questions of authenticity, and with the Sale of Goods Act breathing down their necks, many auctioneers now have a safety net, in the form of extensions. These enable successful bidders to delay payment for two or three weeks while they seek expertisation of doubtful material. In other words, the law allows a cooling-off period, but only for he legitimate purpose of verifying the authenticity of items over which there may be some doubt. This is only operative in cases where a coin or medal is sold as genuine, and described and estimated in value accordingly. In many doubtful cases, however, an auctioneer will cover himself by adding the crucial words "as is" to the description of a lot. Then, indeed, it is a case of *caveat emptor*. The auctioneer has done everything humanly possible to draw attention to the controversial nature of the item, and it must then rest on the judgment of purchaser.

On the subject of auctions there are legal aspects which are not always apparent, as well as subtle differences in law and practice between England and Scotland. These tend to arise in cases where coins and medals come up for sale at provincial general mixed auctions, rather than in the sales conducted by numismatic auctioneers. Goods up for auction may be subject to an upset price which is made public as the price at which the bidding will start. A reserve price, on the other hand, is known only to the auctioneer, and if it is not reached, the goods will not be sold. Upset prices are common in Scotland, reserve prices in England. If no upset price is specified and the goods are not subject to a reserve price then the highest bid secures them, even though it may not be as high as the vendor hoped for. If a seller notifies other bidders that he is bidding for his own goods, or that he has employed an agent to bid for him, the bidding is legal. If he does not give notice and bids himself, or gets someone to bid for him, thus forcing up the price, the sale is fraudulent, and the buyer can purchase the goods for the amount of the last bid he made before fraudulent bidding started.

One frequently hears dark, but usually apocryphal, tales of "the ring" in action to depress the bidding and secure items below the price commensurate with their actual value. This is a fraudulent practice and in law is regarded as a criminal conspiracy. In practice, however, it would be very difficult for a group of dealers or other individuals to keep the bidding down merely by sitting on their hands. This practice could only operate successfully in sales which were largely, if not entirely, frequented by dealers. But coin sales, like other specialist collector-orientated auctions, are characterised by a high proportion of private bidders in attendance. Any conspiracy by a ring would merely allow some private bidder to step in and secure the lot at a bargain price. Rings are illegal, but in practice prosecutions are very rare as it is extremely difficult to obtain proof of their operations. What is more likely to happen is that dealers have been known to act in concert to force up the bidding to frighten off some unwelcome interloper. Here again, such tales are legion, but astonishingly lacking in specific details. The golden rule in attending auctions is to know what you are going after, and to have a pretty precise idea of how much you are prepared to pay. Do not be stampeded in the heat of the moment into going way beyond your limit.

Taxation of Profits on Disposal

The Inland Revenue define an asset as "any form of property (other than sterling) wherever situated". A disposal includes a sale, exchange or gift of an asset, or the receipt of a capital sum in respect of them. In layman's terms you dispose of an asset when you sell it, give it away, exchange it or lose it. A transfer of assets between husband and wife doesn't count (unless they are legally separated), nor does the transfer of an asset you leave when you die. If a disposal results in a profit you could be liable to tax. Any profit made on the sale of certain assets, including coins, medals and other collectables, constitutes a capital gain and is subject to Capital Gains Tax (CGT) which is now charged at the same 25% and 40% rates as income tax. However the government allows you to make a total capital gain in the current tax year of £5,500 before tax becomes chargeable. If this is the case, and the total proceeds from disposal do not exceed £10,000, then a simple declaration to this effect is all you need to make in the relevant section of your annual tax return.

Computing the actual capital gain is a complicated matter. Suppose you purchased a coin in 1960 for £5,000 and sold it in 1993 for £12,000. On the face of it, you've made a capital gain of £7,000 and you might think that you were liable to CGT because the gain was over £5,500. However, the *length of time* you've held the asset also has to be taken into consideration. From April 6, 1988 the

law was altered so that only gains made after March 31, 1982 are now taxable. In effect, you are taxed as if you acquired the coin on March 31, 1982. The initial value of the coin is deemed to be its market value at that date. If the gain from March 1982 to the time of disposal is greater than the overall gain from acquisition in 1960 to disposal in 1993, you take the lesser of the two figures. If this produces a gain, whereas the old method of working it out would have produced a loss, you will be regarded, for tax purposes, as having made neither a gain nor a loss on disposal. You have a choice of opting for computing from the time of actual acquisition or from March 1982, whichever seems the more advantageous; but once you've made your choice you cannot subsequently change your mind.

How do you establish what the coin was worth in March 1982? The Inland Revenue tend to regard Seaby, Krause or other relevant catalogues as their yardstick. The difference between the nominal or catalogue value in 1982 and what you eventually got for the coin *assuming that the latter was greater*, might be regarded as the capital gain, but even then the position is complicated by inflation in the intervening years eroding the real value of the coin.

At this stage things get really complicated as you have to work out the indexation allowance. This is determined by the Retail Prices Index (RPI), and you need to know the RPI for (a) the month of disposal, and (b) the month in which you acquired the asset, or March 1982, if later. The RPI is announced each month by the Departmenrt of Employment and is published in its *Employment Gazette* which ought to be available in your local public library. Take the RPI for the month of the disposal and subtract the RPI for the month when indexation commenced. Then divide the result by the RPI for the month when indexation began, and work out this figure to the nearest third decimal place. This is known as the indexation factor, which you then multiply by the initial value of your coin. Simple isn't it? In most cases, however, I expect you will have made a capital loss in real terms, so these sums, though necessary to satisfy the Inland Revenue, are largely academic.

TREASURE
and the Law

Until the introduction of the new Treasure Act, the legal position regarding articles of value, found long after they were hidden or abandoned, was not as simple and straightforward as it might be supposed. Furthermore, this was a case where the law in England and Wales differed fundamentally from that in Scotland.

Treasure Trove was one of the most ancient rights of the Crown, deriving from the age-old right of the monarch to grave treasure. In England and Wales, the law applied only to objects made of, or containing, gold or silver, whether in the form of coin, jewellery, plate or bullion. Moreover, the object had to be shown to have been deliberately hidden and the owner could not be readily found. The English law therefore excluded precious stones and jewels set in base metals or alloys such as bronze or pewter. It also took no account of artifacts in pottery, stone, bone, wood or glass which might be of immense antiquarian value.

In recent years, as a result of the rise in metal-detecting as a hobby, the archaeological lobby brought pressure to bear on Parliament to change the law and bring it into line with Scotland where the rules on Treasure Trove were far more rigorously interpreted. In Scotland the Crown is entitled to *all* abandoned property, even if it has not been hidden and is of little value. This applies even to objects dumped in skips on the pavement. Strictly speaking you would be committing a criminal offence if you removed an old chair from a skip without the owner's permission, although in practice such helping oneself rarely proceeds to a prosecution. In 1958 an archaeological expedition

Metal detecting can be fun—but be sure you know the rules!

from Aberdeen University found several valuable artifacts on St Ninian's Isle, Shetland. These included silver vessels and ornaments, as well as a porpoise bone which had incised decoration on it. The archaeologists challenged the rights of the Crown to this treasure, arguing that the Crown would have to prove that the articles had been deliberately hidden, and that a porpoise bone was in any case not valuable enough to count as treasure. The High Court, however, decided that as long as the property had been abandoned, it belonged automatically to the Crown. Its value, intrinsic or otherwise, or whether or not it was hidden, did not make any difference. Since then, as a result of this decision in case law, the criteria for Treasure Trove have been very strictly applied in Scotland. It would have only required a similar test case in England or Wales to result in a similar tightening of the rules. This has been resisted, mainly by the detectorist lobby, but inevitably the government considered legislation to control the use of metal detectors, if not to ban them altogether.

In England and Wales a find of gold or silver coins, artifacts or ornaments, or objects which contain some of these metals, which appears to have been concealed by the original owner, was deemed to be Treasure Trove. It was not even necessary for the articles to be buried in the ground; objects concealed in thatched roofs or under the floorboards of buildings have been judged to be Treasure Trove. Such finds had to be notified immediately to the police who then informed the district coroner. He then convened an inquest which decided whether all or part of the find was Treasure Trove. Establishing the gold or silver content was straightforward, but the coroner's inquest had to decide whether the material was hidden deliberately and not just lost or abandoned, and that the owner could not be located. A gold coin found on or near a country footpath might reasonably have been dropped by the original possessor through a hole in pocket or purse and in such cases it was very unlikely that it would be deemed Treasure Trove, even if the coin turned out to be very rare. In this instance the coroner would then have had to determine who was the lawful owner of the find: the actual finder, the owner of the land where it was found or even the tenant of the land. As a rule, however, it was left to the finder and landowner to decide between them who the owner of the coin should be, and in some cases the matter could only be resolved by referring to a civil court. For this reason it was vital that metal detectorists should secure permission *in writing* from landowners before going on to their land, defining rights and obligations on both sides, in order to determine

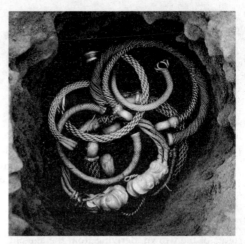

The Snettisham torcs—one of our country's greatest finds.

the disposal or share-out of any finds or proceeds from the sale of finds, *beforehand*.

If the coroner decided that the articles were deliberately concealed, and declared them to be Treasure Trove, the find automatically reverted to the Crown. In practice the find was considered by the Treasure Trove Reviewing Committee of the Treasury. They might decide that although the articles *invariably coins* were gold or silver, they were so common that they were not required by the British Museum or one of the other great national collections, and would return them to the finder to dispose of at his discretion. If some or all of the coins were deemed vital for inclusion in a national collection the finder was recompensed with the full market value of the material. On the other hand, if someone found gold or silver which might be Treasure Trove and failed to declare it at the time, that person was liable to prosecution under the Theft Act should the find subsequently come to light. Not only could he face a heavy fine but the articles would be forfeit to the Crown, and of course no reward or recompense was then payable either.

The anomalies and inconsistencies of existing law on Treasure Trove were eliminated and the position considerably tightened up by the passage, on July 5, 1996, of the Treasure Act.

Announcing that the Treasure Act had received the Royal Assent, Lord Inglewood, National Heritage Minister, said, "This represents the first legislation on treasure trove to be passed in England and Wales and will replace common law precedents and practices dating back to the

Middle Ages. The Act, which offers a clearer definition of treasure and simplified procedures for dealing with finds, will come into force after a code of practice has been drawn up and agreed by both Houses of Parliament". The Act came into force in England, Wales and Northern Ireland on September 24, 1997, replacing the common law of treasure trove.

The act was introduced as a Private Member's Bill by Sir Anthony Grant, after the failure of an earlier attempt by Lord Perth. For the first time, it would be a criminal offence to fail to report within 14 days the discovery of an item which would be declared Treasure Trove. Finders will continue to be rewarded for reporting their discoveries promptly, while landowners and occupiers will also be eligible for rewards for the first time.

The Treasure Act covers man-made objects and defines treasure as objects other than coins which are at least 300 years old and contain at least 10 per cent by weight of gold or silver; coins more than 300 years old which are found in hoards (a minimum of two coins if the precious metal content is more than 10 per cent, and a minimum of 10 coins if the precious metal content is below 10 per cent). The act also embraces all objects found in clear archaeological association with items which are treasure under the above definitions. It also covers any object which would have been Treasure Trove under the previous definitions (e.g. hoards of 19th century gold or silver coins).

The maximum penalty for failing to report the discovery of treasure within 14 days will be a fine of £50,000 or three months imprisonment, or both.

In Scotland the police pass the goods on to the procurator fiscal who acts as the local representative of the Queen's and Lord Treasurer's Remembrancer. If the articles are of little value, historically or intrinsically, the finder will usually be allowed to keep them. If they are retained for the appropriate national collection then a reward equal to the market value is payable.

A favourite haunt of metal-detectorists these days is the beach, and many hobbyists make quite a lucrative living by sweeping the beaches especially just after a Bank Holiday. It's surprising how much loose change gets lost from pockets and handbags over a holiday weekend. Technically the coins recovered from the beach are lost property, in which case they ought to be surrendered to the police, otherwise the finder may be guilty of theft. In practice, however, the

law turns a blind eye to coins, on the sensible grounds that it would be impossible to prove ownership. On the other hand, banknotes are treated as lost property since someone could in theory at least identify a note as his by citing the serial number.

In the case of other objects, such as watches and jewellery, of course the law governing lost property is enforced, and the old adage of "finders keepers" does not apply. Any object of value, identifiable as belonging to someone, that is washed up on the foreshore or found in territorial waters is known technically as "wreck". This includes not just a wrecked ship, but any cargo that was being carried by a ship.

If wreck is not claimed by its owner, it falls to the Crown. In this case it is not necessary to prove deliberate concealment, as in the case of Treasure Trove. This law has a specific numismatic application in the case of the gold and silver coins washed up after storms around our shores, from Shetland to the Scillies. Such coins, emanating from wrecks of Spanish treasure ships and Dutch East Indiamen in particular, are well documented, and any such finds ought to be reported immediately to the police.

Stray finds of coins, as well as other objects of value, on public places, such as the street, a public park or a sports ground, are also subject to law. In this case the finder must take all reasonable steps to locate the owner. Anyone who keeps a coin without making reasonable effort to find the owner could be prosecuted for theft. As with the beach, however, such "reasonable effort" would clearly be impractical. Finding coins on private premises is another matter. In this case large bodies, such as the Post Office, British Rail, the British Airports Authority, bus companies, municipal authorities, hospitals, the owners of department stores, theatre and cinema proprietors and the like, may have bye-laws, rules and regulations for dealing with lost property found within their precincts, or in their vehicles. If you found a purse or wallet on a bus or train, or in a telephone kiosk or a shop, common sense (and your conscience) would tell you to hand it over to the driver, conductor, shopkeeper or official in charge. As a rule, unclaimed lost property reverts eventually to the finder, but not always; British Rail and some other organisations have a rule that in such cases the property reverts to the organisation. In any event, failure to disclose the find immediately might render you liable to prosecution for stealing by finding.

Treasure Act
CODE OF
PRACTICE
—a summary

For easy reference a summary of the main points of the new law is reproduced here*. Further information will be found in the *Code of Practice on the Treasure Act,* which can be obtained free of charge from the Department for Culture, Media and Sport (formerly the Department of National Heritage) (telephone: 020 7211 6200). Metal detectorists are strongly advised to obtain a copy of the Code of Practice which, among other things, contains guidance for detectorists, sets out guidelines on rewards, gives advice on the care of finds and has lists of useful addresses.

What is the definition of treasure?

The following finds are treasure under the Act (more detailed guidance is given in the Code of Practice):

1. *Objects other than coins:* any object other than a coin provided that it contains at least 10 per cent of gold or silver and is a least 300 years old when found (objects with gold or silver plating normally have less than 10 per cent of precious metal).

2. *Coins:* all coins from the same find provided they are at least 300 years old when found (but if the coins contain less than 10 per cent of gold or silver there must be at least 10 of them; there is a list of these coins in the Code of Practice).

An object or coin is part of the same find as another object or coin if it is found in the same place as, or had previously been left together with, the other object. Finds may have become scattered since they were originally deposited in the ground.

Only the following groups of coins will normally be regarded as coming from the "same find":

(a) hoards that have been deliberately hidden;

(b) smaller groups of coins, such as the contents of purses, that may have been dropped or lost and

(c) votive or ritual deposits.

Single coins found on their own are not treasure and groups of coins lost one by one over a period of time (for example those found on settlement sites or on fair sites) will not normally be treasure.

3. *Associated objects:* any object, whether it is made of, that is found in the same place as, or that had previously been together with, another object that is treasure

4. *Objects that would have been treasure trove:* any object that would previously have been treasure trove, but does not fall within the specific categories given above. These objects have to be made substantially of gold or silver; they have to have been buried with the intention of recovery and their owner or his/her heirs cannot be traced. The following types of find are not treasure:

(a) objects whose owners can be traced;

(b) unworked natural objects, including human and animal remains, even if they are found in association with treasure;

(c) objects from the foreshore, which are wreck.

If you are in any doubt, it will probably be safest to report your find.

What about objects found before the Act came into force?

You should report objects that come into any of the four categories just described (if found after September 23, 1997). There is no need to report any objects found before that date unless they may be treasure trove (see 4 above)

What should I do if I find something that may be treasure?

You must report all finds of treasure to the coroner for the district in which they are found *either* within 14 days after the date on which you made the find *or* within 14 days after the day on which you realised that the find might be treasure (for example, as a result of having it identified). The obligation to report finds applies to everyone, including archaeologists.

How do I report a find of treasure?

Very simply. You may report your find to the coroner in person, by letter, telephone or fax. The coroner or his officer will send you an acknowledgement and tell you where you should deliver your find. The Code of Practice has a list of all coroners with their addresses, telephone and fax numbers.

There are special procedure for objects from a few areas for which treasure franchises exist, but they should be reported to the coroner in the usual way. The main franchise-holders (the Duchies of Lancaster and Cornwall, the Corporation of London and the City of Bristol) have confirmed that they will pay rewards for finds of treasure from their franchises in the normal way.

Where will I have to take my find?

You will normally be asked to take your find to a local museum or archaeological body. Local agreements have been drawn up for each coroner's district in England and Wales to provide the coroner with a list of such museums and archaeological organisations. The Department is publishing a series of leaflets, roughly one for each country of England and one for Wales, listing the relevant coroners, museums and archaeological services in each area.

The body which receives the find on behalf of the coroner will give you a receipt. Although they will need to know where you made the find, they will keep this information confidential if you or the landowner wish—and you should do so too.

The body receiving the find will notify the Sites and Monuments Record as soon as possible (if that has not already happened), so that the site where the find was made can be investigated by archaeologists if necessary. A list of Sites and Monuments Records is in Appendix 3 of the Code of Practice.

What if I do not report a find of treasure?

If you fail to report a find that you believe or have reasonable grounds for believing to be treasure without a reasonable excuse you may be imprisoned for up to three months or receive a fine of up to level 5 on the standard scale (currently £5,000) or both. You will not be breaking the law if you do not report a find because you do not initially recognise that it may be treasure, but you should report it once you do realise this.

What happens if the find is not treasure?

If the object is clearly not treasure, the museum or archeological body will inform the coroner, who may then decide to give directions that the find should be returned without holding an inquest.

What happens if the find is treasure?

If the museum curator or archaeologist believes that the find may be treasure, they will inform the British Museum or the National Museums & Galleries of Wales. The museums will then decide whether they or any other museum may wish to acquire it.

If no museum wishes to acquire the find, the Secretary of State will be able to disclaim it. When this happens, the coroner will notify the occupier and landowner that he intends to return the object to the finder after 28 days unless he receives an objection. If the coroner receives an objection, the find will be retained until the dispute has been settled.

What if a museum wants to acquire my find?

If a museum wants to acquire part or all of a find, then the coroner will hold an inquest to decide whether it is treasure. The coroner will inform the finder, occupier and landowner and they will be able to question witnesses at the inquest. Treasure inquest will not normally be held with a jury.

If the find is declared to be treasure, then it will be taken to the British Museum or the National Museums & Galleries of Wales, so that it can be valued by the Treasure Valuation Committee.

How do I know that I will receive a fair price for my find?

Any find of treasure that a museum wishes to acquire must be valued by the Treasure Valuation Committee, which consists of independent experts. The Committee will commission a valuation from one or more experts drawn from the trade. You, together with the museum that wishes to acquire the find and any other interested party, will have an opportunity to comment on the valuation and to send in a separate valuation of your own, before the Committee makes its recommendation. If you are dissatisfied you can appeal to the Secretary of State.

What if the coroner or museum loses or damages my find?

They are required to take reasonable steps to ensure that this does not happen; but, if it does, you should nonetheless be compensated.

Who will receive the reward?

This is set out in detail in the Code of Practice. To summarise:

— where the finder has permission to be on the land, rewards should continue to be paid in full to him or her (the burden of proof as to whether he or she has permission will rest with the finder). If the finder makes an agreement with the occupier/landowner to share a reward, the Secretary of State will normally follow it;
— if the finder does not remove the whole of a find from the ground but allows archaeologists to excavate the remainder of the find, the original finder will normally be eligible for a reward for the whole find;

— rewards will not normally be payable when the find is made by an archaeologist;
— where the finder has committed an offence in relation to a find, or has trespassed, or has not followed best practice as set out in the Code of Practice, he or she may expect no reward at all or a reduced reward. Landowners and occupiers will be eligible for rewards in such cases.

How long will it take before I receive my reward?

The Code of Practice states that you should receive a reward within one year of you having delivered your find, although this may take longer in the case of very large finds or those that present special difficulties. If no museum wants to acquire the find it should be disclaimed within six months or within three months if it is a single object.

Reproduced from "The Treasure Act, Information for Finders of Treasure (England and Wales)" leaflet DCMSJ0229NJ, published by the Department for Culture, Media and Sport.

INDEX
TO COIN NEWS

Once again, in response to popular demand, we have included this basic subject index to the COIN YEARBOOK's parent magazine COIN NEWS, covering the period from October 1998 to September 1999. Entries are indicated by numbers signifying the month (e.g. 10–12 relate to October to December 1998 and 1–9 signify January to September 1999), followed by the page number.

BOOKS